Societal Impact on Aging Series

Series Editor

K. Warner Schaie, PhD
Evan Pugh Professor of Human Development and Psychology
College of Health and Human Development
The Pennsylvania State University
University Park, PA

K. Warner Schaie, PhD, is Evan Pugh Professor of Human Development and Psychology at the Pennsylvania State University. He also holds an appointment as Affiliate Professor of Psychiatry and Behavioral Science at the University of Washington. He received his PhD in psychology from the University of Washington, an honorary Dr. Phil. from the Friedrich-Schiller University of Jena, Germany, and an honorary Sci. D. degree from West Virginia University. He was honored with the Kleemeier Award for Distinguished Research Contributions from the Gerontological Society of America and the Distinguished Scientific Contributions Award from the American Psychological Association. He is author or editor of 40 books including the textbook *Adult Development and Aging* (with S. L. Willis) and the *Handbook of the Psychology of Aging* (with J. E. Birren), both of which are now in their 5th editions. He has directed the Seattle Longitudinal Study of cognitive aging since 1956 and is the author of more than 250 journal articles and chapters on the psychology of aging. His current research interest is the life course of adult intelligence, its antecedents and modifiability, as well as methodological issues in the developmental sciences.

Neal Krause, PhD, is Professor of Health Behavior and Health Education in the School of Public Health at the University of Michigan, and Senior Research Scientist at the Institute of Gerontology. His work focuses on three areas. First, as the principal investigator of the research project funded by the National Institute on Aging (NIA), *Well-Being among the Aged: Personal Control and Self-Esteem,* he is continuing analysis of longitudinal data he has gathered from a nationwide sample of older adults examining relationships among current stressful events, lifetime trauma, social support, health, and well-being. Second is the relationship between religion and health in late life. This more recent NIA-funded project, *Religion, Aging, and Health,* involves developing measures of religion to assess how its various facets bolster and maintain the health and well-being of older people. Finally, Dr. Krause is continuing research with Dr. Jersey Liang on his study assessing the dynamic linkages among social relations, financial well-being, and health status among the older-old in Japan and the United States. Dr. Krause has authored 123 refereed articles and 22 chapters and invited papers over the course of his career, one of which is a recent chapter on neighborhood conditions and health for the *Annual Review of Gerontology and Geriatrics.*

Alan Booth, PhD, is Distinguished Professor of Sociology, Human Development, and Demography at the Pennsylvania State University and senior scientist in the Population Research Institute. He has authored more than 100 articles and three books. He has edited nine books, seven of which have stemmed from the Pennsylvania State University National Symposium on Family Issues of which he is a co-organizer. He served as editor of the *Journal of Marriage and the Family* from 1986 to 1991 and was the recipient of the American Sociological Association Family Section Distinguished Career Award in 2002. He is principal investigator of two major research projects. The first, *Marital Instability Over the Life Course,* is a longitudinal study of more than 2,000 married persons and their offspring funded by the National Institute on Aging. Commencing in 1980, the focus of study has been on factors that influence and are influenced by divorce, changes in marital quality, and alterations in parent-child relations. The second, *Hormones, Family Relations, and Child Development,* is a longitudinal study of 400 families with children residing in central Pennsylvania. Funded by the W. T. Grant Foundation in 1996, the study is designed to examine the inter-relationships between hormones known to be related to behavior (e.g., testosterone and cortisol) and family processes.

Religious Influences on Health and Well-Being in the Elderly

K. Warner Schaie, PhD
Neal Krause, PhD
Alan Booth, PhD
Editors

 Springer Publishing Company

Springer Publishing Company, Inc.
536 Broadway
New York, NY 10012-3955

Acquisitions Editor: Helvi Gold
Production Editor: Jean Hurkin-Torres
Cover design by Joanne Honigman

04 05 06 07 08 / 5 4 3 2 1

Library of Congress Cataloging-in-Publication Data

Schaie, K. Warner (Klaus Warner), 1928-
  Religious influences on health and well-being in the elderly / K. Warner Schaie, Neal Krause, Alan Booth.--1st ed.
        p. cm. -- (Societal impact on aging series)
  Includes bibliographical references and index.
  ISBN 0-8261-2404-6
  1. Older people--Religious life. 2. Older people--Health and hygiene. 3. Health--Religious aspects. I. Krause, Neal M. II. Booth, Alan, 1935- III. Title. IV. Societal impact on aging.
BL625.4.S33 2004
201'.76219897--dc22
                                                            2004010460

Printed in the United States of America by Integrated Book Technology, Troy, NY

Contents

Contributors

Gene G. Ano
Department of Psychology
Bowling Green State University
Bowling Green, OH

Giacomo Bono, PhD
Department of Psychology
University of Miami
Coral Gables, FL

Linda M. Chatters, PhD
School of Public Health, School
  of Social Work and the
  Institute for Social Research
University of Michigan
Ann Arbor, MI

Kenneth F. Ferraro, PhD
Department of Sociology and
Center on Aging and the Life
  Course
Purdue University
West Lafayette, IN

Roger Finke, PhD
Department of Sociology
Pennsylvania State University
University Park, PA

Elizabeth P. Flint, PhD
Center for the Study of Aging
  and Human Development
Duke University Medical Center
Durham, NC

Linda K. George, PhD
Center for the Study of Aging
  and Human Development
Duke University Medical Center
Durham, NC

Judith C. Hays, PhD, RN
Center for the Study of
  Aging and Human
  Development
Duke University Medical Center
Durham, NC

Ellen L. Idler, PhD
Institute for Health,
  Health Care Policy and
  Aging Research
Department of Sociology
Rutgers University
New Brunswick, NJ

Kimya I. Jackson
Department of Biobehavioral
  Health
Pennsylvania State University
University Park, PA

Neal Krause, PhD
School of Public Health and the
  Institute of Gerontology
The University of Michigan
Ann Arbor, MI

Christian J. Lalive d'Epinay, PhD
Center for Interdisciplinary
  Gerontology
Department of Sociology
University of Geneva
Thônex/Geneva, Switzerland

Jeff Levin, PhD, MPH
Valley Falls, KS

Michael E. McCullough, PhD
Department of Psychology
University of Miami
Coral Gables, FL

Susan H. McFadden, PhD
Department of Psychology
University of Wisconsin—Oshkosh
Oshkosh, WI

Keith G. Meador, MPH
Center for the Study of Aging
  and Human Development
Duke University Medical Center
Durham, NC

Marc A. Musick, PhD
Population Research Center
University of Texas at Austin
Austin, TX

Kenneth I. Pargament, PhD
Department of Psychology
Bowling Green State University
Bowling Green, OH

Margaret M. Poloma, PhD
Department of Sociology
The University of Akron
Akron, OH

Dario Spini, PhD
Center for Interdisciplinary
  Gerontology
University of Geneva
Center for Life Course and Life
  Style Studies
Universities of Lausanne and
  Geneva
Lausanne, Switzerland

A. Sandra Willis, PhD
Department of Psychology
Samford University
Birmingham, AL

Keith E. Whitfield, PhD
Department of Biobehavioral
  Health
Pennsylvania State University
University Park, PA

Everett L. Worthington, Jr., PhD
Department of Psychology
Virginia Commonwealth
  University
Richmond, VA

Preface

This is the sixteenth volume in a series on the broad topic of "Societal Impact on Aging." The first five volumes of this series were published by Erlbaum Associates under the series title of "Social Structure and Aging." The present volume is the eleventh published under the Springer Publishing Company imprint. It is the edited proceedings of a conference held at the Pennsylvania State University, October 7–8, 2002.

The series of Penn State Gerontology Center conferences originated from the deliberations of a subcommittee of the Committee on Life Course Perspectives of the Social Science Research Council chaired by Matilda White Riley in the early 1980s. That subcommittee was charged with developing an agenda and mechanisms that would serve to encourage communication between scientists who study societal structures that might affect the aging of individuals and scientists who are concerned with the possible effects of contextual influences on individual aging. The committee proposed a series of conferences that would systematically explore the interfaces between social structures and behavior, and in particular identify mechanisms through which society influences adult development. When the first editor was named director of the Penn State Gerontology Center, he was able to implement this conference program as one of the center's major activities.

The previous fifteen volumes in this series have dealt with the societal impact on aging in psychological processes (Schaie & Schooler, 1989); age structuring in comparative perspective (Kertzer & Schaie, 1989); self-directedness and efficacy over the life span (Rodin, Schooler, & Schaie, 1990); aging, health behaviors, and health outcomes (Schaie, House, & Blazer, 1992); caregiving in families (Zarit, Pearlin, & Schaie, 1993), aging in historical perspective (Schaie & Achenbaum, 1993), adult intergenerational relations (Bengtson, Schaie, & Burton, 1995), older adults' decision making and the law (Smyer, Schaie, & Kapp, 1996), the impact of social structures on decision making in the elderly (Willis, Schaie, & Hayward,1997), the impact of the workplace on aging

(Schaie & Schooler, 1998), mobility and transportation in the elderly (Schaie & Pietrucha, 2000), the evolution of the aging self (Schaie & Hendricks, 2000), societal impact on health behavior in the elderly (Schaie, Leventhal, & Willis, 2002), personal control in the elderly (Zarit, Pearlin, & Schaie, 2003), and the impact of technology on successful aging (Charness & Schaie, 2003).

The strategy for each of these volumes has been to commission six reviews on three major topics by established subject-matter specialists who have credibility in aging research. We then invited two formal discussants for each chapter—usually one drawn from the writer's discipline and one from a neighboring discipline. This format seems to provide a suitable antidote against the perpetuation of parochial orthodoxies as well as to make certain that questions are raised with respect to the validity of iconoclastic departures in new directions.

To focus each conference, the organizers chose three aspects of the conference topic that are of broad interest to gerontologists. Social and behavioral scientists with a demonstrated track record are then selected and asked to interact with those interested in theory building within a multidisciplinary context.

The present volume focuses on the impact of religious institutions, religious practices, and religious organizations upon the health and well-being of older persons. Behavioral and social scientists have only recently begun to examine issues such as spirituality and the effects of participation in formal religious structures as they impact upon successful aging. Research has consistently shown that older adults who are religious tend to enjoy better physical and mental health than those who are less involved in religion. This phenomenon has been forcefully demonstrated in several recent studies showing that religion is linked to mortality (e.g., religious elders seem to live longer than their less religious counterparts). We also know that in many sub-cultures, religious institutions may be the most viable social structures that attend closely to the health and well-being of their members and their community.

Even though the work linking religion with health and well-being is compelling, relatively little is known about why this potentially important relationship exists. This lack of knowledge may be due primarily to weakness in theory and in measurement. Consequently there is a need for more rigorous conceptualizations of how religion and religious institutions effect health and well-being in the elderly. This includes a review of ways in which religion and religiosity is currently measured and the specification of alternate models. It also involves the conceptualization of mechanisms that would link religious activities to maintaining health and psychological well-being in the elderly. Given the wide differences in religious involvement in a diverse society, it is also necessary to consider the specific effect of religion and religious institutions by social class, gender, and race.

The volume begins with an overview chapter outlining the issues that must be considered in linking religion and religiosity to health and well-being. This is followed by the first topic which considers the conceptualization and measurement of religion in late life. We begin by specifying what we mean by religion in an aging context. A review of the literature on the relation between church attendance and health addresses the impact of formal aspects of religion. A highlight of the discussion following the chapter is the caution that this relationship may be time-bound and limited to the American culture. We then turn to the more individual aspects of religious experience by a chapter on the role of prayer.

The second topic in this volume is concerned with the question of how religion might affect health in later life. Current theories of religion, aging, and health are poorly developed and we need to know more about whether and why there is a connection between religion and health. The first chapter in this section explores the relationship between religious coping and its possible impact on stress reduction. The second chapter focuses on the role of forgiveness as an alternate mediator that increases well-being by gaining acceptance of self and others in spite of rave feelings of psychological hurt.

The third topic deals with structural variations in the role and impact of religion on health and well-being, We first examine the literature on differential influences due to minority membership. Examined here in detail are differences in the manner in which religious influences might work among older African Americans, elderly Whites, and elderly Hispanics. Finally, we consider structural differences in the religion and health relationship as they occur over the human life course

We are grateful for the financial support of the conference that led to this volume which was provided by conference grant AG 09787 from the National Institute on Aging, and by additional support from the Dean of the College of Health and Human Development of the Pennsylvania State University. We are also grateful to Judy Hall and Anna Shuey for handling the conference logistics, to Jenifer Hoffman for coordinating the manuscript preparation, and to Pamela Evans for help in preparing the indexes.

K. WARNER SCHAIE

REFERENCES

Bengtson, V. L., Schaie, K. W., & Burton, L. (Eds.). (1995). *Adult intergenerational relations: Effects of societal changes.* New York: Springer Publishing.

Charness, N., & Schaie, K. W. (Eds.). (2003). *Impact of technology on successful aging.* New York: Springer Publishing.

Kertzer, D., & Schaie, K. W. (Eds.). (1989). *Age structuring in comparative perspective.* Hillsdale, NJ: Erlbaum.

Rodin, J., Schooler, C., & Schaie, K. W. (Eds.). (1991). *Self-directedness and efficacy: Causes and effects throughout the life course.* Hillsdale, NJ: Erlbaum.

Schaie, K. W., & Achenbaum, W. A. (Eds.). (1993). *Societal impact on aging: Historical perspectives.* New York: Springer Publishing.

Schaie, K. W., & Hendricks, J. (Eds.). (2000). *Evolution of the aging self: Societal impacts.* New York: Springer Publishing.

Schaie, K. W., House, J., & Blazer, D. (Eds.). (1992). *Aging, health behaviors, and health outcomes.* Hillsdale, NJ: Erlbaum.

Schaie, K. W., Leventhal, H., & Willis, S. L. (Eds.). (2002). *Societal impacts on health behaviors in the elderly.* New York: Springer Publishing.

Schaie, K. W., & Pietrucha, M. (Eds.). (2000). *Mobility and transportation in the elderly.* New York: Springer Publishing.

Schaie, K. W., & Schooler, C. E. (Eds.). (1989). *Social structure and aging: Psychological processes.* Hillsdale, NJ: Erlbaum.

Schaie, K. W., & Schooler, C. E. (Eds.). (1998). *Impact of the work place on older persons.* New York: Springer Publishing.

Smyer, M., Schaie, K. W., & Kapp, M. B (Eds.). (1996). *Older adults' decision-making and the law.* New York: Springer Publishing.

Willis, S. L., Schaie, K. W., & Hayward, M. (Eds.). (1997). *Impact of social structures on decision making in the elderly.* New York: Springer Publishing.

Zarit, S. H., Pearlin, L., & Schaie, K. W. (Eds.). (1993). *Social structure and caregiving: Family and cross-national perspectives.* Hillsdale, NJ: Erlbaum.

Zarit, S. H., Pearlin, L., & Schaie, K. W. (Eds.). (2003). *Personal control in social and life course context,* New York: Springer Publishing.

CHAPTER 1

An Introduction to Research on Religion, Aging, and Health: Exploring New Prospects and Key Challenges

Neal Krause

Research on religion is enjoying a renaissance in the social and behavioral sciences (see Koenig, McCullough, & Larson, 2001, for a comprehensive review of this literature). In fact, a good deal of this work is now beginning to appear in the mainstream gerontology journals as well (e.g., Idler & Kasl, 1997; Krause, 2002a; Levin, Taylor, & Chatters, 1994). The purpose of this chapter is to provide a broad overview of the rapidly growing field of religion, aging, and health. This will be accomplished by presenting the rationale and exploring the issues that shaped the chapters in this volume. More specifically, the discussion that follows is divided into three main sections. First, an effort is made to sketch out a wider intellectual context for the chapters that follow. Next, a rationale is provided for selecting the core topics that are explored in each chapter. Finally, topics that are not covered in this volume are identified and discussed briefly.

SETTING THE WIDER CONTEXT

In order to attain a deeper appreciation for the work that follows in this volume, it is helpful to consider three key questions. First, why study religion at all? Second, why study religion and aging specifically? Third, how can a meaningful strategy be devised for approaching the research on religion, aging, and health?

Why Study Religion?

There are two reasons why social and behavioral gerontologists should give careful consideration to the study of religion. The first is historical. Many of the major figures in the social and behavioral sciences devoted considerable attention to religion. For example, in sociology, Durkheim (1915/1965) and Weber (1922/1963) devoted entire volumes to this topic. In addition, many consider William James to be the greatest American psychologist. Like Durkheim and Weber, James wrote an entire volume on religion (1902/1997). It is interesting to note that James wrote extensively on religion even though his private letters indicate he was not a deeply religious man himself (Perry, 1954).

But the strong emphasis on religion does not stop with sociology and psychology. Two of the founding fathers of psychiatry paid considerable attention to the subject as well. More specifically, Sigmund Freud (1913) wrote an entire volume on religion and Carl Jung gave considerable thought to this topic as well. In fact, the following quotation from the work of Jung (1953) leaves little doubt about the importance of religion in his mind: "Everything to do with religion, everything it is and asserts, touches the human soul so closely that psychology least of all can afford to overlook it" (p. 337). If so many of the great minds in so many different disciplines devoted so much time to the study of religion, then it is important for social and behavioral gerontologists to pay more attention to it as well.

In addition to the historical reasons for studying religion, findings from more recent research have generated a great deal of enthusiasm and interest in this subject. More specifically, this work suggests there may be a link between religion and health. This is exciting because, unlike the books by the grand masters, recent empirical work more clearly shows how research on religion may be used to help improve the quality of life of our aging population. Viewed broadly, this intriguing body of empirical findings suggests that people who are involved in religion tend to enjoy better physical and mental health than individuals who are not religious (Koenig, McCullough, & Larson, 2001). Perhaps the most convincing work in this area involves a small cluster of studies on religion and mortality (e.g., Hummer, Rogers, Nam, & Ellison, 1999). This research indicates that people who are more deeply involved in religion are less likely to die over the course of a study follow-up period than individuals who are not involved in religion. If the findings from this research prove to be valid, then scholarly work on religion and health may eventually be used to find ways of improving the health of our aging population.

Why Study Religion and Aging?

Although it is important to study religion and health in the general population, there is reason to believe it may be an especially critical factor for older adults. Research consistently shows that older people tend to be more deeply involved in religion than younger individuals. For example, research summarized by Ehmann (1999) indicates that 45% of people between the ages of 18 and 29 feel religion is important in their lives. However, this figure jumps sharply to 77% for those who are at least 75 years old. Similarly, Ehmann reports that only 23% of those age 18 to 29 attend church on a weekly basis, while twice that many (46%) age 75 and over do so. Finally, a series of nationwide surveys by Barna (2002) indicate that older people are more likely to read the Bible and pray privately than young adults.

Taken at face value, research on age differences in religion may initially appear to suggest that people become more religious as they grow older. However, great care must be taken in drawing such a conclusion. The majority of studies in this area are based on cross-sectional data. In essence, this work shows that those who are presently older are more religious than those who are presently young, but this doesn't necessarily mean that people become more religious with age because it is not possible to separate the influence of age from cohort effects.

Fortunately, a recent study by Wink and Dillon (2001) helps shed more light on this issue. Working with data provided by the same people over a 70-year period, these investigators found a nonlinear relationship between age and the importance of religion. More specifically, their analyses suggest that the importance of religion initially declines between early and middle adult life, but then increases significantly as people enter old age. Although the findings from this unique data set are intriguing, this work nevertheless suffers from two shortcomings. First, researchers are becoming increasingly aware that religion is a complex, multidimensional phenomena (Fetzer Institute/National Institute on Aging Working Group, 1999). Since Wink and Dillon examine only one measure of religion (i.e., the importance of religion), it is not possible to tell if the same conclusion can be drawn for other dimensions of religion, such as private prayer or the use of religious coping responses. Second, even though data were gathered in this study from the same people for nearly seven decades, it does not necessarily follow that cohort effects have been ruled out. In order to more directly address this problem, data must be collected for similar periods of time from individuals in other birth cohorts.

In view of the problems with current data on age differences in religion, it is perhaps best to conclude that while the jury is still out, there is some evidence that people may become more religious as they grow older. If this proves to be the case, and religion is related to health and well-being, then it is especially important for social and behavioral gerontologists to focus on religion when studying health in late life.

What Is the Best Way to Approach the Study of Religion, Aging, and Health?

If the goal is to more tightly integrate research on religion into the study of aging and health, then an obvious issue is how to proceed. At least three factors must be taken into account when devising a good strategy. First, it is important not to overlook research that has already been conducted on religion. Second, researchers must pay careful attention to the content domain and measurement of religion. Third, it is important to construct well-articulated conceptual models that aim to show how religion may influence health in late life.

Prior Research on Religion.   In reading some of the research on religion and health, one sometimes gets the impression that investigators feel they are blazing new trails and exploring territory that no one else has ever examined. The plain truth of the matter is that nothing is further from the truth. The theoretical and empirical study of religion is anything but new. In addition to the theoretical works of the grand masters that were discussed above, the empirical study of religion has been around for a long time as well. For example, the leading specialty journal in the field is the *Journal for the Scientific Study of Religion*. This journal has been published for over 40 years. This simple fact has two important implications for those wishing to pursue research on religion, aging, and health. First, it clearly indicates that social and behavioral gerontologists are not "discovering" religion. Instead, they are attempting to more deeply embed, and more tightly integrate, a long-standing body of research into mainstream gerontology. Second, because a good deal of empirical work on religion is already in place, researchers wishing to study religion, aging, and health would be well advised to immerse themselves more deeply in this literature that is tucked away, outside the purview of the journals and volumes they typically read.

Measuring the Context Domain of Religion. Several years ago, a group of experts in religion and health area were brought together with funds provided by the Fetzer Institute and the National Institute on Aging (Fetzer Institute/National Institute on Aging Working Group, 1999). The group was charged with two tasks. First, they were to identify the dimensions of religion that are most likely to be associated with health. Second, the group was to devise good survey measures of these domains. As the panel began its work, it quickly became evident that religion is a very complex, multidimensional phenomena. In fact, as their deliberations proceeded, it seemed as though the number of dimensions of religion was limitless. Although many previous studies on religion and health measure religion primarily in terms of the frequency of church attendance and the frequency of private prayer, the members of the group were well aware that there is far more to it than this. Ultimately, the group identified 12 key dimensions of religion. Measures of these domains were developed and published in a monograph (Fetzer Institute/National Institute on Aging Working Group, 1999). The dimensions of religion that were identified by this panel are presented in Table 1.1.

Although this panel of experts made a significant contribution to the literature, there are two limitations in their work. First, it is not clear whether the measures of religion they devised adequately capture the content domain of religion as it is experienced explicitly by older people. Instead, the items were devised for use with people of all ages. But if people become more religious as they grow older, then the nature and meaning of religion may change for them as well. If this is true, then measures are needed to assess religion as it is experienced specifically by older people. Second, an impressive body of research suggests that older African Americans are more deeply involved in religion than older whites (Levin, Taylor, & Chatters, 1994), but it is hard to tell if the measures devised by the panel of experts work equally well for members of both racial groups.

In an effort to deal with these problems, Krause (2002b) extended the efforts of the working group by developing and implementing a detailed research program to devise measures of religion that are appropriate for use with older blacks and older whites. Like the members of the working group, Krause (2002b) found that religion is a very complex domain consisting of at least fourteen major dimensions. The different facets of religion identified by Krause (2002b) are presented in Table 1.2.

Although the work by the panel of experts, as well as the efforts of Krause (2002b), help flesh out the content domain of religion more

TABLE 1.1   Dimensions of Religion/Spirituality Identified by the Fetzer Institute/National Institute on Aging Working Group (1999)

1. Religious meaning
2. Religious values
3. Religious beliefs
4. Forgiveness
5. Private religious practices
6. Religious coping
7. Religious support
8. Religious history
9. Religious commitment
10. Organizational religiousness
11. Religious preference
12. Daily spiritual experiences

fully, this work falls short because no effort was made to craft conceptual models that show how the various facets of religion might be related to health. As the discussion in the next section will reveal, this is an enormous undertaking in its own right.

Devising Conceptual Models of Religion and Health.   The work by Krause (2002b) and the Fetzer Institute/National Institute on Aging Working Group (1999) proceeded from the premise that the best way to study religion and health was to first devise sound measures of religion, and then develop good conceptual models that show how the different measures of religion operate. But in retrospect, this may not have been the wisest approach because measurement and modeling are inextricably bound. As the classic work of Blalock (1982) reveals, embedded in measures are theoretical statements about the nature of the constructs being studied. It is important to reflect carefully on what this means. When researchers craft measures, it is often not possible to include everything encompassed in a given theoretical domain, such as religion. Instead, decisions must be made about what to include and what to leave out. Sometimes those who develop survey measures are not fully aware of the implications of this process. The decision to include and exclude certain dimensions of religion is based on implicit theoretical statements about what religion is and how it may influence health. Perhaps the best way to illustrate the nature of this problem is to turn to an example.

Many researchers believe that social support systems in the church have an important influence on the health of people who worship there

TABLE 1.2　Dimensions of Religion Identified by Krause (2002b)

1. Organizational religiousness
2. Social relationships with fellow church-members
3. Social relationships with the clergy
4. Spiritual connectedness
5. Religious music
6. Private religious practices
7. Prayer
8. Religious coping
9. Secondary religious control
10. Religious meaning
11. Forgiveness
12. Religious doubt
13. Religious commitment
14. Religious issues for African Americans

(Krause, 2002a). The Fetzer Institute/National Institute on Aging Working Group (1999) devised measures of church-based social support. However, the indicators they developed assess support from everyone in the church taken together. This is fine, but the literature indicates that support from members of the clergy may have a different impact on health and well-being than assistance provided by rank-and-file church members. In fact, there is some evidence that people may be especially inclined to turn to members of the clergy when difficult times arise. For example, the widely cited work of Veroff, Kulka, and Douvan (1981) reveals that when significant personal problems are encountered, people are more likely to seek assistance from a member of the clergy than from a mental health professional (see also Neighbors, Musick, & Williams, 1998). Moreover, support by the clergy may be more efficacious than assistance provided by rank-and-file church members because providing support to others is often part of the official clerical role. In fact, a growing number of pastors are receiving formal training in professional counseling so they can execute these role obligations more effectively (Worthington, 1993). By failing to devise separate measures of support provided by the clergy, the members of the working group were assuming implicitly that there are no significant differences in the effects of assistance provided by clergy and rank-and-file church members. This problem could have been avoided if a model of church-based support was developed before the measures were devised.

As this example reveals, theoretical issues inevitably come to the foreground when efforts are made to devise measures of constructs like church-based social support. Simply put, whether they like it or not, and whether researchers are aware of it or not, they are building theoretical assumptions and perspectives into the measures of religion they devise.

Given the dilemma created by the dual demands of theory and measurement, it seems that the best strategy involves beginning with explicit conceptual models of religion and then subsequently devising the best measures of the constructs contained in these conceptual schemes. But even this task is not as straightforward as it seems because investigators must choose between two broad approaches to model development. First, some investigators have tried to develop comprehensive models of religion that encompass all of the ways religion may influence health in a single conceptual framework (Koenig, McCullough, & Larson, 2001). Alternatively, others have devised more focused models that attempt to explain how just one facet of religion may influence health. For example, Pargament (1997) has done outstanding work developing conceptual models that show how religious coping responses may influence health and well-being.

A central premise in this chapter is that it probably is not possible to devise one grand model of religion and health at the present time. Instead, it makes more sense to begin modestly by developing a series of more focused models that capture the ways that specific facets of religion operate. There are two closely-related reasons for advocating this strategy. The first may be found in the work of William James (1902/1997). James argued that

> The divine can mean no single quality, it must mean a group of qualities, by being champions of which in alternation, different men may all find worthy missions. . . . So a "god of battles" must be allowed to be the god for one kind of person, a god of peace and haven and home, the god of another. We must frankly recognize the fact that we live in partial systems, and that parts are not interchangeable in spiritual life. (p. 509)

In essence, James is saying that religion means many things to many people, and that as a result, no one model of religion will capture the process equally well for everyone.

The same conclusion is reached in the contemporary literature on causal modeling. For example, Bradley and Schaefer (1998) argue that, "It is therefore unlikely that there is a single model of any particular situation. . . . Reality is too complex and models too limited. It is more likely that several models each shed light on different facets of the real situation" (p. 29).

In addition to the convincing rationale provided by James (1902/1997), as well as Bradley and Schaefer (1998), there are more pragmatic reasons for taking a more focused or circumscribed approach to building conceptual models of religion. In practice, it is very difficult to work with causal models containing more than six or seven constructs because these conceptual schemes quickly become unwieldy and difficult to estimate. Put another way, it is hard to imagine what a conceptual model would look like if it contained all the dimensions of religion listed in Tables 1.1 and 1.2.

Although focusing on more limited conceptual models of religion may provide a good point of departure, care must be taken not to disparage the use of grand comprehensive models in the study of religion. Instead, it makes more sense to develop them incrementally. More specifically, it seems more reasonable to first devise a series of well-articulated models that show how specific domains of religion operate. Then, once this is done, researchers can look across the different models to see how they might fit together to form a larger, more comprehensive whole. This is, of course, just another way of stating what Robert Merton (1949) said sometime ago about the interface between midrange and grand theory.

So in the process of reviewing the chapters that follow in this volume, it would be helpful to think about how the insights provided by the authors might be used to craft better midrange theories of religion and health. And in the process, it would be useful to look across and beyond these emerging conceptual schemes to see if there are ways of merging them to form a larger, more comprehensive, and higher-order whole.

RATIONALE FOR SELECTING THE TOPICS IN THIS VOLUME

If the best strategy for developing the literature begins with devising a series of models that examine specific domains of religion, then difficult decisions have to be made about which domains to investigate. We need to know which domains are most important, and which are likely to have the greatest effect on health. Unfortunately, there are relatively few guidelines in the literature on how to address these fundamental issues. It was out of this dilemma that the planning session for this conference began. In the end, the editors of this volume pooled their expertise in the area and decided to focus on six key areas or facets of religion. These domains, as well as the rationale for selecting them, are presented below.

Church Attendance and Denominational Preference

There are three reasons why church attendance and denominational preference were selected for this volume and why the chapter dealing with these topics appears at the beginning of the volume. First, church attendance and denominational preference were used most often in early research on religion and health. This is especially true with respect to church attendance. Second, and as a result, church attendance and denominational preference are still used as a basis of comparison when new constructs are introduced into empirical research. More specifically, many investigators use these constructs as control variables in an effort to see if measures of new dimensions of religion explain variance in health-related outcomes above and beyond the variance explained by church attendance and denominational preference (Krause, 2003). Third, and perhaps most important, denominational preference operates much like a master status variable because it lies behind, and tends to influence, many of the other topics that are covered in this volume. This means, for example, that one's religious preference or affiliation shapes the beliefs and practices surrounding a number of key domains of religion, including prayer, forgiveness, and religious coping responses. Simply put, church attendance and denominational preference are more remote variables that influence more proximal religious determinants (e.g., prayer and coping) of health.

Prayer

There are two reasons why a chapter on prayer was included in this volume. The first may be found in the classic work of William James (1902/1997). He maintained that prayer is, ". . . the very soul and essence of religion" and that prayer is where the real work of religion is accomplished (p. 486). The second reason for focusing on prayer comes from a series of provocative studies in the medical literature. More specifically, several studies that use an experimental design reveal that praying over people in intensive care units tends to improve their health (e.g., Harris et al., 1999).

Religious Coping Responses

A vast literature conducted in secular settings reveals that stressful life events tend to exert a noxious effect on health and well-being (McEwen & Lasley, 2002). However, research in secular settings further indicates that people typically use a range of coping responses to deal with the problems that confront them and, as a result, the deleterious effects of stress are often offset or avoided (Snyder, 2001). A comprehensive research program by Pargament (1997) suggests that the same may be true for religiously-based coping strategies as well. Religious coping refers to the specific faith-oriented cognitive and behavioral responses that people engage in to reduce, avoid, or eliminate the noxious effects of the stressful life events that confront them. Pargament's studies reveal that people often turn to religion when they are faced with difficult times, and the religious coping responses they adopt often help them deal effectively with the problems they face. This makes sense because the Christian Bible, as well as the Jewish Torah, are replete with recommendations on how to deal with adversity. In view of the compelling work that is already in place on religious coping, as well as the central place that is afforded coping in religious texts, it was important to include a chapter on it in this volume.

FORGIVENESS

Research reveals that about 90% of older adults indicate they are Christians (Princeton Religion Research Center, 1994). One of the core tenets in the New Testament places a heavy emphasis on forgiving others (Marty, 1998). Recent research reveals there may be important health-related benefits from doing so (McCullough, Pargament, & Thoresen, 2000). In fact, entire therapeutic regimens have been devised to teach people how to forgive those who have hurt them (Enright & North, 1998). Given the convincing evidence for the relationship between forgiveness and health, as well as the success in using forgiveness as a therapeutic devise, it was imperative to include a chapter on this topic in the present volume.

Life Course Issues in Religion and Health

The last two topics covered in this volume do not represent domains of religion per se, but instead deal with the way in which any facet of religion should be approached and evaluated. The first stresses the importance of taking a life course perspective. As George (1996) forcefully argues, theory in social and behavioral gerontology can be enhanced greatly if researchers assume a life course perspective. Earlier, research by Wink and Dillon (2001) was reviewed which shows there may be a nonlinear relationship between age and the importance of religion. Knowing that such lifelong patterns exist sets up a series of intriguing research questions. For example, we need to know whether the ebb and flow of religious involvement over the life course is followed by corresponding changes in health and well-being. In addition, far more work is needed to see if the dimensions of religion listed in Tables 1.1 and 1.2 change over the life course, and if they do, we need to learn more about the nature and direction of these changes. Given the importance of the life course perspective and the provocative questions it raises, it was important to devote a chapter to this issue in the present volume.

Socioeconomic Status and Race

Researchers have maintained for decades that people in lower socioeconomic (SES) groups, as well as people of color (especially African Americans) are more involved in religion than individuals who are more well-to-do or who are white (Pargament, 1997; Levin, Taylor, & Chatters, 1994). In fact, a recent series of studies by Krause (2002a, 2003) and Krause and Ellison (2003) reveals that there are pervasive race differences in a wide range of religious factors, including church-based support and forgiveness. In contrast, research on SES is less developed, but given pervasive SES differences in health (Marmot & Wilkinson, 2000), and well-known SES variations in things like church attendance (Lenski, 1961), research on the interface between SES, religion, and health appears ripe for further exploration. A chapter on SES and race was included in this volume in an effort to ensure investigators do not lose sight of the fact that all social behavior takes place within a web of broad social structural influences, and that these factors must be taken into account when every domain of religion is examined.

TOPICS THAT ARE NOT EXPLORED IN THIS VOLUME

Because the content domain of religion is so vast, it was not possible to include all of the relevant dimensions in a single volume. Even so, it is important to touch on what was left on the cutting-room floor because briefly reviewing the excluded domains of religion helps ensure they will be kept in mind as the chapters that follow are reviewed. Five excluded areas and topics are reviewed briefly below.

Church-Based Social Support

Many of the early social theorists believed that social ties and social support were the very essence of religion itself. Evidence of this may be found, for example, in the work of Simmel. He argued that, "The faith which has come to be regarded as the essential, the substance, of religion, is first a relation between individuals" (Simmel, 1905, p. 366). The emphasis on social ties in the church is important, because a compelling number of studies in secular settings reveal that people with strong social support systems tend to have better physical and mental health than individuals who do not maintain close ties with others (Berkman & Glass, 2000). Recently, some evidence has emerged which suggests that the same may be true of church-based social ties as well (Krause, 2002a). It is important to keep church-based social support systems in mind as the chapters in this volume are read because significant others in the church may influence the adoption of many religious practices, such as religious coping responses (Krause, Ellison, Shaw, Marcum, & Boardman, 2001) and forgiveness (Krause & Ingersoll-Dayton, 2001).

Gender

Research consistently shows that women are more deeply involved in religion than men (Barna, 2002). Moreover, there is some evidence that gender differences in religion are present across the life course (Levin, Taylor, & Chatters, 1994). But most of the work that has been done so far focuses solely on mean differences in religion. This means, for example, that women pray more often than men (Barna, 2002). But there is another more subtle issue that needs to be explored here as well. More specifically we need to know whether the impact of various facets of religion on health differ for men and women. A recent study by Krause, Ellison, and Marcum (2002) on church-based social support shows why this distinction may be important. Their study reveals that women receive more church-based support than men. However, their findings further indicate that, compared to older women, church-based support exerts a more beneficial effect on the health of older men. Although it is not clear why this may be so, the general pattern of findings is important to keep in mind as the chapters in this volume are reviewed.

The Negative Side of Religious Involvement

In the process of reviewing research on religion and health, a number of investigators go to great lengths to extol the benefits of religion while saying very little about the potential downside of involvement in religion. In the end, religion and places of worship are largely human endeavors. Because human beings are not perfect, the institutions they create are often flawed as well. As a result, people may encounter difficulties in church as well as problems in implementing and practicing their faith. Evidence of this may be found in at least three areas. First, research by Krause, Morgan, Chatters, and Meltzer (2000) reveals that interpersonal conflict is not uncommon in the church, and that when it arises, it is a source of significant psychological distress (see also Krause, Ellison, & Wulff, 1998). Second, research by Pargament (1997) indicates that while most people find solace in religious coping responses, other individuals do not. Instead, some people adopt negative religious coping responses (e.g., feeling abandoned by God), and those who do are more likely to experience psychological distress. Third, Krause and his associates report that from time-to-time, some individuals tend to have doubts about their faith (Krause, Ingersoll-Dayton, Ellison, & Wulff, 1999). This study further reveals that people who experience religious doubt also encounter more symptoms of psychological distress.

Viewed more broadly, the literature reviewed up to this point presents two very different perspectives on how religion may influence health: On the one hand, involvement in religion appears to enhance physical and mental functioning, while on the other hand, it may also serve to compromise health and well-being. As the research presented in the following chapters will reveal, there is far from a one-to-one correspondence between things like prayer, religious coping, forgiveness, and health. Perhaps adopting a more balanced perspective by considering the negative as well as the positive facets of religion will provide greater insight into how individual variations arise in the effects of religious involvement.

Cross-Cultural and International Issues

The chapter on race and socioeconomic status in this volume provides many valuable insights into how these core social structural components may influence the relationship between religion and health. However, it is possible to throw an even broader net by turning to religion in cultures and countries that are substantially different from those in the West. Unfortunately, there are very few studies in the English literature on this subject (for notable exceptions see Krause et al., 2002; Musick, Traphagan, Koenig, & Larson, 2000). Expanding the scope of inquiry by studying religion in culturally-diverse settings should help isolate the underlying factors that link religion and health and help define the extent to which results generated in Western settings can be generalized to other cultures. In addition, as

American society continues to become more culturally diverse, we need to know a good deal more about the religion of those who immigrate from Asia, Africa, and other markedly different societies.

Spirituality

Many people speak of religion and spirituality in the same breath. Although it is hard to distinguish between the two, the major difference is that religion often takes place within formal institutions while spirituality is not necessarily grounded in the context of a formal organization (George, Larson, Koenig, & McCullough, 2000). Even though spirituality is an important domain in its own right, it was not included in this volume because the range of potential spiritual experiences is almost limitless. Anything from the birth of a child to a walk in the woods might be subsumed under the broad rubric of spirituality. As a result, the measurement, and therefore the conceptual boundaries, of this unwieldy domain remain elusive. Since religion was hard enough to cover by itself, it seemed that a chapter on spirituality is best left to another volume. This does not mean, however, that the study of spirituality is in any way less important. Instead, for the time being, it would be helpful to think of the interplay between spirituality and religion as the chapters in this volume are reviewed.

CONCLUSIONS

Reading research on religion and health can be a frustrating experience because investigators have used a plethora of measures to study a bewildering array of religious domains from a number of different theoretical perspectives. Even so, the very depth and breadth of the field is reassuring because it illustrates how the study of religion can serve as a strategic context for integrating much of what has been learned in the wider social and behavioral sciences. The contributors to this volume are among the very best in the field. Many are responsible for opening up whole new vistas of research on religion and health, and many have devised the state-of-the-art measures that are used to investigate them. As a result, it is hoped that the chapters in this volume will help investigators get a handle on this unwieldy field and find specific guidance on how to integrate newly emerging insights into their own research programs. Ellen Idler discusses issues involving church attendance (i.e., religious observance) in chapter 2, Jeff Levin provides an overview of prayer in chapter 3, Kenneth Pargament and Gere Ano cover religious coping in chapter 4, Giacomo Bono and Michael McCullough delve into issues involving forgiveness in chapter 5, Linda Chatters outlines the importance of taking a life course perspective when studying religion and health in chapter 6, and Linda George, Judith Hays, Elizabeth Flint, and Keith Meador examine the influence of race and socioeconomic status in research on religion and health in late life in chapter 7.

Although those who venture into the field will be confronted by many problems in conceptualization, measurement, and analysis, the rewards that are derived from studying religion and health are commensurate with these costs. Studying the connection between religion and health is exciting because it cuts right to the heart of age-old questions about the interface between mind and body. But more than this, the study of religion, aging, and health provides a venue for systematically tracing the health-related implications of some of the ultimate questions that have faced human beings since time began.

ACKNOWLEDGEMENTS

This chapter was written with support from the National Institute on Aging (RO1 AG14749—"Religion, Aging, and Health").

REFERENCES

Barna, G. (2002). *The state of the church, 2002.* Ventura, CA: Issachhar Resources.

Berkman, L. F., & Glass, T. (2000). Social integration, social networks, social support, and health. In L. F. Berkman & I. Kawachi (Eds.), *Social epidemiology* (pp. 137–173). New York: Oxford University Press.

Blalock, H. M. (1982). *Conceptualization and measurement in the social sciences.* Beverly Hills, CA: Sage.

Bradley, W. J., & Schaefer, K. C. (1998). *Uses and misuses of data and models.* Thousand Oaks, CA: Sage.

Durkheim, E. (1915/1965). *Elementary forms of religious life.* London: George Allen Unwin Ltd.

Ehmann, C. (1999). The age factor in religious attitudes and behavior. July 14, 1999 Poll Release (http://www. gallup.com/poll/releases/pr990714b.asp).

Enright, R. D., & North, J. (1998). *Exploring forgiveness.* Madison, WI: University of Wisconsin Press.

Fetzer Institute/National Institute on Aging Working Group. (1999). *Multidimensional measurement of religiousness/spirituality for use in health research.* Kalamazoo, MI: Fetzer Institute.

Freud, S. (1913). *Totem and taboo: Some points of agreement between the mental lives of savages and neurotics.* London: Routledge.

George, L. K. (1996). Missing links: The case for a social psychology of the life course. *The Gerontologist, 36,* 248–255.

George, L. K., Larson, D. B., Koenig, H. G., & McCullough, M. E. (2000). Spirituality and health: What we know, what we need to know. *Journal of Social and Clinical Psychology, 19,* 102–116.

Harris, W. S., Gowda, M., Kolb, J. W., Strychacz, C. P., Vacek, J. L., Jones, P. G., Forker, A., O'Keefe, J. H., & McCallister, B. D. (1999). A randomized, controlled trial of the effects of remote, intercessory prayer on outcomes of patients admitted to the coronary care unit. *Archives of Internal Medicine, 159,* 2273–2278.

Hummer, R., Rogers, R., Nam, C., & Ellison, C. G. (1999). Religious involvement and U.S. adult mortality. *Demography, 36,* 273–285.

Idler, E. L., & Kasl, S. V. (1997). Religion among disabled and nondisabled persons II: Attendance at religious services as a predictor of the course of disability. *Journal of Gerontology: Social Sciences, 52B,* S306–S316.

James, W. (1902/1997). *Selected writings—William James.* New York: Book-of-the-Month Club.

Jung, C. G. (1953). *C. G. Jung: Psychological Reflections* (edited by J. Jacobi & R. F. C. Hill). Princeton, NJ: Princeton University Press.

Koenig, H. G., McCullough, M. E., & Larson, D. B. (2001). *Handbook of religion and health.* New York: Oxford University Press.

Krause, N. (2002a). Church-based social support and health in old age: Exploring variations by race. *Journal of Gerontology: Social Sciences, 57B,* S332–S347.

Krause, N. (2002b). A comprehensive strategy for developing closed-ended survey items for use in studies of older adults. *Journal of Gerontology: Social Sciences, 57B,* S263–S274.

Krause, N. (2003). Exploring race differences in the relationship between social interaction with the clergy and feelings of personal worth in late life. *Sociology of Religion* (In Press).

Krause, N., & Ellison, C. G. (2003). Forgiveness by God, forgiveness of others, and psychological well-being in late life. *Journal for the Scientific Study of Religion* (In Press).

Krause, N., Ellison, C. G., & Marcum, J. P. (2002). Church-based social support, gender, and changes in health over time. *Sociology of Religion, 63,* 21–47.

Krause, N., Ellison, C. G., Shaw, B. A., Marcum, J. P., & Boardman, J. (2001). Church-based social support and religious coping. *Journal for the Scientific Study of Religion, 40,* 637–656.

Krause, N., Ellison, C. G., & Wulff, K. M. (1998). Church-based emotional support, negative interaction, and psychological well-being: Findings from a national sample of Presbyterians. *Journal for the Scientific Study of Religion, 37,* 725–741.

Krause, N., & Ingersoll-Dayton, B. (2001). Religion and the process of forgiveness in late life. *Review of Religious Research, 42,* 252–276.

Krause, N., Ingersoll-Dayton, B., Ellison, C. G., & Wulff, K. M. (1999). Aging, religious doubt, and psychological well-being. *The Gerontologist, 39,* 525–533.

Krause, N., Liang, J., Shaw, B. A., Sugisawa, H., Kim, H. K., & Sugihara, Y. (2002). Religion, death of a loved one, and hypertension among older adults in Japan. *Journal of Gerontology: Social Sciences, 57B,* S21–S47.

Krause, N., Morgan, D. L., Chatters, L., & Meltzer, T. (2000). Negative interaction in the church: Insights from focus groups. *Review of Religious Research, 41,* 522–545.

Lenski, G. (1961). *The religious factor.* Garden City, NY: Doubleday & Company.

Levin, J. S., Taylor, R. J., & Chatters, L. M. (1994). Race and gender differences in religiosity among older adults: Findings from four national surveys. *Journal of Gerontology: Social Sciences, 49,* S137–S145.

Marmot, M., & Wilkinson, R. G. (2000). *Social determinants of health.* New York: Oxford University Press.

Marty, M. E. (1998). The ethos of Christian forgiveness. In E. L. Worthington (Ed.), *Dimensions of forgiveness: Psychological research, theoretical perspectives* (pp. 9–28). Philadelphia: Templeton Foundation Press.

McCullough, M. E., Pargament, K. I., & Thoresen, C. E. (2000). *Forgiveness: Theory, research, and practice.* New York: Guilford.

McEwen, B., & Lasley, E. N. (2002). *The end of stress as we know it.* Washington, DC: National Academy Press.

Merton, R. K. (1949). *Social theory and social structure: Toward the codification of theory and research.* Glencoe, IL: Free Press.

Musick, M. A., Traphagan, J. W., Koenig, H. G., & Larson, D. B. (2000). Spirituality in physical health and aging. *Journal of Adult Development, 7,* 73–86.

Neighbors, H. W., Musick, M. A., & Williams, D. R. (1998). The African American minister as a source of help for serious personal crises: Bridge or barrier to mental health care? *Health Education & Behavior, 25,* 759–777.

Pargament, K. I. (1997). *The psychology of religion and coping: Theory, research, and practice.* New York: Guilford.

Perry, R. B. (1954). *The thought and character of William James, briefer version.* New York: George Braziller.

Princeton Religion Research Center. (1994). *Religion in America* (supplement). Princeton, NJ: Gallup Poll.

Simmel, G. (1905). A contribution to the sociology of religion. *American Journal of Sociology, 11,* 359–376.

Snyder, C. R. (2001). *Coping with stress: Effective people and processes.* New York: Oxford University Press.

Veroff, J., Kulka, P. A., & Douvan, E. (1981). *Mental health in America: Patterns of help seeking from 1957 to 1976.* New York: Basic Books.

Weber, M. (1922/1963). *The sociology of religion.* Berlin, Germany: J. C. B. Mohr.

Wink, P., & Dillon, M. (2001). Religious involvement and health outcomes in late adulthood: Findings from a longitudinal study of women and men. In T. G. Plante & A. C. Sherman (Eds.), *Faith and health: Psychological perspectives* (pp. 75–106). New York: Guilford Press.

Worthington, E. L. (1993). *Psychotherapy and religious values.* Grand Rapids, MI: Baker Book House.

CHAPTER 2

Religious Observance and Health: Theory and Research

Ellen L. Idler

Observance   I. 1. The action or practice of observing (a law, duty, ceremony, custom, rule, method, etc.). b. The keeping of a prescribed ritual. 2. A customary rite. b. An ordinance to be observed; esp. the rule of a religious order. II. Respectful or courteous attention, dutiful service. III. 1. Observant care, heed. 2. The action of paying attention; notice; watching.

Shorter Oxford English Dictionary, 1933, p. 1352

The title of this chapter uses the word "observance," rather than "religious attendance," in order to convey a larger meaning. The assignment for the paper was first to review theory and research on the relationship between religious attendance and health among elderly persons, and to address what we know about differences between and among various religious denominations in American society. Secondly, I will discuss the mechanisms underlying the relationship, comparing religious observance to some of the more subjective dimensions of religion, and illustrating this with findings from a large representative sample of elderly persons and from a subset of this group who were interviewed during their last year of life. Finally, I will speculate a little about the elements of religious observance, in other words, what it is that individuals are exposed to when we measure the frequency of their attendance at religious services. For all of these purposes, the layers of meaning in the term "observance" are critical.

TWO TRADITIONS IN RESEARCH ON RELIGIOUS OBSERVANCE AND HEALTH

Denominations and the Societal-Level Approach

The first definition given in the Oxford English Dictionary (OED) is "the action or practice of observing a law, duty, ceremony, custom, rule, method, etc." Religious observance means obeying religious laws or rules, particularly with respect to ceremonies. An observance is a behavior that conforms to religious teaching or prescription. The ability of religious groups to constrain and direct human behavior was one of the primary reasons Emile Durkheim, turn of the century French sociologist, argued that religious ties protected individuals against suicide (1897/1951). His book, *Suicide,* marks the origin of both theoretical and empirical research on religion and health. With the use of national and regional statistics, Durkheim demonstrated that there were large variations in suicide rates in the countries of Europe, and that these were to some extent explained by the differing proportions of Protestants, Roman Catholics, and Jews in the populations from which the rates were derived. Protestantism, with its emphasis on free will and individual salvation, put individuals at risk of suicide because of what Durkheim called excessive anomie, by comparison with Judaism and Catholicism, which provide, in Durkheim's words, "a sufficiently intense collective life" (p. 170) to minimize the risk of suicide.

Observance means that members of religious groups observe rules, thereby constraining their behavior to some extent. It also means that they observe *particular* customs, ceremonies, etc., and these particular observances, in Durkheim's research, have different consequences for their health, in this case different risks for the particular cause of death by suicide. A more recent example of research on denominational differences is in an article by Pescosolido and Georgianna (1989). They calculated suicide rates for 27 US religious organizations, and found that groups that increased their county's suicide rate the most were denominations at the heart of liberal Protestantism—Episcopalians, "institutional" (as opposed to evangelical) Methodists, "institutional" Presbyterians, and the United Church of Christ. Groups exerting the strongest protective effect against suicide were the Roman Catholic Church, the conservative Protestant Nazarenes and evangelical Baptists. The authors present a U-shaped diagrammatic interpretive summary of their findings, derived from Durkheim, that includes expected suicide rates for the religious groups they studied, as well as both unaffiliated atheists (at one extreme) and cults such as the Branch Davidians or Heaven's Gate (at the other), none of which were included in their research. In the diagram, religious groups are arrayed by the density of their social network ties, from the unaffiliated atheists with no ties at all, to the members of isolated, extreme cults where all contact with the world outside the religious group is cut off. The relationship between the density of religious ties and suicide rates is curvilinear—this potential for religious groups to exert *too much* control over their members was foreseen by Durkheim, and could hardly be ignored by Pescosolido and Georgianna, who were writing shortly after the suicides at Jonestown (but before those in Waco or Los Angeles).

To summarize, from this line of research on religion and health we see, first, that differences *between* religious denominations matter for health. We will address the mechanisms by which religion affects health in the second part of this paper, but something about the content of beliefs, or specific religious observances appears to have a differential effect on suicide rates. The close correspondence between Pescosolido's findings in late 20th century America and Durkheim's in turn-of-the-century Europe always strikes me as bordering on the miraculous, given their different locations, research methods, and historical eras, not to mention the tendency for large social institutions to change over time. Second, Pescosolido's research, and importantly Durkheim's theory, show a clearly curvilinear effect—that an *excess* of the regulation and constraint imposed by religious groups can have a negative effect on health. Durkheim was concerned with the increasing suicide rate in modern European society, which he attributed to increasing alienation and anomie, or normlessness; his examples of suicide due to excessive social force come from nonwestern societies and are clearly exceptions to the rule that the social integration and regulation provided by religious groups lowers the risk of suicide. What is true for the research on religion and suicide is true for the broader field as well: against a background of generally positive findings about the impact of religious observance on health, there remains the theoretical and actual potential for religion to have detrimental effects on health and well-being in elderly populations.

Social Network Membership and the
Individual-Level Approach

Another strain of research with a bearing on the relationship between religious observance and health comes from the large epidemiological surveys fielded in the late 1960s and 1970s, beginning with Alameda County, California (Berkman & Syme, 1979), Tecumseh County, Michigan (House, Robbins, & Metzner, 1982), and Evans

County, Georgia (Schoenbach, Kaplan, Fredman, & Kleinbaum, 1986). Each of these prospective cohort studies measured religious group membership or attendance at baseline; they also assessed the health of respondents, their health risk behaviors and their other social ties to family, extended family, friends, and neighborhood or voluntary organizations. Deaths from all causes, not just suicide, were ascertained. In each of the three studies, ties to religious groups, along with other social ties, were associated with lower mortality risks. More recently, Robert Hummer and his colleagues, Rogers, Nam, and Ellison (1999) used data from the 1987 National Health Interview Survey, finding that the most frequent category of attendance at religious services added approximately 7 years to life expectancy at age 20, compared with the life expectancy of those who did not attend services at all. In this study, the effect of frequency of religious observance was linear, with those attending more than once per week having the lowest hazard of death, compared to increasing risks among those attending weekly, less than once per week, and never. Specific religious affiliations were not measured in these studies, or at least not reported; the variables assessed simply absence or presence/extent of religious involvement per se.

Our research in a representative sample of elderly persons in New Haven, CT, replicated both of these traditions of research, and tested the impact of differences in religious denomination as well as the impact of attendance at services. In a 1992 paper, we examined religion's effect on later physical health, in the form of functional disability (Idler & Kasl, 1992); frequency of attendance at services was associated with significantly fewer functional limitations after three years, even after we adjusted for baseline functioning and health status. In the same model, there were no differences by religious denomination (Protestants, Jews, and those with Other/No Religion did not differ from Roman Catholics in their follow-up functional disability). However, to examine this issue somewhat more closely, and because we were aware of large socioeconomic differences for blacks and whites within the Protestant group, we analyzed the impact of attendance for each denomination separately. These findings showed that the positive effects of attendance were very strong for Roman Catholics (about half our sample), less strong for Jewish respondents, still weaker for black Protestants, and entirely absent for white Protestants. The ordering, in other words, showed a strong correspondence to the Pescosolido findings regarding suicide.

The Durkheim and Pescosolido research tradition, and other studies, including those of Dwyer, Clarke, and Miller (1990) and Kark et al. (1996) are based on aggregate regional-, county-, or country-level data on the numbers of members of specific religious organizations. The social network tradition, on the other hand, has made use of individual level data on religious participation, with generally little attention to denomination or affiliation. These two traditions should be merged more often than they have been. In Figure 2.1 I propose a theoretical relationship between religious observance (low to high) and religious group affiliations, arrayed in order of increasing social network density, as adapted from Pescosolido and Georgianna (1989). According to this theoretical schema of the joint effects of observance and denomination, we should expect to see weak to absent effects of religion on health among low-level participants of the least dense congregations of the mainline Protestant churches, and the strongest effects among highly observant members of densely knit congregations in Roman Catholic parishes and the "community religions" of the Amish, Mormons, etc. The moderate positive effects of religion, as seen in most studies, would be found not only among individuals with mid-level observance patterns in medium-dense congregations, but also among those with lower levels of observance in denser congregations, and those with high levels of participation in the least-dense congregations. The model balances the social force of religious affiliation (about which individuals have differing degrees of choice) with the individual self-selection of participation levels.

MECHANISMS: MAKING SENSE OF IT

If religion affects the health of individuals in a way that can be studied scientifically, there must be mechanisms by which membership in specific religious groups, or observance levels, can be linked, at least in part, to already-known health risks through which they have their effect. This is not a universally held opinion among researchers in this field, but it is certainly my view and I, think, the conservative one. In my 1985 dissertation, I proposed three mechanisms which have stood the test of time as this research has developed. Religiousness affects individual health by: (1) promoting healthy lifestyles, (2) facilitating social support by and for members of religious groups, and (3) providing coherent schema, or frameworks of meaning that provide coping, comfort, and understanding for the difficult transitions in life, many of which occur in old age. I would also add a fourth to that list: religious participation may also have direct beneficial physiological effects on heart rate, blood pressure, muscle tone, or the immune system. There is evidence from population-based prospective studies

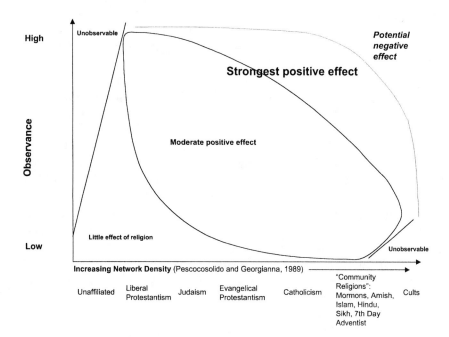

FIGURE 2.1   Joint effects of religious affiliation and observance on health.

supporting each of these mechanisms or mediators. A true mediator is a variable, or set of variables, that is related to the independent variable of interest (in this case religious observance), and also to the dependent variable (health), and, when introduced into a regression equation, significantly reduces the prior adjusted or unadjusted effect of the independent variable (Baron & Kenny, 1986). A mediator variable "explains" some (or on rare occasions all) of the effect of a variable; it gives us a plausible way of understanding how one thing can lead to another. In my view, the mediator variable does not in any way diminish the importance of the independent variable, in the way that effect-reduction might superficially appear to do. Rather, it enhances the importance of the independent variable because it links it to known processes. This is particularly true if more than one mediator is involved—an independent variable with more than one mediator to a health endpoint is a valuable independent variable to know about.

Healthy Lifestyles

In his book *Who Shall Live? Health, Economics, and Social Choice* (1974), the health economist Victor Fuchs has a chapter cleverly titled "A Tale of Two States." It's aptly Dickensian, in describing the best and the worst, the high and the low, the successful and the unsuccessful. In it, he compares the health status of two populations, residents of two neighboring states that are alike in many ways (geography, climate, natural resources, density, average income, and education), and yet have extremely different rates on some of the most important population health indicators: infant mortality, cancer deaths, deaths from suicide and all causes. Nevada's death rate for males aged 40–49 was 54% higher than Utah's; for females it was 69% higher. Fuchs looked specifically at deaths from cirrhosis of the liver, which were 111% higher in Nevada, and from cancer of the respiratory system, which were 296% higher. There were even differences in infant mortality. He attributed these disparities to the "different lifestyles" of Nevadans and Utahans. Of course Utah is the population center of the Mormon church. Mormons do not drink alcohol or smoke cigarettes, and "in general lead stable, quiet lives," with high marriage and low divorce rates, and high birth rates and large families (Fuchs, p. 53). This book was written in 1974; I thought it would be interesting to update Fuchs' data, and I found that little had changed. In the most recent data from the Behavioral Risk Factor Surveillance System (BRFSS), Nevada has by far the highest smoking rate in the U.S. (31.5%), Utah has by far the lowest (13.9%), and Utah also has the lowest rate of lung cancer deaths in the country. Nevada's infant mortality, homicide, and suicide rates are also much higher than Utah's (Centers for Disease Control, 2002). Fuchs' purpose was certainly not to advocate religion in general, or Mormonism in particular; he was simply pointing to the critical role of social conditions in influencing human behaviors that have enormous health consequences.

Of course, most religious groups do not have such strong beliefs about smoking or other health practices as the Mormon church does, but studies in religiously diverse populations also consistently find lower rates of health risk behaviors among the religiously observant, regardless of affiliation. In the New Haven Established Populations for Epidemiological Study of the Elderly (EPESE) study ($N = 2,812$), frequency of attendance at religious services was associated with significantly higher levels of physical activity, lower levels of alcohol use, and a greater probability of never having smoked (Idler & Kasl, 1997a). Selection, no doubt, plays an important role: health risk behaviors in old age are likely to be continuations of health risk behaviors in early and midlife, and more likely to persist among the healthy. The link to lifelong religious affiliation provides an additional means for understanding the stability of health behaviors over the life course. There is strong evidence that religious observance in adolescence is associated with a lower frequency of dangerous or risky behaviors like getting in fights, drinking and driving, carrying weapons, smoking, or using illegal drugs, and also with better health-enhancing behaviors, like exercising, eating regular meals, and getting enough sleep (Wallace & Forman, 1998).

Health behaviors are a mediator of the effect of religious observance on health if introducing one or more health behaviors reduces the initial effect of observance. In a later, 28-year follow-up of the original Alameda County study (N = 5,286), Strawbridge, Cohen, Shema, and Kaplan (1997) found that frequent attenders were both less likely to be smokers at the start of the study, and also more likely to quit smoking during the course of the follow-up, compared with non-attenders. Introducing baseline smoking status to the analysis reduced the effect of attendance on all-cause mortality, and introducing a time-dependent covariate for quitting smoking reduced it even more. Thus part of the initial effect of religious attendance on lower mortality is due to the fact that frequent attenders were less likely to smoke in the first place, and also more likely to quit if they had started smoking, compared with nonattenders. In numerous ways, religion appears to constrain behaviors that put individuals at risk, and thereby protects health. To return to our OED definition of observance, this is the theme of following the rules, observing ordinances, and conforming behavior to meet the expectations of the group.

Support of Social Ties

The OED definition of observance also carries the meanings of: "respectful or courteous attention, dutiful service" and "observant care, heed." These shades of meaning suggest the second mechanism that is often identified: the giving and receiving of social support from other congregation members. Social support networks, religious or otherwise, reduce the risk of mortality. Attendance at religious services, studied from the beginning as an important source of social contacts, offers the individual access to a set of social ties that is distinct from the ties offered by the neighborhood, workplace, voluntary organization, or extended family, although it may overlap with many of these. Since social ties flourish in congregations, members of religious congregations report having larger social networks overall, and also larger networks of both friends and relatives (Ellison & George, 1994). Religious congregations offer both strong and weak ties, which have the potential for providing both emotional and instrumental support to individuals in need. The importance of shared belief systems will be examined below, but one motivating belief shared by all of the major religious traditions is the importance of helping others less fortunate than oneself. Thus congregations offer not only the potential for support to be received by individuals within the group, but also frequent structured opportunities for members to offer support for others, inside and outside the congregation. A small number of recent studies have demonstrated longitudinal health benefits of volunteer activity (Musick, Herzog, & House, 1999; Luoh & Herzog, 2002). This giving and receiving of support over the years of a person's involvement with a particular congregation can build up powerful models of anticipated support, when and if there is need. Thus the benefits of social network embeddedness for health may be magnified by the social support networks of congregations because such a heavy emphasis is placed on support (to and from others) in these settings. However, there are few studies of congregation-based social support (Krause, 2002 is a rare exception) and no studies of the effects of religious versus secular social support from which to generalize.

In the 28-year follow-up Alameda County study (Strawbridge et al., 1997), the higher rate of marriage and social contacts among the frequent attenders was also a partial mediator of the initial relationship between religious attendance and lower rates of all-cause mortality. As was the case with smoking, frequent attenders with few social contacts at baseline were more likely to increase their number of social contacts compared with infrequent attenders, and this post-baseline increase in social attachments was also partially responsible for the reduction in mortality among frequent attenders. The Strawbridge et al. study is important because it demonstrates a clear causal order, in which religious attendance precedes improvement in health behaviors and the growth of social network size, which then subsequently reduce risk. This capacity of religious groups to maintain and even increase the number of available social ties has particular relevance for elderly persons whose close family and friendship ties may be diminished by death, migration, or institutionalization.

Frameworks of Meaning

The final definition of observance is "the action of paying attention; notice; watching." This is an expression of the third mechanism by which religious observance can affect health: by changing the ways in which people see and interpret the world around them and events in their own lives. Bereavement, the serious illnesses of loved ones, and the facing of one's own pain and disability are normative challenges in old age, for which religious beliefs and practices have immediate relevance. Classical sociological theories of religion again anticipate these functions of religious observance in health; Weber's concept of "theodicy" articulates the process by which individual troubles are addressed by religious concepts and language, providing frameworks of meaning for some of the most difficult experiences of human life. Religious texts and stories provide examples of human beings coping with every kind of adversity, and thereby give encouragement, teach lessons, comfort by comparison, and reduce fear of the unknown. Rituals for mourning or healing can assist individuals in making transitions to the understanding of new life stages in which adaptation to loss is required. In fact, studies of a variety of coping methods show that individuals turn to religion in situations such as serious illness, disability, or death, when little control is possible and larger questions of meaning take on urgency.

Outcomes, indicators of successful coping and adaptation, are usually depression or some measure of well-being. In the New Haven EPESE study (Idler & Kasl, 1997a), attendance at services was associated cross-sectionally with lower total Center for Epidemiologic Depression Scale (CESD) scores, particularly with the positive affect, somatic, and interpersonal (but not negative affect) subscales. There were also significant interactions between attendance at services and functional disability associated with positive affect and an indicator of optimism; in other words, disabled members of the sample were particularly likely to experience lower depression levels and higher optimism if they attended services more often. Studies of heart surgery patients (Ai, Dunkle, Peterson, & Bolling, 1998), parents who have lost a child (McIntosh, Silver, & Wortman, 1993), older women caring for elderly parents (Moen, Robison, & Dempster-McLain, 1995), and kidney transplant patients (Tix & Frazier, 1998) all point to the same religious coping process: individuals facing health- or bereavement-related life crises frequently turn to religion for support, and those who do appear to adapt better to difficult circumstances.

PHYSIOLOGICAL PATHWAYS

Religious observance may also provide a buffer against both major and minor stressors, or even prevent them from occurring in the first place, through direct physiological pathways. Certain religious practices, such as prayer, meditation, or participation in rituals may elicit what Benson has famously referred to as the "relaxation response" (Benson, 1996), in opposition to the "stress response" (Selye, 1936) that has provided the dominant paradigm for our understanding of the relationship between the social environment and health. Religious ritual practice, or observance, may be responsible for reduction in the production of stress hormones; high levels of the "flight or flight" hormones epinephrine and norepinephrine circulating in the blood can increase blood pressure, leading to pathological change in blood vessels, and the potential for myocardial infarction or stroke. In addition, stress from adverse life events such as bereavement, divorce, or disasters can result in suppression of the immune system (Watkins, 1995). Repeated elicitation of the relaxation response may result in a reduction in muscle tension, heart rate, the activity of the autonomic nervous system, and a corresponding increase in the effectiveness of the immune system (Koenig, McCullough, & Larson, 2001). The relaxation response may be elicited by an individual's focus on the repetition of a word or phrase, or a repetitive action such as breathing. When given a choice, most individuals choose a prayer or phrase from a sacred text (Benson). Religious rituals, including music, sacred texts, sermons, and communal prayers provide individuals with physical, emotional, and cognitive cues for integrating the experience of the mind, body, and spirit, and achieving transcendent states that are sought as ends in themselves.

Observance *vs.* Other Dimensions of Religiousness

As I have suggested already in this paper, religion is a complex phenomenon with many dimensions. Attendance at worship services, and denomination or affiliation, the subjects of this paper, are only two of a potentially long list of aspects of religion that could be tested for their relationship to health. Observance, or attendance at public worship services, however, with its social and ritual components, may be linked to more of the potential mechanisms we have just reviewed than some other dimensions of religiousness, and therefore might be expected to be more salient. Is public religious observance a more powerful influence than other, more subjective, less behavioral measures of religiousness, such as self-ratings of religiousness or spirituality? The answer, as I will illustrate with data from the New Haven EPESE project, is "it depends."

In the representative sample as a whole, attendance at services was significantly correlated ($b = .49$, $p < .001$) cross-sectionally with our measure of subjective religiousness (getting strength and comfort from religion, and self-rated religiousness), even when adjusted for health and sociodemographic status (Idler & Kasl, 1997b). In these models, black Protestants attended services most frequently, then Roman

Catholics, then Jews, then white Protestants, and finally those with Other/No Affiliation attended least. Black Protestants and Roman Catholics also have the highest levels of subjective religiousness (not different from each other), with white Protestants, Jews, and Other/None significantly less, in that order. When we looked next at the relationship between attendance and subjective religiousness with each of the mediating variables, we saw that attendance was strongly associated with three of the four health practices (more physical activity, lower alcohol use, and never smoking), while subjective religiousness was associated with higher (heavier) body mass index, and weakly with never smoking. Of six social involvement measures, attendance was associated with five (close friends, kin contacts, friend contacts, leisure activities, and holiday celebrations), while subjective religiousness was associated with only two (close kin and kin contacts). Finally, of seven measures of well-being, attendance was associated with four (CESD total score, positive affect, somatic, and interpersonal subscales), while subjective religiousness was associated with none. Thus, at the cross-sectional level, attendance at services was associated with considerably more of the potential mediating mechanisms than was the measure of subjective religiousness. In the longitudinal analysis, it was attendance at services that was associated with better functional disability in every year of follow-up from 1983 to 1988, while subjective religiousness played no role at all. A final step in this analysis was the addition of all possible mediators to the longitudinal models, which resulted in the elimination of the association of attendance with better functioning in four of the years of follow-up, but not in the other three. Thus the better health practices, larger, closer social networks, and higher levels of well-being of those EPESE respondents who attended services frequently accounted for some, but not all, of the association of attendance with better functioning. So we might conclude that at least in this sample and with this health outcome, attendance appears to play a larger and better-explained role in health.

But let's look again at the role of subjective religiousness. We looked cross-sectionally at the relationship between religiousness and several measures of health status which were to be included as covariates in the longitudinal analyses. Adjustment for baseline health status is essential, because of the obvious potential confounding of physical health with the ability to attend services. Attendance was associated at baseline with better functional ability, but not with any of the other health measures—number of prescription medications, stroke, diabetes, angina, congestive heart failure, fractures, amputations, or cognitive function. Subjective religiousness, on the other hand, was significantly associated with *poorer* functional ability, and *more* prescription medications, in other words with worse, not better health. In longitudinal analyses described earlier, with depression as the outcome, we have already mentioned the interaction between subjective religiousness and disability in predicting lower depression among men. Thus there is a suggestion, in the full EPESE sample, that subjective religiousness plays a particular role for elderly persons who are already sick. Those who are ill or disabled at baseline are more, not less, subjectively religious, and feelings of religiousness protect particularly these ill or disabled individuals against depression.

Our measures of subjective religiousness played a much more important, main effect role in our most recent New Haven EPESE analyses, however (Idler, Kasl, & Hays, 2001). An interest in end-of-life issues caused us to re-examine our data, in which respondents were interviewed every 12 months for 6 years, and then again after 5 more years. By subtracting the date of interview from the date of death, we were able to identify a sample of 499 respondents who had been interviewed on the subject of religion by the EPESE project within the 12 months before their deaths. We were interested in their patterns of religious feelings and practice in the year before death, and also in the consequences those feelings and practices might have for well-being. Our results showed, after adjusting for health status, that respondents who were in their last 6 months of life had significantly lower attendance levels than they had had at their previous interview, while those who were not in their last 6 or 12 months of life had not changed; however, subjective religious measures changed very little for any group, with the exception of small *increases* for those in their last six months of life. I would quickly add, however, that while attendance declined from previous levels for the last six months of life group, it was still quite high, averaging 1–2 times per month.

In further analyses, we asked if religious attendance or feelings would have any impact on the quality of life of those in the end-of-life period (Idler & Kasl, 2002). The short answer is yes, and both types of religiousness appear to play a role. Figure 2.2 shows that respondents in their last year of life who attended services at least once per month saw an average of 7+ friends frequently, while those who did not attend saw only 4+. Those who said they were deeply religious saw 8 friends regularly, while those who were not saw only half that many. And those who felt a great deal of comfort from religion saw 7, compared with 4 for those who did not get comfort from religion. These differences are adjusted for SES and health status and are statistically significant where indicated. We then looked at average CESD scores, which could range

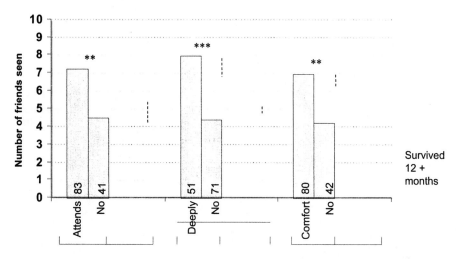

FIGURE 2.2   **Average number of friends seen frequently by religious and non-religious respondents in last year of life. New Haven EPESE, 1982, *N* = 2812.**

from 0 to 60, with 16 being the usual cutoff for approximating clinical depression. In this analysis shown in Figure 2.3, also adjusted for SES and health, respondents in their last year of life who attended services regularly had CESD scores of 9, while those who did not had scores of approximately 14, a very high average score for this group of 36 individuals. There were very similar, and also statistically significant differences for those who were deeply religious, compared with those considered themselves fairly religious or less. Thus in this analysis of a highly unusual sample of individuals interviewed prospectively during their last year of life, we saw a pattern similar to that which we saw among the disabled members of the population. Whereas among the representative sample of community-dwelling elderly persons, we saw a stronger association of attendance at services with better health and more of the potential mediator variables, and much less of a role played by the subjective dimensions of religiousness, which were often associated with poorer health, in the last year of life sample we saw strong positive effects for the more subjective dimensions of religion, equal to those of attendance.

We might sum up the comparison of these two dimensions of religiousness by saying that attendance at religious services is the most frequently measured dimension of religiousness in health surveys, and it is likely to be the dimension of religiousness that has the strongest overall positive effect on health status in large, representative samples.

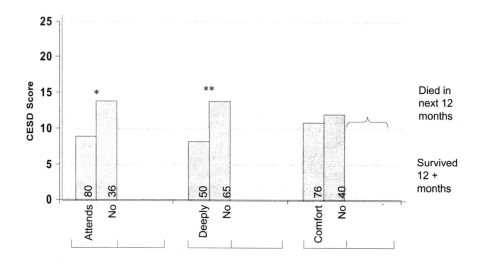

FIGURE 2.3   Average CESD scores of religious and non-religious respondents in last year of life. New Haven EPESE, 1982, *N* = 2812.

The reason for this is that the many layers of meanings of religious observance link the public, social aspects of religiousness to more of the potential mediators of the relationship between religion and health, resulting in both primary and secondary prevention of disease and its resulting disability. However, among vulnerable subsets of the population, such as those with serious chronic illness or disability, or those in their last year of life, subjective dimensions of religion may play a very important role in preventing the depression or social isolation that could easily result from physical limitations.

ELEMENTS OF RELIGIOUS OBSERVANCE

Studies which measure only attendance at religious services are usually, appropriately, criticized for their insufficient operationalization of the full meaning of religiousness. What the critics often seem to have in mind is fuller attention to the more subtle dimensions of beliefs, values, and spirituality, aspects which until recently have been absent from the measurement of religiousness in large representative surveys. (The New Haven and Duke EPESE studies are very rare examples of prospective studies from the 1980s with any attention to these other dimensions at all.) Attendance at services, the only item likely to be included if religion is measured, was thus the familiar item, whose meaning was not questioned. In this last part of the paper I would like to suggest that we look a little more closely at the nature of attendance at religious services, and ask what it is that people are exposed to when they spend one, two, or more hours per week in public worship services. I would like to focus on two areas: rituals in worship and the elements of congregational life.

Congregations

The novelist Mary Gordon once wrote, ". . . the church is the one institution I know where one doesn't have to be rich, or educated, or sophisticated, or attractive, or well-connected, or even necessarily sane, in order to be a member." I don't know about your congregation, but sanity is definitely not a requirement for membership in my congregation either. I would add, as another nonrequirement for membership, that one can be neither too young nor too old for full membership—how many institutions aside from the family can say that? Congregations are collectives; they are social groups with common purposes that draw individuals from many corners of a community and create the potential for social ties that would not exist otherwise. Individuals choose to be there; in modern life in religiously dense and diverse population centers, the choice is more real than ever before in human history. People choose to be parts of groups including others like and unlike themselves, groups with rules and obligations and expectations. By joining they submit to those expectations, and transcend their individuality.

But congregations should be thought of as more than collections of individuals. Congregations have permanence and long histories that transcend the lives of individual members, and even sometimes the histories of the buildings they are housed in. Congregations have structures—roles, committees, positions—and they have many functions. For an illustration of functions, take a look at a church newsletter. All of the mechanisms previously mentioned by which religion might influence health are here, and more. There are food baskets for Easter for the needy in the local community, and blankets and tools for agriculture for those in countries served by the World Council of Churches. Money is raised for Habitat for Humanity, and help is offered to those whose houses were flooded by Hurricane Floyd (which also flooded the church). Congregation members are raising money to help others with multiple sclerosis, Lou Gehrig's disease, and leukemia. One member, a single mother who has suffered with both multiple sclerosis and breast cancer in recent years, expresses her gratitude for the support the congregation has given her family. There are births and deaths. This congregation was founded in 1766, and it has been doing these same things, sharing joys and supporting those in need inside it and outside it, for centuries. It is clearly more than the sum of its parts at any moment.

In his later book on religion, Emile Durkheim (1915) emphasized the essential, social, nature of the religious group: ". . . for it is an eternal truth that outside of us there exists something greater than us, with which we enter into communion" (p. 257). Religion, for Durkheim, was a system of ideas about the sacred that was by necessity shared, held in common, and expressed in collective representations whose meaning was understood by all. Congregations are also much more than the sum of the individuals who make them up; they are actors in their communities, holders of social capital, often the bearers of good will, and frequently the providers of basic, necessary social services to their neighborhoods and communities. It would have made no sense to Durkheim to conceptualize religiousness at the individual level alone, nor should it make sense to us.

Any serious study of religion and health should not stop at the individual level of analysis, but should strive to include congregations as equally important levels of analysis. Sociologists of religion have not forgotten congregations; the recent national study of congregations led by Nancy Ammerman (1997) is a fine example. But the study of religion and health has rarely been graced by this wider view; rather it has been pinioned to the actions and reactions of individuals and their consequences for health, measured always at the individual level. This is both a weakness of the field at the current time, and an important opportunity to move it forward. It is an issue of measurement, analysis, and most of all, perspective. It is one answer to the question of why religious observance is important for health: it is important because religious observance gives purpose and orientation to religious congregations, and brings individuals into contact with them.

Rituals

The earliest examples of practices designed to promote the public health are to be found, among primitive peoples, inextricably mingled with the ritual of religion.
—Winslow, 1937, p. 646

In 1937, Charles-Edward Amory Winslow, professor of public health at Yale School of Medicine, wrote these words for the first *Encyclopedia of the Social Sciences*, under the heading "Public Health." These are the very first words in the article, which ran for many pages. Winslow was a gifted scientist of the early 20th century, known for his studies of the decline in infectious disease mortality. In his discussion of the importance of religious ritual for health, he mentions the documented quarantine efforts in ancient Persia and among the Biblical Hebrews. Other practices from ancient times carried out for religious reasons, with unintended but nevertheless effective public health consequences, include burial of the dead, the controlled preparation of meat for consumption, and the separation of lepers from the community. Durkheim (1915) observed that one function of religious rituals is to separate the sacred from the profane, and this characteristic is as apt today as in ancient times. Religious rituals in the contemporary setting take place in the sacred time of the worship service, and the sacred place of the temple, mosque, or church, places of sanctuary from daily life and profane time.

As Ammerman (1997) points out in her report on congregational life in late 20th century America: "as places of religious ritual, congregations are potential sites for social and personal transformation (1997)" (p. 369). Ritual has the power to alter social arrangements, and to lift individuals who participate in them out of their daily lives, into a state of what Durkheim called "collective effervescence," the experience of the transcendent that takes place in a social context. Rituals are the primary structure of the worship service; their repeated performance, week after week, year after year, brings individuals into sacred space and time in a predictable way. Regular attendance at religious services also then means regular exposure to religious ritual. Life course transitions are often marked by religious ritual—baptisms, confirmations, weddings, funerals. For the elderly, particularly, a lifelong membership in a congregation may place many of these key moments in the same setting, and result in a significant attachment to this sacred place.

Why might this exposure to religious ritual have an impact on health? Returning to the mechanisms proposed earlier, rituals have the effect of reinforcing the social solidarity of the group, which might influence individual behavior with respect to smoking, drinking, or sexuality, assisting individuals in avoiding "temptations" that increase health risks. They may also enhance feelings of emotional closeness, concern, and support for others in the social group, thereby increasing social support levels. And they may certainly also evoke insight and understanding in moments of crisis or suffering. But perhaps above all, religious rituals are experiences that unite the body and its senses with emotions and the cognitive schema of beliefs shared with others. Such "body-mind-spirit" experiences are sought through many extraordinary routes in modern life, but provided regularly in ordinary religious worship services. Kneeling for prayer, smelling incense, drinking wine, eating the communion wafer, being baptized by immersion, are all physical experiences expressing the joining of the body to others in the religious group. Research on the physiological impact of religious ritual has mostly taken the form of studies of meditation; it is still in a very early stage, despite the popular interest (Begley, 2001).

One element of the worship service worthy of particular attention is music. The performance of live music by talented amateurs and/or skilled professionals is a regular feature of Judeo-Christian worship services that may bring joy and pleasure, especially to those who might lack the means to hear music performed in secular concerts. The beauty of the music may also be enhanced by the beautiful physical setting in which it takes place: in high-ceilinged architecture, reflected in stained glass windows, or in sanctuaries that may be filled with painting or sculpture. Moreover, many congregations offer opportunities for performance by congregation members of all ages, in choirs, in instrumental performance, or in unison singing. John Updike said in an interview I heard, when asked (with considerable skepticism from the interviewer) why an intellectual would go to church regularly (which Updike does): "I go to church to sing." We might add to Mary Gordon's list of the inclusive qualities of congregations—anyone can sing here, whether they can hold a tune or not. The study of the physiology of singing is also limited but suggestive (Valentine & Evans, 2001).

In our NIA study of religion in adaptation to heart surgery (Richard Contrada, principal investigator), currently underway, we have taken a closer look at the elements of the worship service. This is a study of what will ultimately be 500 patients undergoing coronary artery bypass or heart valve replacement surgery. Because of the importance of the single variable measuring religious attendance in so many earlier studies, what happened during the "attendance time" seemed like a black box. Our attempt to open this black box, to dissect the meaning of attendance, has taken two forms, with items you can see in Tables 2.1 and 2.2. Table 2.1 shows items that identify behaviors that could take place during a worship service. We were initially interested in the frequency of exposure to these behaviors, but since most would be experienced at every service, we shifted our focus to the importance of the behavior to the respondent. Table 2.2 shows items that measure emotional arousal in response to worship services, including both positive and negative emotions. The responses to these items do assess

TABLE 2.1   Worship Experience

When you attend services, how important is:

- Listening to or performing music
- Praying for yourself or others
- Reading or listening to Scripture or Torah
- Listening to the semon or drasha
- Participating in rituals or sacraments, such as communion, baptism, or lighting Sabbath candles
- Thinking about the beauty of the surroundings and/or sitting in silence

frequency. With the use of these items, we hope to sketch a much fuller picture of activities and responses to them that occur during worship services.

A final example of the connection between religious observance and health, which ties together congregations, denominations, rituals, and the importance of religion to the elderly, comes from our New Haven EPESE study (Idler & Kasl, 1992). The observance of annual holidays can represent important milestones or markers for the seasons of the year. Families, extended families, neighbors, and community groups may offer celebrations, in addition to the formal religious services. Special music, special food, gifts, cards, traditional treats, and the prospect of family reunions create an atmosphere of anticipation that may take on considerable significance for elderly persons because it draws on early memories (Wuthnow, 1999). To examine the importance of religious holiday celebrations, we counted the number of deaths in the sample that occurred 30 days before the holiday, and compared it with the number of deaths that occurred in the 30 days after, in the years 1982 through 1991. Because there were both Christian and Jewish elderly in the sample, we were able to count deaths of respondents around their own holidays (Christmas and Easter for Christians, and Rosh Hashanah, Yom Kippur and Passover for Jews), and also around the holidays that they would not have observed. Our hypothesis was that these annual religious observances would provide goals for survival for vulnerable elderly people, and that there would be significantly fewer deaths before the holidays, but only for those to whom it was relevant. Our results for the Christian holidays provided strong confirmation. For Christians there were 125 deaths in the 30 days before Christmas and Easter in those years, and 171 after, a significant difference. For Jews, for whom these holidays were irrelevant, there were 28 before and 30 after, virtually no difference. For the Jewish holidays,

TABLE 2.2   Worship Emotions

How often does attending religious services make you feel:
- Elated or joyful?
- Choked up?
- Goose bumps or your spine tingle?
- Sad?
- Like crying?
- Peaceful and calm?
- Cleansed or healed?
- Renewed or energized?

there appeared at first to be no differences for Jewish respondents (there were none for Christians), but when we looked at some of the subgroups we saw significant differences for male respondents and particularly for the more observant Jewish respondents who attended services once a month or more often. These findings are quite similar to those obtained in other studies in the U.S. and Israel (Anson & Anson, 2000; Phillips & King, 1988).

This paper has two main messages about the importance of studying the impact of religious observance on health. One is that we ought to try harder to lift the level of analysis up from the individual—to consider the group, the place where the elementary forms of religious life were initially discovered. The other is that religious observance is a powerful influence on health because it is a complex phenomenon with many parts. It means observing ceremonies, customs, rules, rites, and rituals. It means paying attention, being conscious of, and paying respect. It means offering service to others, paying heed and care. These were the dictionary definitions, but they also capture many of the mechanisms by which religious participation is thought to affect health. Most research on religion and health has focused on religious observance, operationalized as attendance at religious services. This research has often been criticized, appropriately, for its inadequate attention to the other dimensions of religiousness. However, the perspective of this paper is that religious observance in public worship services, the most obvious form of religious participation, is also the most important for health. Whether by accident or by wisdom, we have been looking in at least one of the right places for the answers. But despite the at-first-glance unitary aspect, religious observances comprise complex sets of ritual, textual, artistic, musical, narrative, emotional, and social elements, engaged in by groups of people who behave and believe in unison, creating something larger than themselves. With a simultaneously broader and more dissected concept of religious observance, we will be able to explain more of its impact on health.

REFERENCES

Ai, A. L., Dunkle, R. E., Peterson, C., & Bolling, S. F. (1998). The role of private prayer in psychological recovery among midlife and aged patients following cardiac surgery. *The Gerontologist, 38,* 591–601.

Ammerman, N. (1997). *Congregation and community.* New Brunswick, NJ: Rutgers University Press.

Anson, J., & Anson, O. (2000). Death rests a while: Holy day and Sabbath effects on Jewish mortality in Israel. *Social Science & Medicine, 52,* 83–97.

Baron, R. M., & Kenny, D. A. (1986). The moderator-mediator variable distinction in social psychological research: Conceptual, strategic, and statistical considerations. *Journal of Personality and Social Psychology, 51,* 1173–1182.

Begley, S. (2001). Religion and the brain. *Newsweek, 137,* 50–57.

Benson, H. (1996). *Timeless healing.* New York: Simon & Schuster.

Berkman, L. F., & Syme, S. L. (1979). Social networks, host resistance, and mortality: A nine-year follow-up study of Alameda County residents. *American Journal of Epidemiology, 109,* 186–204.

Centers for Disease Control. (2002). *National Center for Health Statistics State Profile Data.* http://www.cdc.gov/nchs/datawh/stprofiles.htm.

Durkheim, E. (1965). *The elementary forms of the religious life.* (J. Swain, Trans.). New York: Free Press (Original work published 1915.)

Durkheim, E. (1951). *Suicide.* (J. Spaulding and G. Simpson, Trans.). New York: Free Press (original work published 1897).

Dwyer, J. W., Clarke, L. L., & Miller, M. K. (1990). The effect of religious concentration and affiliation on county cancer mortality rates. *Journal of Health and Social Behavior, 31,* 185–202.

Ellison, C. G., & George, L. K. (1994). Religious involvement, social ties, and social support in a southeastern community. *Journal for the Scientific Study of Religion, 33,* 46–61.

Fuchs, V. (1974). *Who shall live? Health, economics, and social choice.* New York: Basic Books.

House, J. S., Robbins, C., & Metzner, H. L. (1982). The association of social relationships and activities with mortality: Prospective evidence from the Tecumseh Community Health Study. *American Journal of Epidemiology, 116,* 123–140.

Hummer, R. A., Rogers, R. G., Nam, C. B., & Ellison, C. G. (1999). Religious involvement and U.S. adult mortality. *Demography, 36,* 273–285.

Idler, E. L., & Kasl, S. V. (1992). Religion, disability, depression, and the timing of death. *American Journal of Sociology, 97,* 1052–1079.

Idler, E. L., & Kasl, S. V. (1997a). Religion among disabled and nondisabled persons I: Cross-sectional patterns in health practices, social activities, and well-being. *Journal of Gerontology: Social Sciences, 52B,* S294–S305.

Idler, E. L., & Kasl, S. V. (1997b). Religion among disabled and nondisabled persons II: Attendance at religious services as a predictor of the course of disability. *Journal of Gerontology: Social Sciences, 52B,* S306–S316.

Idler, E. L., & Kasl, S. V. (2002, November). *Impact of religious observance and beliefs at the end of life.* Paper presented at the annual meeting of the Gerontological Society of America, Boston, MA.

Idler, E. L., Kasl, S. V., & Hays, J. (2001). Patterns of religious practice and belief in the last year of life. *Journal of Gerontology: Social Sciences, 56B,* S326–S334.

Kark, J. D., Shemi, G., Friedlander, Y., Martin, O., Manor, O., & Blondheim, S. H. (1996). Does religious observance promote health? Mortality in secular vs religious kibbutzim in Israel. *American Journal of Public Health, 86,* 341–346.

Koenig, H., McCullough, M., & Larson, D. (2001). *Handbook of religion and health.* New York: Oxford.

Krause, N. (2002). Church-based social support and health in old age: Exploring variations by race. *Journal of Gerontology: Social Sciences, 57B,* S332–S347.

Luoh, M-C., & Herzog, A. R. (2002). Individual consequences of volunteer and paid work in old age: Health and mortality. *Journal of Health and Social Behavior, 43,* 490–509.

McIntosh, D. N., Silver, R. C., & Wortman, C. B. (1993). Religion's role in adjustment to a negative life event: Coping with the loss of a child. *Journal of Personality and Social Psychology, 65,* 812–821.

Moen, P., Robison, J., & Dempster-McLain, D. (1995). Caregiving and women's well-being: A life course approach. *Journal of Health and Social Behavior, 36,* 213–301.

Musick, M. A., Herzog, A. R., & House, J. S. (1999). Volunteering and mortality among older adults: Findings from a national sample. *Journal of Gerontology: Social Sciences, 54B,* S173–S261.

Pescosolido, B. A., & Georgianna, S. (1989). Durkheim, suicide, and religion. *American Sociological Review, 54,* 33–48.

Phillips, D. P., & King, E.W. (1988). Death takes a holiday. *The Lancet 24,* 728–732.

Schoenbach, V. J., Kaplan, B. H., Fredman, L., & Kleinbaum, D. G. (1986). Social ties and mortality in Evans County, Georgia. *American Journal of Epidemiology, 123,* 577–591.

Selye, H. (1936). A syndrome produced by diverse noxious agents. *Nature, 138,* 32.

Strawbridge, W. J., Cohen, R. D., Shema, S. J., & Kaplan, G. A. (1997). Frequent attendance at religious services and mortality over 28 years. *American Journal of Public Health, 87,* 957–961.

Tix, A. P., & Frazier, P. A. (1998). The use of religious coping during stressful life events: Main effects, moderation, and mediation. *Journal of Consulting and Clinical Psychology, 66,* 411–422.

Valentine, E., & Evans, C. (2001). The effects of solo singing, choral singing and swimming on mood and physiological indices. *British Journal of Medical Psychology, 7,* 115–120.

Wallace, J. M., & Forman, T. A. (1998). Religion's role in promoting health and reducing risk among American youth. *Health Education & Behavior, 25,* 721–741.

Watkins, A. D. (1995). Perceptions, emotions and immunity: An integrated homeostatic network. *Quarterly Journal of Medicine, 88,* 283–294.

Winslow, C.-E. A. (1937). Public health. In E. R. A. Seligman (Ed.), *Encyclopedia of the social sciences* (pp. 646–657). New York: MacMillan.

Wuthnow, R. (1999). *Growing up religious: Christians and Jews and their journeys of faith.* Boston: Beacon.

Commentary

Religion and Health:
A European Perspective

Christian J. Lalive d'Epinay and Dario Spini

The chapter by Idler on religious observance and health brings together basic conceptual statements, the building of a theoretical paradigm based on earlier theoretical and empirical work, and an attempt at empirical validation, as well as what she calls speculation. Her chapter represents a thorough review of published work on the relationship between religious observance and health. It also offers a heuristic model which enables one to predict a main positive effect of religion on health on the basis of religious observance and network density. A negative effect is also expected when religious observance and network density are very high. This model is very thought-provoking. However, our comments will challenge some basic assumptions on which this model is grounded on the basis of two main questions.

A first question concerns the epistemological bases of this model. More particularly we raise questions about content. Is it correct to transfer Emile Durkheim's ideas about suicide to the field of health? Is it possible to evacuate the content of religious orthodoxy when we are dealing with issues like religion and health? A second question raised in these comments concerns the validity of Idler's model outside the U.S.A. Is it possible to generalize from empirical results concerning the relationship between religious observance and health mainly obtained in the U.S.A. to other parts of the world? In order to answer this second question we will compare American and Western European research on the link between religion and health on the basis of a literature search.

THEORETICAL AND
EPISTEMOLOGICAL COMMENTS

A Bidimensional or a Tridimensional Model?

The Durkheimian model developed by Idler for analyzing the link between religion and health is basically bidimensional; the degree of (individual) observance is plotted on one axis and the density of the network, or community life, on the other. Between the two, a curvilinear distribution is postulated with possible positive and negative effects of religious observance on health (see Idler, this volume, Figure 2.1). This model is validated by the data of Pescosolido and Georgianna (1989), and by Durkheim's work (Durkheim, 1986). The convergence between both studies is evident, but we would not describe it as "bordering on the miraculous."

At the theoretical level, why should a paradigm not work in two different space/time contexts, if it is a good one? But at the empirical level, a question mark hangs over this convergence: Durkheim did not discuss the reliability of the official sources on which his analyses were based. It is well known that at the end of the 19th century, in communities in which suicide was altogether a sin and a crime, and in which access to religious ceremonies and the cemetery was denied to anyone who had committed suicide, such a death was the cause of great stigmatization of the family. A very normal reaction was therefore to disguise a suicide as some other, religiously and socially acceptable, form of death. The question of Durkheim's sources has been extensively discussed (Besnard, 1976; Douglas, 1967; Pope, 1976; Van Poppel & Day, 1996), the conclusion of these studies being that more recent analyses of Durkheim's data fail to demonstrate that Catholics have lower suicide rates than Protestants (Pope, 1976, p. 143). But the fact that this statistical part of Durkheim's analysis is subject to caution in no way detracts from the theoretical interest of Durkheim's paradigm. It remains a good example of a great theory based on flawed data!

Another main difficulty with Idler's model concerns the hypothesis underlying the vertical axis: the higher the level of observance, the stronger the positive effect on health. This proposition might be valid within the context of American Christian and Jewish communities, because it is postulated that they share the same basic beliefs—what Herberg called "The American Religion"—but if the model is to be more generally applicable, should we not ask: *observance of what?*

Such a question would lead to the introduction of a third dimension: the substantive content of the religious beliefs, norms, and rites. There is for example the case of religious groups that forbid vaccination. And what about the impact on mental health and well-being of very Christian beliefs, such as the Last Judgment and Hell?

In 1979, Lalive d'Epinay and colleagues (Lalive d'Epinay et al., 1983) carried out a survey on the elderly population in two areas of Switzerland, one being the alpine and semi-rural, very religious (Catholic) canton of Valais, and the other the more urban and cosmopolitan canton of Geneva. A surprising result was that the gender-social group with the highest level of depressive symptoms was that of the farmers' wives (one in two of whom showed four or more depressive symptoms). This result did not fit the stereotype about the quality of life in villages, in "*Gemeinschaft*-like" communities. We could not find any explanation on the basis of the closed-ended questionnaire, but the complementary narratives we gathered (about 140 from a sample of more than 1,600 individuals) revealed a typical grievance that we dubbed the "farmer's wife's complaint" (Lalive d'Epinay, 1985).

The basic elements of the complaint were (a) at the individual level, a harsh experience of daily life, and of religious beliefs and control; (b) at the contextual level, rapid change from a traditional, agricultural, *gemeinschaftlich,* and Catholic form of society toward a modern, urban, secular society. As a result of this change, the older generation of women could compare their situation with that of younger women (typified by the example of a daughter, a granddaughter, or a niece).

Daily life was described as tough, too tough. With aging, life left them worn out and debilitated. In the villages, the social structure tended to be egalitarian, but with a strict gender hierarchy, sustained by the Christian doctrine: "Wives, submit yourselves unto your own husbands . . ." (Ephesians, 5.22). Thus, an aggravating element was the "bad" husband. A bad husband drank too much (the Valais is a wine-growing region) and beat his wife and children (domestic violence). Catholicism condemns excessive drinking and domestic violence, but there was a structural male connivance between the priests and the men. When a woman complained at confession, the standard answer was: "I'll try to talk with your husband, but remember, a wife must submit to her husband."

Some women said: "It is a cross we have to bear; and it is God who gave us that cross. Nothing can be changed." But was it true that nothing could be changed? The world around them was changing fast. One daughter quit the village and now lives in a city like Geneva. "She has," her mother says, "a much easier life. Well, her marriage went wrong, but she got rid of her husband, she divorced. Divorce is bad, it is a sin, so the daughter is a sinner and may well be damned for that. But she has a better life and looks so much happier." The aged mother concluded by saying: "Sometimes I wish I were single; I have a friend who is a widow; she is lucky!" But such thoughts are bad; she can repress them but they frighten her: "How will I face the Last Judgment?" As one woman from such a village wrote in her autobiography: "We women were trapped between two infernos: the inferno of our everyday life, and the threat of the inferno in eternal life" (Brumagne, 1980).

The interpretation suggested in this study is also a very Durkheimian one, relying on a changing social context and, let's say, oppressive integration. But the oppressive integration derives neither from too high observance nor from too dense a network. It derives from the interplay between the content of rules (here related to gender) and beliefs (related to the Last Judgment) on the one hand, and integration and social control on the other. The collective suicides (or mass murders) of Jonestown and Waco were associated with "too much control," as Idler writes, but also with an apocalyptic doctrine.

Durkheim was well aware of the ideological (content) dimension of religion. For him, for example, the most important difference between Catholicism and Protestantism was the status of "free examination" ("libre examen": *Suicide,* part II, chap. 2.3), which makes Protestantism more individualistic, thus less "integrative." Exploring "primitive" societies, he also observed that in some of them, suicide resulted from the observance of religious rules. To sum up, we suggest adding to Idler's model a third dimension related to the content of religious doctrines concerning health and death.

Status of the Durkheimian Paradigm

The first section of this chapter was oriented towards theory and research; this shorter one is more, let us say, epistemological. A paradigm can be borrowed from another science, or another area of a specific science, and tentatively applied to another scientific field. For example, the functionalist paradigm in sociology owes much to biology, in an implicit way with Durkheim, and in a much more explicit one with Radcliffe-Brown (1935), for example. Alternatively, a paradigm can be borrowed from a study on a given phenomenon, and tentatively extended to cover the broader field to which the phenomenon is said to belong.

Both procedures (transfer or generalization) are legitimate when correctly applied, and very promising. It seems clear that Idler's chapter belongs to the second category ("What is true for research on religion and suicide is true for the broader field as well . . . ," p. 22 this volume). This means that suicide is conceptualized either as a disease, or as a result of a disease. The first noun, *observance,* is defined and discussed, but not the second, *health,* which seems to be taken as consensual and obvious, the best way to make it a protoplasmic notion. Health refers here to the 1958 World Health Organization's definition (absence of disease) or to the 1968 one (state of total well-being). Durkheim used the expression "social disease," and the suicide rate for him could reach a "pathological" level (according to his distinction between the normal and the pathological in a given state of a society). But then he had in mind the rate as a collective, meta-individual expression. At the individual level, it was clear for him that it could not be reduced to a state of madness or to a form of sickness (*Suicide,* part I, chap. 1).

As mentioned above, suicide has been condemned as a sin in Christian denominations (and still is in some), and as a crime in Christian societies. Classifying suicide as a disease, with its consequent "medicalization," represents a step forward, both in terms of knowledge and of social action. Social scientists collaborating with medical practitioners tend to accept some of their basic assumptions and definitions, but we, social scientists, have a duty to direct some attention to the sociology of knowledge and to challenge the assumptions that underpin our research. The current, heated debate in an aging society like ours on the end of life, suicide and euthanasia, provides an illustration. The individual decision of an elder to depart from life is a function of his or her awareness of frailty, often in a context of physical pain and psychological distress; but it is also an expression of a desire not to be a burden to the family, or to society. This latter motivation fits the Durkheimian category of "altruistic suicide" and cannot be fully understood in a health-related perspective. The point here is that implicitly categorizing suicide as a disease—medical or social—appears to be somewhat judgmental. As a private opinion, it should be respected; as a scientific one, it must be analyzed and discussed.

APPLICABILITY TO WESTERN EUROPE

Our question here is twofold. First, is the model formulated by Idler applicable to the Western European context? Second and more generally, to what extent is the question we are dealing with here (religiousness and health) a pertinent one in Europe?

Is the Topic of Religion and Health Exportable to Western Europe?

For European observers, the "American religious exception," where church attendance and adherence to beliefs have remained very high and stable over recent decades, is a matter of astonishment. This stability in religious involvement is at odds with what we observe in Western Europe, where a wave of secularization is under way, with huge declines since the sixties in church attendance, participation in the basic socialization rites (baptism and confirmation), and adherence to Christian beliefs.

There is in the U.S.A. something that Herberg (1955) called the "American religion," a religion associated with the Judeo-Christian heritage and widely shared up to now by the great majority of the population. According to 1990/93 data (see Table 2.3), roughly 60% of Americans attend a church service at least once a month, with a slight age gap (age group 16–29: 48%; age group 50+: 62%) but almost no gender, education, or income gap. With very few exceptions everybody believes in God, 8 out of 10 believe that there is a life after death and a Heaven, and 7 out of 10 still share the traditional Christian beliefs in the existence of the Devil and of a Hell.

The countries of Western Europe display a wide range of situations. At one extreme, we have Catholic Ireland with a very high rate of church attendance, higher than in the U.S.A., but with more doubts about the frightening images of the Devil and Hell. At the other extreme, we have the Scandinavian countries and France, where participation in church services has long (since the 1980s at least) been low and where (with the exception of Sweden) most people believe in God, but a God disconnected from the other traditional Christian beliefs. Between the extremes, we find two groups of countries, one with a strong Catholic tradition (three Southern European countries and Austria), where 40 to 50% of the population regularly attend church services, and the other comprising West Germany, the United Kingdom, the Netherlands, and Belgium, where church attendance drops to between one in four and one in three, with a low level of belief in the Devil and Hell.

The situation in Western Europe is thus quite disparate from that prevailing in the U.S.A., but most European countries share two common features. First, church attendance and adherence to traditional beliefs are clearly differentiated by age group, gender, education and/or income, with the younger age groups, males, and more educated (or wealthier) persons generally showing lower adherence. Second,

TABLE 2.3   Church Attendance and Adherence to Beliefs, by Country (1989–1990)

Country	Attend services once a month or more	God	Life after death	Devil	Hell
			Believe in		
U.S.A.	58	96	78	70	71
Ireland	88	98	83	55	53
Italy	53	91	68	42	42
Austria	44	87	56	23	20
Portugal	41	86	39	28	25
Spain	39	86	52	32	22
W. Germany	34	78	50	18	15
Belgium	31	69	44	19	17
Netherlands	30	64	47	16	13
United Kingdom	24	78	52	33	28
France	17	62	44	20	17
Norway	13	65	45	24	19
Denmark	11	64	34	10	8
Sweden	10	45	38	12	8

Note. From Inglehart, R., Basañez, M., & Moreno, A. (1998).

although a systematic and in-depth time lag comparison cannot be made at this stage, the trend from 1980 to 2000 is that of a decline in participation and adherence, apparently due to cohort differences.

The interpretation of cohort differences is supported by data from Campiche and colleagues (Campiche & Dubach, 1992; Campiche, in press) concerning the current decline in church attendance in Switzerland (see Table 2.4). In 1989, one in three Swiss inhabitants still went to church once a month or more; ten years later, this ratio had fallen to one in four, with about half of the inhabitants not attending church at all. These numbers can also be interpreted in terms of cohort or generational change. The cohorts aged 46 to 65 in 1999 were about 20 years old during the 1950s and 1960s. Most of them were baptized and received a Christian education; subsequently, during adult life, some stopped going to church. One new feature of the younger cohorts is that fewer and fewer of them have had any religious education or have been baptized.

This is not the time or place to analyze in depth the religious differences between the U.S.A. and Western European countries, although it would be helpful for our discussion. According to Boudon (2001) "the American exception" is well explained by a combination of

TABLE 2.4   Church Attendance (Once a Month or More) in Comparable Samples From Switzerland by Age Group and Period

	Year	
Age group (yrs)	1989	1999
16–24	31.8	13.5
25–34	24.2	19.2
35–44	31.5	22.9
45–54	35.1	21.7
55–64	44.2	36.2
65–74	52.0	41.0
All ages	34.3	24.4

Note. From Campiche & Dubach (1992) and Campiche (in press).

Adam Smith, Alexis de Tocqueville, and Max Weber hypotheses. The first underlined the diversification of the Christian religious experience, an effect of the immigration. A consequence drawn by de Tocqueville was the strong link between religion and the national consciousness, but the absence of any monopolistic "State-Church" (in sharp contrast with the European situation until the 20th century). Adding to that, Weber (1964) analyzed denominational membership as an organizing principle of social stratification in an egalitarian society.

To Boudon's argumentation, we would like to add another hypothesis, also drawn from de Tocqueville's "Democracy in America" (1981). In the U.S.A., the religious community was at the time of colonization, and still is today, the mainstay of social integration and social life, performing important social functions in domains like health or education (the word "community," incidentally, being so common in American everyday language, and so rare in French, German, or Scandinavian languages). In this regard, religiousness in the U.S.A. is more closely bound up with the experience of social networks and a matter of belonging, rather than being a set of beliefs as it is in Europe. The European wave of secularization, for its part, reflects the decline in the control exercised by the Church over individuals.

Does this mean that the question of the link between religiousness and health should be regarded as obsolete or marginal in Western Europe? Before answering, we now want to scrutinize first whether the question is seen as an important one in the European scientific community, and second whether the recent research literature from the U.S.A. and Western Europe validate the hypothesis of a positive link between religion and health.

Literature Search: A Comparison of American and Western European Sources

In order to examine the validity of the association between religious observance and health, four databases (MEDLINE, PREMEDLINE, PsycINFO, and Sociological Abstracts) were searched. Only journal articles referring to community-dwelling samples (excluding studies on religious communities such as monks) in the U.S.A. or in Western European countries (European Union, Norway, and Switzerland) and published between 1990 and 2003 were included. Studies based on historical records for periods such as the end of the 19th century were excluded. The search was based on pairing the keywords religion/religiosity/religiousness/religious with the words health/longevity/mortality/survival/life expectancy/suicide in the abstracts. Only empirical papers that clearly indicated the direction of association between the two terms of the search (religion and health, survival and suicide) were considered. With respect to health-related studies, we included studies covering different aspects of health: functional, physical, depressive symptoms, self-rated health, personality disorders. Studies on suicide were included in spite of our theoretical position that would exclude this phenomenon from health-related issues in order to correspond to Idler's definition of health. Suicide articles were included if they concerned behavior, but not if they only mentioned attitudes toward or thoughts about suicide.

All the abstracts were thus screened according to the direction of the association between religion and health. We classified the reported results into three categories: (1) *confirming*, if the main association expected between the two variables—positive for health and survival and negative for suicide—was clearly mentioned in the abstract (when the association was evaluated but not clearly reported in the abstract, the result was not coded); (2) *partially confirming*, if the association was confirmed in one situation, but not in another (for example confirmed in a specific group or dimension and not in another, using a specific method and not another, or valid in a first model but not when other variables were introduced in the model); and (3) *contradicting*, when no association or an association in the opposite direction was reported.

A first result, which supports the idea that studies evaluating the association between religion and health, survival, and suicide are more relevant in the U.S.A. than in Western Europe, concerns the number of studies done in each region. Overall we recorded 237 journal articles, of which 166 concerned health (physical or mental), 33 survival and 38 suicide. Here, for reasons of space and because the studies covering mortality and suicide are far less numerous than those concerning health, we group all three dimensions (health, mortality, and suicide) together under the general heading of health.

With regard to the difference between the two geographical areas in the context of religion and health, we observed that the studies based on American samples ($n = 180$; 76%) greatly outnumber the European studies ($n = 57$; 24%; binomial test, $p < .001$). Moreover we evaluated the association between the two geographical areas and the obtained results, which proved significant, $\chi^2(2) = 9.76$; $p < .01$. This association was due to the fact that in the U.S.A., the number of confirming studies ($n = 96$; 53.3%) was higher than expected (86) and the number of contradicting studies (n = 39; 21.7%) was lower than expected (45). In the Western European countries, the reverse was the case. The number of confirming studies ($n = 17$; 29.8%) was lower than expected (27) and the number of contradicting studies ($n = 20$; 35.1%) higher than expectated (14). It should, however, be pointed out that the general pattern of differences we have described was observed for health and mortality but not for suicide as the differences between the two geographical areas, while similar to the pattern for the other two dimensions, were not statistically significant. This short survey of the literature leads to three main conclusions: (1) Less interest is to be found for this line of research in Western Europe than in the U.S.A.; (2) the positive link between religion and health is better attested in the U.S.A. than in Western Europe, where only a minority of studies sustain the hypothesis; and (3) neither in Western Europe nor in the U.S.A. is the link a "mechanical" one: in the latter geographical area, it is confirmed only by a slight majority (53%) of the studies. These facts run in favor of the argument that, scrutinizing the hypothesis, it is important to classify the religious communities according not only to the level of their members' observance, but also to the substantive content of their beliefs and norms.

An Example of European Contradictory Results in Research on Religion and Health: The Swiss Interdisciplinary Longitudinal Study on the Oldest Old (SWILSO-O)

Our own research on the "oldest old" provides a good example of the ambivalent and sometimes contradictory results obtained in Western Europe. SWILSO-O records data on two cohorts; both samples were randomly selected among community-dwelling elders aged 80 to 84 at baseline, and interviewed from 1994 for the first cohort (n = 340 individuals born 1910–1914) and from 1999 for the second (n = 376 individuals born 1915–1919) in two regions of Switzerland—Central Valais, a region containing a large majority of practicing Catholics, and the canton of Geneva, which is more temporal and cosmopolitan in nature but where Catholicism and Protestantism are both well represented. Samples were stratified by gender and region (Lalive d'Epinay, Pin, & Spini, 2001). From a religious point of view, the members of these two cohorts belong to the same generation: at baseline almost all identify themselves as members of a Christian church (with only 4.7% indicating a non-Christian community or no religious community at all), 65.6% attend church services (or participate through media) at least once a month, and 59.8% pray almost every day. Although region and gender differences are significant (with a higher religiosity in Valais and among women), no difference is observed between the cohorts on these religious variables.

In 2001, we published a paper based on the data of a five-year follow-up of the first cohort (1994–1999) (Spini, Pin, & Lalive d'Epinay, 2001), whose results clearly indicated a strong relationship between the three measures of religiousness (praying and participation in church services personally or via mass media, separately or combined in a composite measure of religiousness) and survival over a period of five years. Interestingly enough, when our sample was split according to denomination (Catholic versus Protestant) or to geographic area (Geneva versus Valais), the link remained. At that time, we were very satisfied to be, to our knowledge, among the first in Europe able to confirm the existence of a positive impact of religiousness on longevity among the "oldest old."

Taking advantage of the fact that the data from the three first waves (1999–2001) of the second cohort became available, we recently decided to replicate the logistic regression analysis reported in Spini et al. (2001) in order to test the effect of the composite measure of religiousness on mortality in the two cohorts across three waves. It must be noted that, contrary to the published study in which survival was based on an administrative follow-up, mortality is measured here from the broader information we gathered concerning reasons for dropping out of the study.

Results showed that, in the first cohort, there was a significant effect of the composite index of religiousness on mortality (odds ratio = 0.77; $p < .01$). This effect confirms that religious practice was negatively linked to mortality in the first cohort. But in the second cohort, no such effect appeared (odds ratio = 1.03, ns). At this stage, we have no explanation for these contradictory results, nor for the general variability of the results obtained across European studies.

CONCLUSION

Idler's chapter (this volume) provides an overview of the relationship between religion and health based on the work of Durkheim (1986) and of Pescosolido and Georgianna (1989) on the link between suicide and religion. More specifically, it presents a model in which religious observance and network density are the two main dimensions yielding an insight into the effects of religiousness on health. Apart from situations where the network density and religious involvement is extremely high, in which case the effect is potentially negative, this model predicts positive effects from the combination of network density and religious observance. Our intention in these comments, while recognizing the great heuristic scope of the model, is to highlight two particular aspects that are worthy of further reflection. First, we question the epistemological validity of transferring Durkheim's postulates on suicide to the field of health and we propose incorporating as a third dimension the content of the religious orthodoxy; and second, we query indirectly the relevance to other parts of the world of results obtained in the U.S.A., drawing on a number of examples in Western Europe and Switzerland.

As far as Idler's epistemological assumptions are concerned, serious doubt has been cast on the reliability of the suicide data Durkheim used to support his theory, with the result that the link between suicide and religious adherence has been contested. From a sociological viewpoint, we also have doubts about including suicide in the sphere of health. This may be justifiable medically but the sociological theory underpinning Idler's work holds that suicide is a social phenomenon and not essentially a matter of pathology. Lastly, it is our view that the heuristic power of the model first proposed by Pescosolido and Georgianna (1989) and later extended by Idler (this volume) would be enhanced by introducing a third dimension, corresponding to the content of the religious doctrines.

In the second part of our comments, we discuss the relevance to Western Europe of the religion-and-health model developed in the U.S.A. First, we introduced a short discussion about the status of religion in these two continents. Unlike the citizens of the U.S.A., those of the various countries of Western Europe have widely disparate relations with religious institutions and large differences in religious observance are to be found across countries. In most Western European countries, unlike in the U.S.A., religion is no longer a shared component of culture. Life expectancy is nevertheless on the rise, even in countries where the level of religious practice is lowest. This suggests that longevity and health in general are more closely associated in Western Europe with socio-economic variables, health-care policies and education than with religion.

Second, we try to establish whether the health social scientists are or are not similarly concerned with our topic in the U.S.A. and in Western Europe. Our inquiry, based on a survey of the literature published from 1990 to 2003, leads us to the answer that it is a much more central issue among the American scientific community than among the European one.

Third, on the basis of the same survey, we compared the results on the link between religion and health in European and in American research publications. The conclusion is that in the U.S.A. a majority of studies confirmed the hypothesis, but that is not the case in Europe. Our own study on two cohorts of the "oldest old" was then used as an illustration of the very diversified and contradictory results that are to be found in Western Europe. Shall we conclude that the topic of the present conference is not a salient one for Europe?

In terms of public interest, due to the secularized situation of most of the Western European countries, it is surely not as relevant as it is in the U.S.A. But from a strictly scientific point of view, the fact that religious belonging is now limited to a minority in the Old Continent, and seen as a very private and personal matter, does not make the topic less interesting. On the contrary: it would be of great interest if it can be proved that a phenomenon shared by a minority makes a difference in terms of health and longevity. But the fact is that the current state of field research does not lead to convincing results, and the state of the theory brings no help to understand the variability of the results across and inside countries. All that lends weight to the argument that the model and explanations concerning the association between religious observance and health have to take into account the social meaning of religion in various societal contexts. It seems very important to establish not only whether there is a link between religion and health but, when such is the case, how this link works. A convincing theoretical explanation should be able to explain why the link is attested in some studies, but not in other. Idler's chapter makes a distinction between three channels: worldviews, community, and life styles. It would be useful to disentangle the impact of each channel on health and test their interactions. This would also help to elaborate another, more prospective, question: among the more and more secularized societies of Western Europe, is there an equivalent, a functional substitute to religion to be found?

Our final conclusion is that in the field of religion and health, the scientific deficit is not due to the lack of empirical research, but to the lack of theoretical explanatory models. We hope that Idler's chapter will stimulate new theoretical developments. If this will be the case, then her chapter will represent as a cornerstone for research on the link between religion and health.

ACKNOWLEDGMENTS

The research described in this chapter was funded by the Swiss National Science Foundation Priority Program "Switzerland: Towards the future" (No 5004-047750/047752). The "Département de la Santé et de l'Action sociale de la République et Canton de Genève" and the "Département de la Santé du Canton du Valais" are thanked for their financial support. Thanks are due to Myriam Girardin for her help in screening the journal articles and to Ian Hamilton for his editorial assistance.

REFERENCES

Besnard, P. (1976). Anti- ou antédurkheimisme. Contribution au débat sur les statistiques officielles [Anti- or antedurkheimism. Contribution to the debate on official statistics.] *Revue Française de Sociologie (Juin)*, 313–341.

Boudon, R. (2001, December 13). L'exception américaine [The American exception]. *Le Monde*.

Brumagne, M.-M. (1980). *La Poudre de sourire: Le témoignage de Marie Métrailler [The powder of smile: The account of Marie Métrailler]*. Lausanne, Switzerland: Editions Clin d'Oeil.

Campiche, R. J. (in press). *Religion et lien social* [Religion and social bond]. Lausanne, Switzerland: L'Age d'Homme.

Campiche, R. J., & Dubach, A. (1992). *Croire en Suisse(s)* [Believing in Switzerland]. Lausanne, Switzerland: L'Age d'Homme.

Douglas, J. D. (1967). *The social meanings of suicide*. Princeton, NJ: Princeton University Press.

Durkheim, E. (1986). *Le Suicide [Suicide]*. Paris: Presses Universitaires de France. (Original work published 1897)

Herberg, W. (1955). *Protestant, Catholic, Jew*. Chicago: Chicago University Press.

Inglehart, R., Basañez, M., & Moreno, A. (1998). *Human values and beliefs: A cross-cultural sourcebook*. Ann Arbor: University of Michigan Press.

Lalive d'Epinay, C. J. (1985). Depressed elderly women in Switzerland: An example of testing and of generating theories. *The Gerontologist, 25*, 6, 597–604.

Lalive d'Epinay, C., Christe, E., Coenen-Huther, J., Hagmann, H.-M., Jeanneret, O., Jundo, J.-P., Kellerhals, J., Raymond, L., Schellhorn, J.-P., Wirth, G., de Wurstenberger, B. (1983). *Vieillesses [Old ages]*. Saint-Saphorin Switzerland: Georgi.

Lalive d'Epinay, C., Pin, S., & Spini, D. (2001). Présentation de SWILSO-O, une étude longitudinale suisse sur le grand âge: L'exemple de la dynamique de la santé fonctionnelle [Presentation of SWILSO-O, a Swiss longitudinal study on the oldest old: The example of the dynamics of functional health.] *L'Année Gérontologique*, 78–96.

Pescosolido, B. A., & Georgianna, S. (1989). Durkheim, suicide, and religion: Toward a network theory of suicide. *American Journal of Sociology, 54*(1), 33–48.

Pope, W. (1976). *Durkheim's suicide*. Chicago: Chicago University Press.

Radcliffe-Brown, A. R. (1935). On the concept of function in social science. *American Anthropologist, New Series, 37,* 3, Part 1, 394–402.

Spini, D., Pin, S., & Lalive d'Epinay, C. (2001). Religiousness and survival: A five-year follow-up under the Swiss interdisciplinary longitudinal study on the oldest old. *Zeitschrift für Geronto-Psychologie und -Psychiatrie, 14,* 4, 181–186.

Tocqueville, A. de (1981). *De la démocratie en Amérique [Democracy in America]*. Paris: Flammarion Garnier. (Original work published 1835/1840)

Van Poppel, F., & Day, L. H. (1996). A test of Durkheim's theory of suicide— without committing the "ecological fallacy." *American Journal of Sociology, 61*(3), 500-507.

Weber, M. (1964). *L'éthique protestante et l'esprit du capitalisme [The Protestant ethic and the spirit of capitalism]*. Paris: Plan. (Original work published 1905–1906).

Commentary

Observing Religion and Health

Roger Finke

W hen research initially reported that religion increases life satisfaction and improves health, the nearly 300,000 religious
congregations in America treated the revelation as a welcome
confirmation. The scholarly community was far more suspect. Over the
last fifteen years, however, a growing volume of research has confirmed
the finding and is now prompting a host of new research questions. The
research is moving beyond a mere proclamation of a "religion effect"
and is sorting out why and when religion has an effect.

Progress is being made on multiple fronts. Conceptually the many
dimensions of religion are being recognized and new measures are
being used to quantify religion. Whereas researchers were once content
with survey questions on church attendance or denominational affiliation, they are now striving for multiple measures of religious beliefs and
actions. The research designs have also improved. Larger, more representative samples increase our confidence in the results reported and
longitudinal surveys are allowing more serious attempts at sorting out
the causal effects of religion. The initial stage of proclaiming the new
findings is over; researchers are now tending to the arduous task of
explaining why and when religion matters.

Idler's work (this volume) has played a significant role in the
progress of this research, and her chapter offers an excellent overview
of the progress she and others have made. Although I find myself in
nearly full agreement with Idler's review, and appreciative of her
research, I still have several comments and a few concerns. My comments are organized around the three major sections of the chapter:
"Two Traditions in Research on Religious Observance and Health,"

"Mechanisms: Making Sense of It," and "Elements of Religious Observance." I suggest that her first section on the "Two Traditions in Research" ignores a growing literature contesting Durkheim's initial findings, relies on a denominational continuum in need of revision, and sometimes blends the two levels of analysis being reviewed. For the final two sections, "Mechanisms" and "Elements of Religious Observance," I will highlight some of the significant progress made in these areas and offer suggestions for extending the research.

TWO TRADITIONS

The opening section introduces two traditions of research. One uses ecological units of analysis, such as nations and counties, to focus on the collective effects of religion. The second relies on epidemiological surveys and focuses on personal religious observance and individual health. Drawing on the work of Durkheim (1951) in the late 19th century and the work of Pescosolido and Georgianna (1989) in the late 20th, Idler suggests that the first tradition shares two common findings. First, religious denominations matter for health. Regardless of the century or the continent, areas with high rates of Catholics tend to have lower rates of suicide. Second, the denominational differences are due to the group's ability to integrate members into the group. With the exception of a few small groups that overregulate behavior, and could potentially call for suicide as an act of commitment, higher levels of integration lead to reduced levels of suicide.

Idler then applies a similar argument to her review of the relationship between social networks and health at the individual level (the second research tradition). She explains that religious observance shows a strong relationship with health for Catholics, a weak relationship for Jews and black Protestants, and no relationship for white Protestants. Building on the work of Pescosolido and Georgianna (1989), she proposes that religion has the strongest effect on health "among highly observant members of densely-knitted congregations in Roman Catholic parishes and the 'Community Religions' of the Amish, Mormons, etc." In other words, a high level of religious involvement combined with tight social networks tends to improve a person's health.

I agree with much of this review, both theoretically and substantively. I am convinced that religion can have a collective as well as an individual-level effect on social action (see Finke & Adamczyk, 2003). The religious involvement of an area and the religious properties of a social group can affect health, just as the personal beliefs and involvement can affect health. Exploring the effects of denominational differences is also important. Sharp denominational differences in the areas of involvement, commitment, and beliefs will each alter the effects religion has on behavior and health. Finally, I strongly agree that social networks and level of involvement in a religious organization are two critical variables for understanding how religion affects health.

As currently presented, however, I think the review of the two traditions ignores important research in some areas and needs revision and clarification in others. A review of previous research is always challenged to tell a coherent story and still stay true to existing findings; when discussing the consistent findings of Durkheim in the 19th century and Pescosolido and Georgianna's work in the 20th, I am concerned that too many details were sacrificed. The most serious omission is that many have challenged Durkheim's methods and data showing a Protestant and Catholic difference. One of the most detailed critiques came from Pope (1976). Pope criticized Durkheim's theory for a conceptual "fuzziness" between integration and regulation, but his most devastating critique was that the Catholic effect reported by Durkheim never existed. After correcting Durkheim's rates and arithmetic, he found no consistent suicide differences between Catholics and Protestants.

Pope is not alone in failing to confirm this finding. In an article appearing in the *American Sociological Review* seven years after Pescosolido and Georgianna's work, Poppel and Day used turn of the century Dutch data to conclude that the "gap between Protestant and Catholic suicide rates . . . [was] the result of nothing more mysterious than differences in how deaths to Catholics and deaths to Protestants were recorded" (Poppel & Day, 1996, p. 505). After reviewing data from multiple time periods and countries (including data from the United States and Durkheim's late 19th century France), Stark and Bainbridge (1996) conclude that Durkheim was correct to stress the importance of social integration and religious involvement, but that the Catholic effect on suicide is often missing or spurious. Ellison, Burr, and McCall (1997) have added that it is a high level of religious activity combined with religious consensus or homogeneity that explains the deterrent effect. Each of these studies suggests that the effect of a uniquely Catholic context is not as consistent or as powerful as suggested by Durkheim or by Idler's review.

If support for the effect of a Catholic context is eroding, Idler's own research suggests that it remains strong at the individual level. Personal religious observance affects health more for Catholics than Protestants. She notes that high levels of religious observance in groups with a high social density helps to explain the Protestant/Catholic difference. On the one hand, I find the argument on the joint effects of observance and networks very plausible: high levels of involvement in groups holding tight social networks should increase the effects of religion on health. But I don't find this to be a convincing explanation for the Catholic/Protestant differences she reports.

Thus, my second concern is Idler's attempt to explain the Protestant/Catholic difference (at the individual level) as a product of differential social density. She describes Catholics as holding "densely-knitted congregations," and Figure 2.1 in her chapter suggests that network density for Catholics exceeds that of Evangelical Protestants and Jews, and far exceeds the network density of liberal Protestants. If defined as the number of close interpersonal relationships one holds in the local congregation, then I would question the current placement of the denominations on this network density continuum. When a large sample of church members was asked to list their five closest friends in the mid-1960s, Catholics were far less likely than members in Protestant sectarian groups (e.g., Assemblies of God, Nazarenes, etc.) to report that at least one of their closest friends was a fellow member and were only modestly higher than mainline Protestants (Stark & Glock, 1968). Since the 1960s, the distinctive Catholic subculture has gradually eroded, with fewer Catholics attending Catholic schools and living in distinctively Catholic neighborhoods. When the religion module of the 1998 General Social Survey asked respondents if one of their five closest friends attended the same congregation, only 35.1% of the Catholic respondents reported a close friend in their congregation. Using the denominational categories proposed by Steensland et al. (2000), each of the other religious groups reported a higher percentage, with Evangelical Protestants reporting 41.8%, Jews 42.3%, mainline Protestants 37.1%, black Protestants 35.3%, and other faiths 50.8%. The only religious category with a sharply higher percentage of friends in their local congregation was the "other faiths" category, which included a disparate assembly of conservative sects (e.g., Jehovah's Witness, Mormons, etc.), other world religions (e.g., Islam, Hinduism, etc.), and a small group of liberal churches (e.g., Unitarians, New Age, etc.).

My point is twofold. One, the placement of the denominations on the network density continuum needs to be revised using appropriate data. Based on my initial glance at this data, the network density of Catholics is similar to mainline Protestants, with only the "other faiths" being sharply different. Two, if being Catholic has a more positive effect on health, there are variables other than social density that explain this effect. If social networks are similar for Protestants and Catholics, then we need to explore how being Catholic (e.g., unique religious beliefs or rituals) might affect health.

My final concern is that the unique contributions of the two research traditions need to be clarified and explained. Despite recognizing the importance of the two traditions, much of the discussion blends the two levels of analysis. How are the religion effects at the "societal level" and the religion effects at the "individual level" separated? For example, the extended discussion on the importance of social networks and the "Catholic effect" in the two traditions often fails to offer clear conceptual distinctions between the two levels. How might social networks or a "Catholic" area change the social context, norms, and institutions affecting health? How might the congregational friendships and Catholic beliefs of an individual affect his or her health?

I would argue that each level of analysis can offer unique insights. For example, in areas where religious observance is high, the local religious institutions or religious norms might become part of a subculture that affects the health of all residents, regardless of their own personal beliefs and practice. In contrast, religion might have very little contextual effect in areas failing to have a dominant religious culture. Many questions remain about how the contextual effects interact with individual religious observance. I will offer a few additional comments on the study of contextual effects later in this note, and the remainder of Idler's review offers a rich discussion of the individual-level effects, but much work remains on sorting out the contextual and individual-level effects of religion on health.

MECHANISMS

Idler offers four mechanisms for explaining how religiousness affects individual health: (1) promoting healthy lifestyles; (2) facilitating social support by and for members of religious groups; (3) providing coherent schema, or frameworks of meaning which provide coping, comfort, and understanding; and (4) religious participation may also have direct beneficial physiological effects on heart rate, blood pressure, muscle tone, or the immune system. I'll give little attention to the first two mechanisms, because they are less contested and their effects are better understood. If Utah Mormons smoke less and are less likely to drink to excess than their Nevada neighbors, I'm not surprised that they are healthier. Both parental and government warnings would suggest that this should be the case. The second mechanism is also widely accepted. Social networks have been a powerful mechanism for improving health for the elderly and churches are a rich source of these networks. The fourth mechanism, religious involvement producing beneficial physiological effects on heart rate, blood pressure, muscle tone, or the immune system, is intriguing, but I am unqualified to comment.

But the third mechanism, providing coherent schema, or frameworks of meaning which provide coping, comfort, and understanding, is an area where I think Idler and others are making significant progress. As social scientists we have often felt more comfortable talking about how the social networks of churches shape health, well-being, and behavior. Yet, we should know that the meaning systems people hold can be equally powerful. Weber (1978) wrote at length about how an individual's religious beliefs can shape individual behavior and even major social change. Although not writing about religion, Thomas' (Thomas & Thomas, 1928) oft-quoted theorem—"if [actors] define situations as real, they are real in their consequences"—tells us that the truth of the beliefs is not the issue. Regardless of how bogus someone's religious beliefs might seem to an outsider, they cannot be deemed as inconsequential.

As a quick aside, I would comment that these religious schemas are alive and well. Although early social scientists, such as Durkheim, thought advancements in science threatened the plausibility of religion, the majority of the U.S. population is confident in their beliefs. When the 1988 General Social Survey asked respondents to rank their religious doubts on a scale of one to seven, with one being "completely free of doubts" and seven being "my faith is mixed with doubts," 61.4% ranked themselves as a one, two, or three. They were also given four reasons why they might experience doubts, including "evil in the world," "personal suffering," "conflict of faith and science," and "feeling that life really has no meaning." Fifty-five percent attributed doubts to personal suffering; 50% said that "evil in the world" contributed to their doubts; only 30% agreed that a "conflict of faith and science" caused them doubt. Thus, to some extent, the vast majority of the population is relying on religious schemas and frameworks of meaning (see Stark & Finke, 2000).

What most impresses me about the work of Idler and others is the progress they are making in their theoretical definitions and their research. They are refining the concepts they use to define religious dimensions as they provide better measures for these concepts and develop research strategies to more effectively sort out the effects of these various dimensions. Let me offer a couple examples. First, they are using conceptual definitions and measures that clearly distinguish different dimensions of religion. Worship attendance, subjective beliefs, and religious practices such as the prayer, meditation, and religious rituals are all treated as distinctive dimensions. Whereas the early studies on religion and health were often confined to church attendance and denominational affiliation, the measures have greatly improved and so have their theoretical descriptions. Second, the research strategies are now designed to sort out the effects of these different religious dimensions. Idler and Kasl's (2002) efforts to sort out the effects of subjective religion and worship attendance offer one example. I was especially impressed with their efforts to show how the effects differ for the end-of-life period, with subjective religion playing a more important role during this time period.

ELEMENTS OF RELIGIOUS OBSERVANCE: PROPOSALS

In the final section of the paper, Professor Idler proposes that additional research in religious observance and health needs to give attention to congregational life and to the ritual elements of worship. As she notes, congregations should be viewed as "more than the sum of the individuals who make them up" and we must better understand why exposure to religious ritual might have an impact on health. I strongly agree with each of these proposals, but I would like to expand on her requests.

In the opening paragraph of *Foundations of Social Theory,* Coleman (1990) laments that the gap between theory and research is growing because "[s]ocial theory continues to be about the functioning of social systems of behavior, but empirical research is often concerned with explaining individual behavior" (p. 1). The research designs used most frequently by social scientists, such as surveys, continue drawing attention to the individual, as social theories continue posing questions about the effects of social groups and social structure. Idler's suggestion to move beyond the individual level of analysis to the congregation is one example of how we can strive to not only understand the effects of individual beliefs, involvement, and networks, but also understand the effects of the larger group. How do congregations affect the health and end-of-life experiences for individuals and what impact do they have on the community? Rather than merely use denomination as a proxy for the type of congregation, we need to know more about the effects of individual congregations.

But I would like to extend this proposal beyond the congregation to the community and even the nation. How does the religious context of a community affect health and well-being? Borrowing from Fuchs'

(1974) research, Idler contrasts the healthy lifestyles of Mormon Utah to lifestyles in Nevada. I would suggest that the differences between the two states go well beyond the beliefs and involvement of individuals. If you are Mormon, the Mormon community will hold you more accountable. Even if you aren't Mormon, your behavior will be altered by community expectations. Thus, the question I think we should address is: does the religious context of a community have an effect above and beyond the effects of individual religious belief and involvement? Similar questions could be posed at the national level. Does the religious context of a nation affect health and well-being? When attempting to explain international attitudes on sexual morality, Adamczyk and I are finding that both the religious context of the nation and the individual's religious beliefs and involvement help to explain a respondent's views on morality (Finke & Adamczyk, 2003).

The second area Idler proposes additional research in is the area of religious ritual. She poses the question "Why might this exposure to religious ritual have an impact on health" and states that they "hope to sketch a much fuller picture of activities and responses . . . during worship services." Once again, answering this question will force us to advance our understanding and our measurement of religion beyond a simple measure of worship attendance. But I think that Idler's emphasis on religious ritual and her earlier emphasis on observance offer additional research advantages. These measures will allow us to more easily generalize to other world religions that place less emphasis on attendance at a weekly service and more on the performance of selected rituals. As this research is expanded to the international arena, or even to the other world religions increasingly represented in the United States, there will be a continual groping for forming concepts and measures that can be generalized to all groups. I think that placing emphasis on more general measures of observance, such as ritual, is one promising avenue.

Although not addressed by Idler, I think that we also need to be more aware of how the teachings of different world religions will vary on issues related to the elderly and to health. We all know from our brief introduction to Greek and Roman mythology in high school or college that not all gods demanded the same level of morality. In fact, some of the gods were quite immoral by our cultural standards. Yet there are times when research regards all religions as promoting the same moral codes. As this research expands to include other world religions, we need to be more aware of how religious teachings and practices vary in the areas of health and aging.

CONCLUSION

Professor Idler and her colleagues have made significant progress in the area of religion, health, and aging, but they have an even more exciting and demanding agenda ahead of them. Recent improvements in measurement, sampling, and research design are beginning to sort out the "religion effect" on health and aging. Still, many challenges remain. For example, the contextual effects of religion are poorly understood by theory and research. How does the level of religious observance in a community affect health and aging and how do congregations vary in the effect they have on individuals? How and why do these effects vary by different religious faiths? Finally, social scientists need to better understand the effects of religious beliefs. After all, if they are defined as real, they might be real in their consequences.

REFERENCES

Coleman, J. S. (1990). *Foundations of social theory*. Cambridge, MA: Belknap Press of Harvard University Press.

Durkheim, E. ([1897] 1951). *Suicide*. Glencoe, IL: Free Press.

Finke, R., & Adamczyk, A. (2003). Explaining morality: Using international data to reestablish the micro/macro link. Unpublished manuscript.

Ellison, C. G., Burr, J. A., & McCall, P. L. (1997). Religious homogeneity and metropolitan suicide rates, *Social Forces 76*: 273–299.

Fuchs, V. (1974). *Who shall live? Health, economics, and social choice*. New York: Basic Books.

Idler, E., & Kasl, S. (2002). *Impact of religious observance and beliefs at the end of life*. Meeting of the Gerontological Society of America. Boston.

Pescosolido, B. A., & Georgianna, S. (1989). Durkheim, suicide, and religion. *American Sociological Review, 54*(1), 33–48.

Pope, W. (1976). *Durkheim's suicide: A classic analyzed*. Chicago: University of Chicago Press.

Poppel, F. van, & Day, L. H. (1996). A test of Durkheim's theory of suicide— Without committing the "ecological fallacy." *American Sociological Review*, 500–507.

Stark, R., & Bainbridge, W. S. (1996). *Religion, deviance, and social control*. New York: Routledge.

Stark, R., & Finke, R. (2000). *Acts of faith: Explaining the human side of religion*. Berkeley: University of California Press.

Stark, R., & Glock, C. Y. (1968). *American piety*. Berkeley: University of California Press.

Steensland, B., Park, J. Z., Regnerus, M. D., Robinson, L. D., Wilcox, W. B., & Woodberry, R. D. (2000). The measure of American religion: Toward improving the state-of-the-art. *Social Forces, 79*(1), 291–318.

Thomas, W. I., & Thomas, D. S. (1928). *The child in America.* New York: Alfred A. Knopf.

Weber, M. (1978). *Economy and society.* G. Roth & C. Wittich (Eds.). Berkeley: University of California Press.

CHAPTER 3

Prayer, Love, and Transcendence: An Epidemiologic Perspective

Jeff Levin

"All prayer seems to be our cry for access, our attempt in word or deed to touch God's hem."

—Marsha Sinetar (1997, p. 162)

Since Moberg's early work in the 1950s (see Moberg, 1990), study of religion and health within gerontology has emphasized effects of behavioral markers of public religious participation. Foremost are measures of the frequency of religious attendance. Religious attendance has been especially relied upon in epidemiologic studies of disease outcomes (Levin & Vanderpool, 1987). Systematic reviews published over the past two decades have established religious attendance as a key determinant or correlate of a wide range of health-related, psychosocial, and quality-of-life indicators for older adults (Larson, Sherrill, & Lyons, 1994; Levin, 1997; Witter, Stock, Okun, & Haring, 1985). Additional work has systematically focused on patterns, predictors, and measures of this and related constructs in older adults and throughout the life course, especially among African Americans (Chatters & Taylor, 1994).

Recently, it has been noted that this focus on health outcomes of public religious behavior may be responsible for neglect of other less public and more personal expressions of religiousness (Sherrill, Larson, & Greenwold, 1993). Gerontologists have distinguished between religious involvement expressed through organized behavior sponsored by a religious institution and religiousness expressed through behavior conducted privately or outside a congregational setting. This distinction between "organizational" and "nonorganizational" religiousness, first articulated in gerontology by Mindel and Vaughan (1978), also has been languaged as public vs. private, formal vs. informal, and institutional vs. noninstitutional religiousness.

In the middle 1990s, a working group convened by the National Institute on Aging (NIA) was charged with cataloguing, developing, and validating multi-item and multidimensional measures of a wide range of religious measures for use in gerontological research. Motivation was to expand awareness of the breadth of constructs studied by religious scholars in the social sciences over the past decades and to make good measures available to scientists working in the area of aging and health. This was achieved, under the direction of Krause, and a report was issued (Fetzer Institute/National Institute on Aging Working Group, 1999).

This proved to be a signal contribution for religious gerontology. Underemphasis of private, informal, noninstitutional, and nonorganizational religious behaviors does not do justice to their salience in older adult cohorts, especially with relative declines in functioning and disengagement from certain roles (Levin, 1989). Among private forms of religious expression neglected in gerontological studies, most notable has been prayer. This is ironic, as prayer, in one form or another, is the most widely recognized and ubiquitous religious behavior (Castelli, 1994). Yet for the most part, prayer is still a gerontological mystery.

For an epidemiologist, this makes prayer an attractive topic. Among epidemiologists, a principal professional function is to solve epidemiologic mysteries. A recent essay in a leading medical journal extolled the virtues of tackling epidemiologic mysteries, especially taboo or forbidden topics like religion (Levin & Steele, 2001). For any epidemiologist, there is a standard approach that is taken in investigating an epidemiologic mystery. Ideally, this consists of answering, in sequence, several successive questions: what, who, where, when, how, and why.

In a large-scale epidemiologic investigation, the first step addresses the "what" question. This is about conceptual development—definitions, models, taxonomies, inclusionary and exclusionary criteria, and validating measures. The second step addresses the "who," "where," and "when" questions. This is the stuff of descriptive epidemiology—identifying patterns of expression of a disease outcome or exposure variable by characteristics of person, place, or time. The third step addresses the "how" question. This involves analytic epidemiology—study of the association between exposures and outcomes, including investigation of potential mediating or effect-modifying factors, sometimes referred to as mechanisms. Finally, the fourth step addresses the "why" question—expounding upon the ultimate meaning underlying mechanisms that lie at the core of associations confirmed in analytic-epidemiologic studies.

Obviously, not all epidemiologic studies address all of these questions. Answers to the "why" question, especially, are rarely sought, and even speculation is rare in discussion sections of reports of population-based studies. These questions, however, provide a nice template for an overview of a new or still mysterious field. For an epidemiologist of religion seeking to explore something as treacherous as prayer—the most marginal topic within a marginal field—stepping through each question, surveying what is and is not currently known, is a prudent way to initiate a deeper engagement of this topic among religious gerontologists.

"WHAT": CONCEPTUAL AND MEASUREMENT ISSUES IN ASSESSING PRAYER

The first step that an epidemiologist undertakes in any study is to ask "what" questions. What is the phenomenon under study? What is its definition? What are its subtypes or dimensions? What measures exist or can be developed for this construct? Addressing these questions involves positing a working definition of the disease outcome or exposure variable under study, settling on any taxonomies of the construct that might exist, selecting inclusionary or exclusionary criteria, and conducting requisite preliminary psychometric work. For most epidemiologic studies, these are not enormous tasks. Disease outcomes are usually dealt with as population rates of clinical entities defined according to conventional clinical criteria, whether assessed through single questions or through established batteries. Exposure variables are usually single-item measures of physiological parameters or environmental exposures, except where behavioral or psychosocial constructs are involved.

In the language of epidemiology, prayer is a behavioral host-factor exposure variable—a behavioral characteristic of human hosts that may potentially influence the risk or odds of subsequent health-related events. As with other behaviors, before epidemiologists can study its effects it must be conceptualized and then operationalized. That is, a working definition must be settled on, issues of dimensionality addressed, and valid measures readied for empirical use.

Definitions of Prayer

For prayer, these are no small tasks. Prayer has been described in many ways across faith traditions. Considerable diversity also exists within respective traditions.

Judaism provides a good illustration. Prayer has been described in a diversity of ways throughout sacred writings (e.g., *Torah, Gemara, Midrash*) and across historical movements (e.g., the Rishonim and Acharonim, Hassidism, Kabbalism, Reform, Jewish Renewal). A variety of themes emerge: prayer as sacrifice, a means of connecting to God's ubiquitous presence, an expression of gratitude, a point of access to God's will, an opportunity given by God enabling us to approach Him, and a means of exploring the symbolism of inner spiritual spaces.

In *Sefer Tehillim*, David exclaims, "Let my prayer be set forth before thee like incense; and the lifting up of my hands like the evening sacrifice" (Psalms 141:2). Rabbi Ovadiah Sforno, 15th-century sage, commenting on *parsha vayetzei* (Pelcovitz, 1997), taught "that man can pray to the Almighty in any house, thereby creating a House of God through the medium of prayer" (pp. 150–151). In Rashi's commentary on *parsha breishit* (Doron, 2000), the great 11th-century elucidator of *chumash* underscored "the very essence of prayer—the realization that man is dependent on God for *everything* and must show gratitude for His bounty" (p. 12).

Contemporary Jews have added their voices. Rabbi Abraham J. Twerski (1992), Hassid and psychiatrist, offers an insightful critique: "Some people think that prayer means telling God what He is supposed to do for them. . . . We should pray for God to make His will known, and to help and guide us in fulfilling that will" (p. 348). In the shoulder notes to 18th-century rabbinic authority Rabbi Moshe Chaim Luzzatto's classic *Derech Hashem*, Rabbi Yosef Begun (1997) interpreted the Ramchal's position: "Prayer is God's gift of love, allowing man to elevate himself and draw closer to God" (p. 303). Rabbi Zalman Schachter-Shalomi (1993), psychologist and human potential pioneer, has likened inner realms of consciousness to subtle, higher spiritual planes spoken of in the Four Worlds concept of Kabbalistic Judaism. *Davvening*, or daily prayer, "is a journey up through these spaces and down again" (p. 173).

Among 20th-century Western religious scholars, various perspectives on prayer can be identified. These invoke concepts corresponding to respective domains of human psychology, such as affect, collective behavior, conation, reason, will, and consciousness.

In *Dimensions of the Sacred,* Smart (1996), an authority on comparative religions, identified two functions or motivations underlying ritual prayer: "pure praise or *bhakti,* involving humility before God; and pure contemplation, involving a series of steps towards the achievement of pure consciousness" (p. 128). In *Sociology of Religion,* Wach (1944), another noted historian of religions, identified a collective function of prayer. Rituals such as prayer "not only serve to articulate the experiences of those taking part but contribute in no small measure to the shaping and determining of the organization and spirit of the group" (p. 40).

In *Dynamics of Faith,* theologian Paul Tillich (1957), while not speaking to prayer directly, expounded on motivations behind expressions of faith, such as prayer. His words are familiar to students of Western religious thought: "Faith is a total and centered act of the personal self, the act of unconditional, infinite and ultimate concern" (p. 8); "It transcends both the drives of the nonrational unconscious and the structures of the rational conscious" (p. 6).

In *Lost Christianity,* Needleman (1980), renowned religious scholar, described prayer as a means of "centering" oneself, using language similar, in respects, to both Tillich and Schachter-Shalomi: "We are talking about a mode of attention or consciousness that is a bridge between our present level of being and the level of being described not only in the contemplative literature of Christianity, but in the mystical and contemplative literature of all the traditions. We are not speaking only about the development of the inner world, but of the balance between the inner and the outer world" (p. 157).

A simple distillation of these perspectives on prayer might render something akin to a useful working definition: "Communication with God." This is not dissimilar to the description of prayer by philosopher William James (1958) in *The Varieties of Religious Experience:* "every kind of inward communion or conversation with the power recognized as divine" (p. 352). James also referenced "a liberal French theologian," Auguste Sabatier, who used the colorful phrase "intercourse with God" (p. 352). (A *very* liberal theologian, apparently!) One must recognize, of course, that each of the three words in "communication with God," even "with," means dramatically different things across respective traditions.

Types of Prayer

How is communication with God expressed? There are fewer categorizations of prayer than there are definitions of prayer. About half a dozen taxonomies were developed in the 1990s (Ladd & Spilka, 2002). Across these models were dimensions tapping constructs such as prayer for purposes of adoration, thanksgiving, intercession, confession, sacrament, or rest.

The earliest of these taxonomies, and an outstanding and useful model, was developed by Poloma and Pendleton (1989). It not only differentiates among four distinct types of prayer, but it has the additional advantage of being the basis for both instrument development and subsequent data collection in a national probability survey. Dimensions are termed ritualist or ritual prayer, colloquial or conversational prayer, petitionary prayer, and meditative prayer. Psychometric analyses confirmed this schema, and highly reliable indices were developed for the latter three dimensions, each of which assesses verbal praying.

A couple of years later, Poloma and Gallup (1991) reported on results of a national probability survey which used this taxonomy of prayer. Psychometric analyses again confirmed the presence of four dimensions, and again ritual prayer was least reliably assessed.

According to this taxonomy, ritual prayer entails reading from a book of prayers or reciting memorized prayers, such as those appearing in daily devotionals or in the Jewish *siddur.* Conversational prayer can be characterized as an informal conversation with God. Petitionary prayer is the requesting of spiritual or material things in response to felt needs. Finally, meditative prayer includes quietly thinking about, experiencing, or worshipping God or listening for God's voice, as well as more formal systems of prayerful meditation.

As noted elsewhere (Levin & Taylor, 1997, p. 85), these types of prayer are not entirely discrete. They overlap both in the affinity and predilection for them among some people and in their manifestation in the same worship experience, such as a congregational service. Moreover, "[t]hese types of prayer are not mutually exclusive; for instance, many individuals who utilize ritual prayer also engage in more informal conversational prayer. If there is a sine qua non to these disparate styles of prayer, it may be, as James (1958 [1902]) long ago noted, the seeking of an 'inward communion' (p. 352) with the divine, leading the pray-er 'into the presence of the ultimate mystery of God' (Meserve, 1991, p. 275)."

To summarize, despite considerable diversity in functional definitions, motivations, and expressions, prayer is widely recognized across faith traditions as a means of communication with God or the divine. We will now turn our attention to the descriptive epidemiology of prayer—evidence for its prevalence and distribution across characteristics of person, place, and time.

"WHO," "WHERE," "WHEN":
DESCRIBING PATTERNS OF PRAYER

The second step in any epidemiologic study, after successfully answering "what," is to address "who," "where," and "when" questions. This is known as descriptive epidemiology, and has to do with identifying patterns of distribution of a disease outcome or exposure variable across categories of person, place, and time (in epidemiologic jargon, "PPT"). For prayer, in gerontological context, conducting a PPT analysis or review involves posing several questions: What is the prevalence of prayer throughout the life course? Are there sociodemographic differences in or correlates of the frequency of prayer? Do these vary by types of prayer, by the identity of the one who prays, or by stages of the life course?

While scientific literature on religion and health is largely gerontological, the empirical literature on prayer for the most part is not gerontological. If religion has been a marginal topic for mainstream sociology and psychology until recently, then prayer research may be the very most marginal niche within religious social science. Despite available taxonomies, most empirical findings on prayer in both aging and health studies are based on single-item measures of the frequency of prayer. Further, prevalence estimates for the most part are not based on systematic or probability samples or drawn on national sampling frames.

It is important not to overdramatize these limitations. Reliable data of recent vintage are available for prayer, in contrast to the early years of religious research in gerontology. The well-known annotated bibliography, *Religion & Aging*, compiled by Fecher (1982), referenced 504 articles or reports pertaining to issues in religious gerontology. According to titles and abstracts, little if any of this writing addressed prayer, especially in an empirical way.

Two recent bibliographies show increased attention to prayer by gerontologists. A systematic review of research on religion and aging from 1980–1994, commissioned by the NIA, identified 73 studies published in mainstream gerontology, religion, and social science journals (Levin, 1997). Of these, 40 used multiple religious measures as independent variables, and 13 included indicators of private or nonorganizational religiousness such as prayer. A similar effort, targeting the 1980–1995 period, with an expanded focus on clinical and geriatric research, identified three dozen studies with significant prayer content (Koenig, 1995).

The Prevalence of Prayer

Throughout these studies, stable national estimates of current or life-time prevalence of prayer are rare. Exceptions are findings from the Gallup organization, from the National Opinion Research Center's (NORC's) General Social Survey (GSS), and from the University of Michigan's National Survey of Black Americans. Each of these studies was based on data collected in the 1980s.

Poloma and Gallup (1991) present findings based on a 1988 Gallup survey using area probability sampling. Out of a weighted sample of 1,980 respondents, 88% reported that they "ever pray to God." The prevalence in the youngest age cohort (18–24 years) was 80%. Across the four older cohorts (25–29, 30–49, 50–64, 65+), the prevalence was consistently between 88 and 91%. Additional stratification by multiple categories of education, race/ethnicity, geographical region, and annual income also showed minimal variation: The lowest prevalence was 82% and the highest was 94%.

Findings from the 1988 GSS ($N = 1481$) categorized frequency of current prayer ("About how often do you pray?") not by raw prevalence but by scores on a six-point metric ranging from never to several times a day (Levin & Taylor, 1997). Across four age cohorts (18–30, 31–40, 41–60, 61+), the percentage of "never"s ranged from 0 to 0.5%, confirming the adage that hardly anyone never prays. Prayer at least once a day, however, rose across these successive cohorts from 40.1% to 45.4% to 57.7% to 72.9%. Data were remapped over 13 successive five-year cohorts, the slope of the line indicating a sharp rise ($r = .27$, $p < .001$). Additional analyses revealed significant gender differences in each cohort, with more frequent prayer by females, and significant racial differences in some cohorts, with more frequent prayer by African Americans. Finally, socioeconomic and geographic correlates were found across cohorts, but few remained statistically significant in predictive models.

These findings confirm the Gallup results, in which only small differences were found across socioeconomic and sociodemographic categories. Further confirmation is provided by a study combining data from the 1984, 1985, 1987, and 1988 GSSs (Chalfant & Heller, 1991). Geographic variation in frequency of prayer was not found in a rural vs. urban comparison, but when regional differences were explored ($p < .001$). Upon closer scrutiny, these differences were small and probably not substantively significant (i.e., Easterners = 4.045, Westerners = 4.159, Midwesterners = 4.382, Southerners = 4.479, on a six-point metric).

The first wave of the National Survey of Black Americans, a multi-stage area probability survey of adults (N = 2107) conducted in 1979–1980, contained an item similar to the GSS prayer variable (Levin & Taylor, 1993). This variable ("How often do you pray?") was scored across a five-category metric ranging from never to nearly every day. An analysis of gender and age differences in religion identified consistently high rates of prayer across seven age cohorts (≤24, 25–34, 35–44, 45–54, 55–64, 65–74, 75+). With scores of 5 indicating prayer nearly every day and scores of 4 indicating prayer at least once a week, only males 24 years old or younger had a score below 4 (3.92). Every other gender category in every other age cohort had a score above 4. Further, prevalence rose consistently across age cohorts, from 3.92 to 4.86 in males and from 4.40 to 4.99 in females. This age effect was strong and statistically significant (F = 25.05, $p < .001$), even after controlling for effects of a variety of socioeconomic and sociodemographic variables (F = 17.16, $p < .001$). Likewise, African-American females prayed more frequently than African-American males, in every age cohort, again even after controlling for effects of other correlates of prayer (gross F = 64.12, $p < .001$; net F = 78.10, $p < .001$).

In summary, most Americans pray and do so quite often. National data indicate that prayer is increasingly frequent in successively older age cohorts, and point to considerable prayer outside of congregational settings. Besides small but significant gender and race/ethnicity differences, on average, social-structural variables do not seem to pattern the frequency of prayer. This mirrors findings on predictors or correlates of mystical religious experiences (Levin, 1993). According to Poloma and Gallup (1991), prayer is more likely to be patterned by markers of general religiousness or by specific religious beliefs or attitudes.

The Distribution of Prayer

Findings referenced above are from studies conducted using U.S. data from samples of primarily professing or self-identifying Christians. Further, where racial or ethnic comparisons are made, they are typically drawn along simple Black vs. White or Black vs. Hispanic vs. Anglo lines. Estimates for the prevalence of prayer in more diverse settings cannot be derived from these data. What about denominational contrasts, other ethnicities, and other nations? Are multi-ethnic, transdenominational, and/or cross-national data available for prayer?

Using data on ethnicity and religious affiliation from early GSSs, including special religious supplements, Greeley (1979) constructed what he termed a religio-ethnic typology. He found that more than half of adult Americans pray every day, but stratifying by religio-ethnic categories yielded interesting contrasts. For example, 76% of Slavic Catholics prayed daily, compared to 52 to 58% of Irish, Italian, German, and Hispanic Catholics. Among Protestants, 66% of Irish prayed daily, compared to 51 to 57% of British, Scandinavians, and Germans. Finally, 68% of African Americans, undifferentiated by religious affiliation, and only 10% of Jewish respondents, undifferentiated by denominational movement, reported daily prayer.

Data from the original World Values Survey of 22 nations, conducted from 1981–1983, enable cross-national comparisons of religious indicators, including prayer. While wording is problematic ("Do you take some moments of prayer, meditation, or contemplation or something like that?"; coded: yes vs. no vs. don't know), this offers the best look at how the prevalence of prayer, however faultily assessed, varies throughout the world (Campbell & Curtis, 1994). In the U.S. sample ($N = 2,315$), 85.3% of respondents reported praying, the highest prevalence of any nation. Among nations, only Finland (14.2%), Sweden (33.2%), and Australia (33.9%) had a prevalence below 40%, and only Mexico (82.5%) and South Africa (85.2%) had a prevalence above 80%. Japan, with by far the lowest prevalence of belief in God (38.6%) and sin (15.0%) and of religious feelings (24.2%), had a higher prevalence of prayer (41.1%) than four other countries.

These studies are admittedly not ideal for answering PPT questions about prayer. A major limitation is reliance upon single-item measures, which do not always enable even rough estimates of frequency. Little advantage has been taken of the taxonomies of prayer referenced earlier (Ladd & Spilka, 2002; Poloma & Pendleton, 1991). The most recent U.S. data, derived from a special supplement to the 1998 GSS and sponsored by NIA (Fetzer Institute/National Institute on Aging Working Group, 1999), was typical, relying on a single item ("How often do you pray privately in places other than at church or synagogue?"). An upside is that comparisons with previous studies was enabled. Indeed, the prevalences of ever praying (86.8%) and praying at least daily (50.9%) coincide with prior findings and point to the stability in this behavior across settings and over time, at least among Americans.

"HOW": THE EPIDEMIOLOGY OF PRAYER

The third step in an epidemiologic investigation, after negotiating "what," "who," "when," and "where," is to address "how." This is known as analytic epidemiology, in contrast to descriptive epidemiology, and is about identifying determinants of physical or mental illness. This is typically expressed in terms of risk or odds with respect to population rates of disease or other health indicators, although sometimes the conventions of social research are used.

The "how" question, in principle, is a two-part endeavor. Typically, an epidemiologist seeks to identify an association between an exposure variable, or class of variables, and a disease outcome, or class of outcomes. On occasion, an epidemiologist seeks to explain any relationship that emerges. By this is meant using analytic techniques such as modeling of one sort or another to uncover mediating or effect-modifying factors that help to account for the initial association. In the language of epidemiology, this involves ruling out confounding effects and specifying the type of association—that is, direct, indirect, synergistic, etc.

Not every epidemiologic study achieves, or attempts, the second part of this endeavor. Most studies are limited to identifying exposure variables as either risk or protective factors, with some modicum of controls, typically for age, to insure adjusted rates (epidemiologese for net effects). By professional convention, the discussion section of empirical papers in major epidemiology journals is the principal place for "how" sorts of questions to be posed. It is uncertain what proportion of epidemiologists actually get around to addressing these questions by incorporating additional variables into their models in subsequent studies.

Within the religion and health field, both aspects of the "how" question have been addressed repeatedly. Hundreds of empirical studies have documented statistically significant associations between religious variables and health outcomes (Koenig, McCullough, & Larson, 2001; Levin, 2001a), including many gerontological and geriatric investigations. By now, this is old news. Less widely recognized is the presence of many competing models positing various biobehavioral and psychosocial factors as potential mediators of religion-health associations.

For example, Idler (1987), a sociologist, has proposed that religious beliefs and practices influence health through promoting social cohesiveness, theodicy, coherence, and healthy behaviors. Psychologists McIntosh and Spilka (1990) have added to this list the salutary effects of internal locus of control beliefs and faith in God. Ellison (1994), also a sociologist, has emphasized the capability of religion both to provide tangible and emotional resources and support and to offer cognitive and institutional frameworks that serve to buffer deleterious effects of stress. The present author has integrated social-epidemiologic theory into a comprehensive model of psychosocial, behavioral, and biological factors connecting religion and health at the population level (Levin, 1996; Levin, 2001a; Levin & Vanderpool, 1989).

Another stream of theoretical work has sought to posit competing theoretical models linking religion, physical health, psychological well-being, and mediating factors in a variety of configurations. These include what have been termed suppressor, distress-deterrent, prevention, moderator, and health effects models (see Levin & Chatters, 1998). Each of these models specifies a different set of linkages of varying magnitude and directionality.

It has recently been observed that despite these often sophisticated efforts to propose pathways of connection between religion and health, few empirical studies have taken the necessary steps to do so (George & Ellison, 1999). Moreover, there is not much empirical evidence that psychosocial constructs alone account for the variation in health outcomes attributed to religious measures. Paradoxically, then, for epidemiologic investigation of religion, when it comes to the study of potential mechanisms we are long on theory and short on data.

With reference to prayer, the situation is identical. Health research, while not as plentiful as for religion in general, is nonetheless present, and has been reviewed elsewhere (e.g., Duckro & Magaletta, 1994; McCullough, 1995). This literature includes studies of effects of prayer, characterized as a behavior of respondents, on various health-related and quality-of-life outcomes, including dimensions of subjective well-being, coping with chronic and acute stress and illness, and psychiatric symptoms and disorders (McCullough, 1995). Throughout, prayer has been found to exert salutary effects. In the *Handbook of Religion and Health,* which emphasizes clinical and epidemiologic investigations and other medical research, studies were identified which found associations implicating prayer as a generally protective factor against anxiety disorders, cancer survival, cardiovascular disease, depression, functional disability, pain, somatic symptoms, and substance abuse (Koenig, McCullough, & Larson, 2001).

Prayer and Health: Empirical Findings

Many prayer-health studies provide information of interest to gerontologists due to (a) samples which draw on older respondents or on the entire adult life course, (b) prospective designs, or (c) analyses featuring explicit age comparisons or controls for age effects. An overview of studies published since about 1990 serves to illustrate the high quality of research on prayer and health conducted recently by gerontologists.

One group of investigations has focused on *private prayer as a potentially protective factor against psychological distress,* primarily depression.

Findings from the 1998 GSS determined that prayer was associated with fewer past-month depressive symptoms due to an indirect effect operating through increased religious coping (Nooney & Woodrum, 2002). Findings from the Duke sample of the Established Populations for Epidemiologic Studies of the Elderly (EPESE) project, conducted from 1986 to 1989, revealed a protective effect of religious devotion (including private prayer) on depression and somatic-retarded activities among elderly African-American cancer patients (Musick, Koenig, Hays, & Cohen, 1998). Findings using the same data determined that the protective effect of religious devotion on depression operated directly as well as indirectly through increased social support and better health (Koenig et al., 1997).

Some cross-sectional studies have produced conflicting results. Findings from the 1994 Alameda County Study of adults aged 50 and up found that nonorganizational religiosity (including frequency of prayer) was unrelated to depression (Strawbridge, Shema, Cohen, Roberts, & Kaplan, 1998). Likewise, a 1987 study of suddenly bereaved adults in a southwestern U.S. urban area found that personal prayer was not significantly associated with depression (Sherkat & Reed, 1992). Findings from Wave II of the Piedmont Epidemiologic Catchment Area (ECA) study, conducted from 1983 to 1984, showed that private religious devotion (including prayer) was associated with greater depressive symptomatology (Ellison, 1995).

A second set of studies has explored *prayer as a factor promoting positive well-being or health*. Findings from the Duke EPESE study showed that religious devotion had a statistically significant positive net effect on subjective health in both African-American and White elderly respondents (Musick, 1996). Findings from the 1983 GSS revealed that devotional intensity (including frequency of prayer) had a significant and positive net effect on a measure of overall life satisfaction (Ellison, Gay, & Glass, 1989). In the Australian Community Survey, conducted from 1997 to 1998, frequency of personal prayer was strongly associated with both positive and balanced affect, even after controlling for effects of age and sex (Francis & Kaldor, 2002). Analyses of data from the nationally representative 1997 Presbyterian Panel Survey found that frequent prayer was associated with significantly higher scores on the vitality, general health, and mental health subscales of the SF-36 among pastors (Meisenhelder & Chandler, 2001), and with significantly higher scores on the physical functioning, role functioning-physical, bodily pain, and mental health subscales among church members (Meisenhelder & Chandler, 2000).

Two recent clinical studies of middle-aged and older cardiac bypass patients at the University of Michigan affirm the salience of prayer for psychosocial status. One study, from 1993, found that private prayer promoted postoperative psychosocial recovery (Ai, Dunkle, Peterson, & Bolling, 1998). The authors hypothesized that this was due to fostering of a sense of optimism. Their second study, from 1999 to 2000, confirmed that private prayer was indeed a strong determinant of dispositional optimism (Ai, Peterson, Bolling, & Koenig, 2002).

As with the studies of prayer and depression, results are not uniform. An Israeli study of secular and religious *kibbutzim* in the western Negev found that private spontaneous praying is associated in an adverse direction with a measure of subjective health status (Anson, Levenson, Maoz, & Bonneh, 1991). Using data from two waves (1996 and 1999) of the National Survey of the Japanese Elderly, a measure of private religious practices (including prayer offerings made at home) was associated with a small but significant increase in the odds of developing hypertension (Krause et al., 2002).

A limitation of nearly every study is reliance upon single-item measures of prayer, almost always assessed as frequency of praying. Three exceptions, not surprisingly, are studies by Poloma and Pendleton (1988, 1989, 1991), authors of the taxonomy of prayer described earlier. One study (Poloma & Pendleton, 1989) supplemented a single-item prayer frequency variable with a scale of religious experiences during prayer. This was a good decision, as frequent prayer was significantly associated with existential well-being but with neither life satisfaction nor happiness, whereas the prayer experiences scale was a strong and significant correlate of all three indicators. A second study (Poloma & Pendleton, 1988) found an interesting pattern of differential associations between respective types of prayer, assessed with validated scales, and respective well-being indicators. Meditative prayer was a significant predictor of existential well-being, colloquial prayer significantly predicted happiness, ritual prayer was predictive of negative affect (perhaps as a response to depression), and the same prayer experiences scale as in the previously reviewed study strongly predicted existential well-being, happiness, and life satisfaction. A third study (Poloma & Pendleton, 1991) reported similar findings, and also that more frequent prayer was associated with greater existential well-being.

These studies are a considerable departure from the others reviewed in this section. Their use of multiple prayer measures, namely prayer frequency, an index of prayer-related experiences, and validated scales for distinct types of prayer, are an ideal approach that religious gerontologists would be wise to duplicate. Unfortunately, not only is this not being done, but these three studies actually predate all of the other studies reviewed in this section.

Prayer and Health: Postulated Mechanisms

Perhaps because of the paucity of research utilizing anything but the simplest measures of prayer, little is known about mechanisms of effect underlying an apparently salutary impact of prayer on physical and psychological well-being. Oddly, greater efforts exist to elucidate mechanisms for a prayer-healing association (Levin, 1996), as distinct from a prayer-health association. This is ironic, as scholarly discourse on prayer and healing is a separate research literature, addresses a different stage of the natural history of disease, emphasizes studies using experimental methods such as randomized controlled trials, and focuses on effects of distant prayer as a potentially therapeutic intervention in clinical samples of sick individuals (Levin, 2003). Despite current controversy over research in this area, in contrast to social and epidemiologic studies of prayer and health, along with a much smaller number of well-executed human studies (see Benor, 2001), there is nonetheless a stimulating ongoing debate on the "how" question among investigators into the healing effects of prayer (see Dossey, 1997, 1998, 2001). The same cannot be said for the relationship between prayer and health.

Few speculations on mechanisms underlying a prayer-health connection have surfaced in the past decades. A psychosocial explanation proposed that prayer represents a coping and defensive response that buffers the adverse effects of stress which typically produce ill-being (Caplan, Naidu, & Tripathi, 1984). A psychophysiological explanation implicated health-impacting psychodynamic motives and reflexes for prayer, as well as neurological correlates and sequelae (Marinier, 1954). A neurophysiological explanation based on laboratory observation identified particular brainwave patterns and electrocortical activity in Christians at prayer reminiscent of experienced meditators and highly adept yogis (Surwillo & Hobson, 1978).

"WHY": FINDING A CONTEXT FOR A PRAYER-HEALTH ASSOCIATION

Addressing "how" questions, if done at all, is about as far as epidemiologists usually go. For prayer, it is apparent that much of the "how" of a prayer-health relationship is unclear or unaddressed. The best that we can say is that evidence from population-based studies exists which, despite being mixed, appears to support a conditionally salutary influence for prayer on certain indicators of health and well-being. Further, some combination of social, behavioral, and biological variables likely mediates, moderates, or antecedes—and thus helps to account for—a prayer-health association. But still a nagging question remains: what underlies *that*?

For a religion-health association, biobehavioral and psychosocial candidate mechanisms have been proposed (see Levin, 1996), but these still do not give a satisfactory indication of just why religion ultimately may be good for one's health. The "why" question, for epidemiology in general and for the religion-and-health field especially, is thus mainly an existential issue. It represents, more than anything else, an attempt to gauge, simply, "what does this all mean?"

The present author has begun reflecting on this "why" question for religion and health in lectures, popular writing, and interviews. This work, summarized in this section in the context of prayer and health, represents a preliminary effort to address a simple but profound issue—why prayer matters—with special reference to existential and end-of-life concerns.

Why Prayer Influences Health

In addressing the "why" of a prayer-health relationship, six words come to mind. Each of these words identifies a concept that helps to shed light on just why it is that prayer should be expected to exert a salutary influence in the lives of aging humans. These six words are motivation, connection, meaning, hope, love, and transcendence. The last two words, especially, may be keys to understanding the apparent health benefits of prayer.

Through regular prayer, people may maintain a sense of relationship with God and their faith tradition. This communion may instill the *motivation* requisite to act diligently in a manner consistent with the holy writings and teachings of one's religion or spiritual path. Scriptural prescriptions and proscriptions regarding health, hygiene, and the body—such as admonitions regarding a wholesome life style found throughout holy writings such as the *Torah*—may be more apt to be taken to heart by people for whom prayer is an open and vital communication link to the divine. Maintaining an active life and making wise health choices throughout the life course, in turn, are strong determinants of reduced morbidity (Fried & Bush, 1988) and greater longevity (House, Robbins, & Metzner, 1982) in older adults.

Congregational prayer and worship may engender a rich sense of *connection* to others or to the eternal. Among Jews, for example, praying in synagogue connects one not just to God or to fellow congregants but to *klal Yisrael*, the community of Jews that exists and has existed across space and time for thousands of years and which, to this day, remains plugged into the tradition through common prayers and rituals that occur like clockwork in congregations throughout the world. If prayer can help to defeat loneliness and isolation, then it may serve to prevent, delay, or curtail illness, as loneliness and isolation are killing. This we know, for example, from the famous studies of mortality after bereavement (e.g., Helsing & Szklo, 1981).

Feeling and experiencing the sense of relationship with God and tradition engendered by collective and private prayer can provide *meaning* to life. In the presence of external chaos, loss of loved ones, and possibly involuntary disengagement from self-defining roles, prayer can provide a sense of order or context that brings with it reassurance that everything will be all right—that, in the words of the Prophet Isaiah, "no weapon that is formed against thee shall prosper" (Isaiah 54:17). Presence or absence of meaning is a much underrated variable among health researchers, and the therapeutic salience of context is backed by considerable anecdotal evidence from clinicians (Dossey, 1991; Frankl, 1984). Prayer as a coping response to physical symptoms among older adults is of obvious relevance for social and religious gerontology, but remains a much underinvestigated topic by researchers (see Bearon & Koenig, 1990).

Belief in the efficacy of prayer—whether for soliciting miracles or for maintaining a link to the divine—may offer *hope* in the face of hopeless situations. Optimism and positive expectation may not come as easily for those whose life has been filled with struggle and disappointment. By clinging tightly to faith, through the agency of prayer, incongruence between life's early goals and ultimate results may lose its destructive salience for psychological distress. Evidence suggests that hopeful thoughts and attitudes, whether regarding this world or the world to come, are powerful determinants of an ability to withstand pain (Snyder, 2000).

An active prayer life may both reflect and foster a deep sense of *love*—for God, fellow religionists, all people, all sentient beings, and all of creation. Developing such a reverence for all beings may not come effortlessly, except perhaps for the saintly. It may only be the fruit of a lifelong commitment to "practicing the presence of God," in Brother Lawrence's (1985) words. Experiencing a loving relationship with God—loving God and feeling God's love—may be especially salutary.

Recent findings show that such a relationship is strongly associated with higher self-ratings of health (Levin, 2001b) and fewer depressive symptoms (Levin, 2002).

Prayer of all kinds, whether quiet reflection, intent meditation, or ecstatic worship, and whether private or collective, may engender moments of true *transcendence*—of the body, of space, of time. How much does the approaching end of life deepen prayer? Is this attributable to onset of illness or declines in physical functioning? Or is it attributable to a concomitant deepening of wisdom and sensitivity with age? Numinous, mystical, and unitive experiences of many types are common elements of both Western and Eastern spirituality. For the Spanish monastic St. Teresa of Avila, the Sufi mystic Jalaluddin Rumi, the Kabbalist Abraham Abulafia, and contemporary self-realized yogic masters like Ram Dass, moments of unitive connection to the Source of being, ecstatic or peaceful, or more lasting transformation are typical manifestations of maturation along respective spiritual paths. The transcendent experience, in turn, has identifiable etiologic antecedents, a natural history or course, and substantive health effects, and various competing psychophysiological and neurophysiological models exist which seek to make sense of effects of transcendence on the body (see Levin & Steele, in press).

These six concepts—motivation, connection, meaning, hope, love, and transcendence—together offer insight into why prayer seems to be such a powerful resource for human well-being. If this reasoning is correct, then these concepts may be of considerable epidemiologic significance. Investigating the underrated role of love and transcendence may be especially key in making sense of empirical findings linking private and nonorganizational religious behaviors such as prayer to physical health, to indices of mental and emotional well-being, and to biomarkers of underlying processes, throughout the life course.

With this in mind, the present author has worked for the past few years to fashion theoretical models integrating current scientific knowledge about love and transcendence into both epidemiologic and gerontological theory. This includes proposing new fields of study dedicated to the epidemiology of love (Levin, 2000) and the epidemiology of the transcendent experience (Levin & Steele, in press), and asserting that investigation of mysticism may be central to the future of religious gerontology (Levin, 2003a). Implicit is the thesis that modern epidemiology—and one could read into that mainstream biomedicine—has lost its way in its embrace of "hard" markers of biological function as both key determinants of health and key explanans for any persistent health or healing effects of nonbiological host characteristics.

Likewise, the medical social sciences, social gerontology included, have placed their greatest focus on observable behaviors and quantifiable statuses as determinants of quality of life and explanans of links between psychosocial constructs and health, whereas a focus on the inner life of aging adults might prove more fruitful (Levin & Taylor, 1997; McFadden & Levin, 1996).

Missing in these discussions is the realm of experience. Even such subtle expressions of human psychology as beliefs, thoughts, values, motivations, and attitudes have received greater attention than experience. The domain of experience may be the ultimate epidemiologic and gerontological mystery. And what human experiences are more profound, more indescribable, more subtle—more ultimate—than love and transcendence? If prayer—communication with God—is the ultimate expression and experience of spirituality, and if this experience has a salutary impact, then perhaps the loving transaction ideally experienced through prayer and prayer's transcendental sequelae are the best places to begin searching if we are to gain a deeper understanding of the connection between prayer and health.

"SO": IMPLICATIONS OF A PRAYER-HEALTH ASSOCIATION

Having addressed "what," "who," "where," "when," "how," and "why," a seventh question now presents itself: "so?" This is not meant flippantly.

Over a decade ago, Tobin (1993) authored an editorial in *The Gerontologist* entitled, "So What?" It was written in response to a study by the present author, published in the same issue of the journal, which explored the prevalence and sociodemographic and religious predictors of mystical experiences in successive age cohorts of adults in a national probability sample (Levin, 1993). Tobin (1993) commended this investigation into "the power of the transcendental in aging" (p. 439) and encouraged research into "the essential psychological processes" (p. 439) that define and determine the sacred beliefs and experiences which "make meanings" (p. 439) for older adults. This was a principal theme of his book, *Personhood in Advanced Old Age* (Tobin, 1991), in which he described how religion can provide continuity across life-course stages by emphasizing the intrinsic and enduring meaning of life. The six concepts described in the last section—motivation, connection, meaning, hope, love, and transcendence—are an effort to develop this idea in a way that can be engaged by researchers.

For gerontologists interested in exploring prayer—its dimensions, patterns, predictors, outcomes—much work remains. Prayer is a vital resource in the lives of adults, perhaps increasingly so at later stages of the life course, and is an almost universal expression of piety and spirituality across faith traditions. It deserves greater and more systematic scrutiny than it has received to date among social and religious gerontologists. If religion is to continue to become a more mainstream topic within gerontology and within the sociomedical fields, then prayer will need to become a less marginal topic within the study of religion.

A Methodological Agenda for Gerontological Research on Prayer

This may be easier said than done. One impediment is a lack of sophistication in most gerontological research on prayer and health. Critiques and suggestions have been offered throughout this chapter. A few specifically methodological advances are also worth noting, including improvements involving measurement, sampling, study design, and analysis.

First, the status quo in prayer assessment in gerontological research is simply not good enough. Single-item frequency measures are useful, to a point, but by now sufficient data are available from probability surveys. The frequency of praying, in general, is a useful datum, but just scratches the surface of the substantive issues that can be engaged in research on prayer. It is time to explore the various types and expressions of prayer experienced by people in their daily lives. It is recommended that greater advantage be taken of the various multidimensional scales of prayer and prayer experiences, described earlier, such as found in the work of Poloma and colleagues (Poloma & Gallup, 1991; Poloma & Pendleton, 1988, 1989, 1991). These tools have been available for over a decade, but have been underutilized by gerontologists.

Second, researchers have done a poor job of reflecting the rich diversity of religious expression found among older Americans and older adults throughout the world. Aside from rare publications about older Jews (e.g., Harel, Biegel, & Guttmann, 1994) and Thomas' fascinating work on elderly Hindu *sadhus* (e.g., Thomas, 1991, 1992; Thomas & Chambers, 1989), most of what we know or think we know about the religious life of older adults derives from studies of North American Christians. There is no compelling reason to believe that the experiences of those most studied to date are identical to the millions of Americans who find spiritual expression through alternative means: new religious movements, esoteric or transpersonally oriented paths, recovery-of-transcendence movements within mainstream religions (e.g., charismatic renewal, Jewish renewal), or East-West syncretisms (e.g., JUBUs, the Sufi Order in the West, Christians living in ashrams or practicing Zen). While these spiritual expressions may seem marginal now for gerontology, they will become increasingly prevalent as the babyboomer cohort ages into older adulthood (Levin, 2003a).

Third, this paper has taken an epidemiologic perspective on research into the connection between prayer and health. This is not to say that most research on the topic is epidemiologic in design. It is not. The norm for studies in this area is the non-probability cross-sectional survey. Even where national probability samples were used, results are mostly expressed in terms of structural relationships. In understanding risk and protection, however, much can be gained by a more explicitly epidemiologic approach, especially use of case-control and prospective cohort designs. Expressing etiologic or determinant effects in terms of estimated risk or odds, population attributable risk, or age-adjusted proportionate mortality ratios, for example, can be enlightening and may more directly answer the sorts of questions most often raised when people think of the possible connection between prayer and health.

Fourth, age-period-cohort (APC) analysis is a useful and underutilized strategy for religious gerontologists. Perusal of national data suggests the presence, to some extent, of both aging and cohort effects and possibly period effects in the patterning of how often Americans pray. But this has not been systematically examined. Multiple panels of stable longitudinal data are required to conduct an APC analysis, and, further, modeling procedures are very sophisticated and one's interpretive reasoning must be keen. Nevertheless, excellent and creative APC analyses have been conducted of both denominational membership (Hagenaars, 1990) and religious attendance (Miller & Nakamura, 1996). In order to conduct an APC analysis of prayer, one is limited, of course, to tracking indicators present throughout multiple decades of data collection. For prayer, this would by necessity limit any such analyses to consideration of single-item assessments of frequency, assuming such an item has been present consistently in an annual survey. The GSS, for example, in operation for over 30 years, has included such an item, but only since 1983 (Davis & Smith, 1990). This may not be a sufficient number of rounds of data for conducting an APC analysis of prayer.

One recently published study took a simpler age-comparative approach to prayer (Peacock & Poloma, 1999). National probability data were used to examine differences across seven age cohorts (covering 18–98 years of age) in scales assessing prayer experience and each type of prayer in the Poloma and Pendleton (1988) taxonomy. The authors found generally higher levels of prayer across successive age cohorts, for all prayer measures. This study uniquely addresses key limitations of prior gerontological research on prayer, notably an absence of an explicit life-course perspective. Existing national datasets could be utilized in similar fashion. This would go a long way toward jump-starting a new generation of more sophisticated research on prayer and aging.

REFERENCES

Ai, A. L., Dunkle, R. E., Peterson, D., & Bolling, S. F. (1998). The role of private prayer in psychological recovery among midlife and aged patients following cardiac surgery. *The Gerontologist, 38,* 591–601.

Ai, A. L., Peterson, C., Bolling, S. F., & Koenig, H. (2002). Private prayer and optimism in middle-aged and older patients awaiting cardiac surgery. *The Gerontologist, 42,* 70–81.

Anson, O., Levenson, A., Maoz, B., & Bonneh, D. Y. (1991). Religious community, individual religiosity, and health: A tale of two kibbutzim. *Sociology, 25,* 119–132.

Bearon, L. B., & Koenig, H. G. (1990). Religious cognitions and use of prayer in health and illness. *The Gerontologist, 30,* 249–253.

Begun, Y. (1997). Quoted in M. C. Luzzatto, *The way of God* [ca. 1734], 6th rev. ed. Trans. by A. Kaplan. Jerusalem: Feldheim Publishers.

Benor, D. J. (2001). *Spiritual healing: Scientific validation of a healing revolution.* Southfield, MI: Vision Publications.

Campbell, R. A., & Curtis, J. E. (1994). Religious involvement across societies: Analyses for alternative measures in national surveys. *Journal for the Scientific Study of Religion, 33,* 215–229.

Caplan, R. D., Naidu, R. K., & Tripathi, R. C. (1984). Coping and defense: Constellations vs. components. *Journal of Health and Social Behavior, 25,* 303–320.

Castelli, J. (Ed.) (1994). *How I pray.* New York: Ballantine Books.

Chalfant, H. P., & Heller, P. L. (1991). Rural/urban versus regional differences in religiosity. *Review of Religious Research, 33,* 76–86.

Chatters, L. M., & Taylor, R. J. (1994). Religious involvement among older African-Americans. In J. S. Levin (Ed.), *Religion in aging and health: Theoretical foundations and methodological frontiers* (pp. 196–230). Thousand Oaks, CA: Sage Publications.

Davis, J. A., & Smith, T. W. (1990). *General Social Surveys, 1972–1990: Cumulative codebook* (p. 154). Chicago: National Opinion Research Center.

Doron, P. (2000). *Rashi's Torah commentary: Religious, philosophical, ethical, and educational insights.* Northvale, NJ: Jason Aronson.

Dossey, L. (1991). *Meaning and medicine: A doctor's tales of breakthrough and healing.* New York: Bantam Books.

Dossey, L. (1997). The forces of healing: Reflections on energy, consciousness, and the beef stroganoff principle. *Alternative Therapies in Health and Medicine, 3* (5), 8–14.

Dossey, L. (1998). Prayer, medicine, and science: The new dialogue. In L. VandeCreek (Ed.), *Scientific and pastoral perspectives on intercessory prayer: An exchange between Larry Dossey, M. D. and health care chaplains* (pp. 7–37). New York: Haworth Pastoral Press.

Dossey, L. (2001). Spirituality, science and the medical arts. *Subtle Energies and Energy Medicine, 12,* 1–15.

Duckro, P. N., & Magaletta, P. R. (1994). The effect of prayer on physical health: Experimental evidence. *Journal of Religion and Health, 33,* 211–219.

Ellison, C. G. (1994). Religion, the life stress paradigm, and the study of depression. In J. S. Levin (Ed.), *Religion in aging and health: Theoretical foundations and methodological frontiers* (pp. 78–121). Thousand Oaks, CA: Sage Publications.

Ellison, C. G. (1995). Race, religious involvement and depressive symptomatology in a southeastern U. S. community. *Social Science and Medicine, 40,* 1561–1572.

Ellison, C. G., Gay, D. A., & Glass, T. A. (1989). Does religious commitment contribute to individual life satisfaction? *Social Forces, 68,* 100–123.

Fecher, V. J. (Comp.). (1982). *Religion & aging: An annotated bibliography.* San Antonio: Trinity University Press.

Fetzer Institute/National Institute on Aging Working Group. (1999). *Multidimensional measurement of religiousness/spirituality for use in health research.* Kalamazoo, MI: John E. Fetzer Institute.

Francis, L. J., & Kaldor, P. (2002). The relationship between psychological well-being and Christian faith and practice in an Australian population sample. *Journal for the Scientific Study of Religion, 41,* 179–184.

Frankl, V. E. (1984). *Man's search for meaning* [1946], revised and updated. New York: Washington Square Press.

Fried, L. P., & Bush, T. L. (1988). Morbidity as a focus of preventive health care in the elderly. *Epidemiologic Reviews, 10,* 48–64.

George, L. K., & Ellison, C. G. (1999). Psychosocial mediators of the relationship between religious involvement and health: State of the evidence and future directions. Paper presented at the Workshop on Spirituality, Religion, and Health, National Institutes of Health, Bethesda, MD, October 26–27.

Greeley, A. M. (1979). Ethnic variations in religious commitment. In R. Wuthnow (Ed.), *The religious dimension: New directions in quantitative research* (pp. 113–134). New York: Academic Press.

Hagenaars, J. A. (1990). Cohort analysis. In *Categorical longitudinal data: Log-linear panel, trend, and cohort analysis* (pp. 314–359). Newbury Park, CA: Sage Publications.

Harel, Z., Biegel, D. E., & Guttmann, D. (Eds.) (1994). *Jewish aged in the United States and Israel: Diversity, programs, and services.* New York: Springer Publishing.

Helsing, K. J., & Szklo, M. (1981). Mortality after bereavement. *American Journal of Epidemiology, 114,* 41–52.

House, J. S., Robbins, C., & Metzner, H. L. (1982). The association of social relationships and activities with mortality: Prospective evidence from the Tecumseh Community Health Study. *American Journal of Epidemiology, 116,* 123–140.

Idler, E. L. (1987). Religious involvement and the health of the elderly: Some hypotheses and an initial test. *Social Forces, 66,* 226–238.

James, W. (1958). *The varieties of religious experience* [1902]. New York: Mentor.

Koenig, H. G. (Comp.) (1995). *Research on religion and aging: An annotated bibliography.* Westport, CT: Greenwood Press.

Koenig, H. G., Hays, J. C., George, L. K., Blazer, D. G., Larson, D. B., & Landerman, L. R. (1997). Modeling the cross-sectional relationships between religion, physical health, social support, and depressive symptoms. *American Journal of Geriatric Psychiatry, 5,* 131–144.

Koenig, H. G., McCullough, M. E., & Larson, D. B. (2001). *Handbook of religion and health.* New York: Oxford University Press.

Krause, N., Liang, J., Shaw, B. A., Sugisawa, H., Kim, H.-Y., & Sugihara, Y. (2002). Religion, death of a loved one, and hypertension among older adults in Japan. *Journal of Gerontology: Social Sciences, 57B,* S96–S107.

Ladd, K. L., & Spilka, B. (2002). Inward, outward, and upward: Cognitive aspects of prayer. *Journal for the Scientific Study of Religion, 41,* 475–484.

Larson, D. B., Sherrill, K. A., & Lyons, J. S. (1994). Neglect and misuse of the *r* word: Systematic reviews of religious measures in health, mental health, and aging. In J. S. Levin (Ed.), *Religion in aging and health: Theoretical foundations and methodological frontiers* (pp. 178–195). Thousand Oaks, CA: Sage Publications.

Lawrence, B. (1985). *The practice of the presence of God* [1692]. Trans. by R. J. Edmonson. Ed. by H. M. Helms. Orleans, MA: Paraclete Press.

Levin, J. S. (1989). Religious factors in aging, adjustment, and health: A theoretical overview. In W. M. Clements (Ed.), *Religion, aging and health: A global perspective* (pp. 133–146). Compiled by the World Health Organization. New York: Haworth Press.

Levin, J. S. (1993). Age differences in mystical experience. *The Gerontologist, 33,* 507–513.

Levin, J. S. (1996). How prayer heals: A theoretical model. *Alternative Therapies in Health and Medicine, 2* (1), 66–73.

Levin, J. S. (1997). Religious research in gerontology, 1980–1994: A systematic review. *Journal of Religious Gerontology, 10,* 3–31.

Levin, J. (2000). A prolegomenon to an epidemiology of love: Theory, measurement, and health outcomes. *Journal of Social and Clinical Psychology, 19,* 117–136.

Levin, J. (2001a). *God, faith, and health: Exploring the spirituality-healing connection*. New York: John Wiley and Sons.

Levin, J. (2001b). God, love, and health: Findings from a clinical study. *Review of Religious Research, 42*, 277–293.

Levin, J. (2002). Is depressed affect a function of one's relationship with God?: Findings from a study of primary care patients. *International Journal of Psychiatry in Medicine, 32*, 379–393.

Levin, J. (2003a). "Bumping the top": Is mysticism the future of religious gerontology? In M. A. Kimble & S. H. McFadden (Eds.), *Religion, spirituality, and aging: A handbook, volume 2* (pp. 402–411). Minneapolis: Fortress Press.

Levin, J. (2003b). Spiritual determinants of health and healing: An epidemiologic perspective on salutogenic mechanisms. *Alternative Therapies in Health and Medicine, 9*(6), 48–57.

Levin, J. S., & Chatters, L. M. (1998). Research on religion and mental health: An overview of empirical findings and theoretical issues. In H. G. Koenig (Ed.), *Handbook of religion and mental health* (pp. 33–50). San Diego: Academic Press.

Levin, J., & Steele, L. (2001). On the epidemiology of "mysterious" phenomena. *Alternative Therapies in Health and Medicine, 7*(1), 64–66.

Levin, J., & Steele, L. (In press). The transcendent experience: Conceptual, methodological, and epidemiologic perspectives. *Alternative Therapies in Health and Medicine.*

Levin, J. S., & Taylor, R. J. (1993). Gender and age differences in religiosity among Black Americans. *The Gerontologist, 33*, 16–23.

Levin, J. S., & Taylor, R. J. (1997). Age differences in patterns and correlates of the frequency of prayer. *The Gerontologist, 37*, 75–88.

Levin, J. S., & Vanderpool, H. Y. (1987). Is frequent religious attendance *really* conducive to better health?: Toward an epidemiology of religion. *Social Science and Medicine, 24*, 589–600.

Levin, J. S., & Vanderpool, H. Y. (1989). Is religion therapeutically significant for hypertension? *Social Science and Medicine, 29*, 69–78.

Marinier, P. (1954). Reflections on prayer: Its causes and its psychophysiological effects. In P. A. Sorokin (Ed.), *Forms and techniques of altruistic and spiritual growth* (pp. 145–164). Boston: Beacon Press.

McCullough, M. E. (1995). Prayer and health: Conceptual issues, research review, and research agenda. *Journal of Psychology and Theology, 23*, 15–29.

McFadden, S. H., & Levin, J. S. (1996). Religion, emotions, and health. In C. Magai & S. H. McFadden (Eds.), *Handbook of emotion, adult development, and aging* (pp. 349–365). San Diego: Academic Press.

McIntosh, D., & Spilka, B. (1990). Religion and physical health: The role of personal faith and control beliefs. *Research in the Social Scientific Study of Religion, 2*, 167–194.

Meisenhelder, J. B., & Chandler, E. N. (2000). Prayer and health outcomes in church members. *Alternative Therapies in Health and Medicine, 6* (4), 56–60.

Meisenhelder, J. B., & Chandler, E. N. (2001). Frequency of prayer and functional health in Presbyterian pastors. *Journal for the Scientific Study of Religion, 40,* 323–329.

Meserve, H. C. (1991). The human side of prayer. *Journal of Religion and Health, 30,* 271–276.

Miller, A. S., & Nakamura, T. (1996). On the stability of church attendance patterns during a time of demographic change: 1965–1988. *Journal for the Scientific Study of Religion, 35,* 275–284.

Mindel, C. H., & Vaughan, C. E. (1978). The multidimensional approach to religiosity and disengagement. *Journals of Gerontology, 33,* 103–108.

Moberg, D. O. (1990). Religion and aging. In K. F. Ferraro (Ed.), *Gerontology: Perspectives and issues* (pp. 179–205). New York: Springer.

Musick, M. A. (1996). Religion and subjective health among Black and White elders. *Journal of Health and Social Behavior, 37,* 221–237.

Musick, M. A., Koenig, H. G., Hays, J. C., & Cohen, H. J. (1998). Religious activity and depression among community-dwelling elderly persons with cancer: The moderating effect of race. *Journal of Gerontology: Social Sciences, 53B,* S218–S237.

Needleman, J. (1980). *Lost Christianity: A journey of rediscovery to the center of Christian experience.* Toronto: Bantam Books.

Nooney, J., & Woodrum, E. (2002). Religious coping and church-based support as predictors of mental health outcomes: Testing a conceptual model. *Journal for the Scientific Study of Religion, 41,* 359–368.

Peacock, J. R., & Poloma, M. M. (1999). Religiosity and life satisfaction across the life course. *Social Indicators Research, 48,* 321–345.

Pelcovitz, R. (Trans.) (1997). *Sforno: Commentary on the Torah.* Brooklyn, NY: Mesorah Publications.

Poloma, M. M., & Gallup, G. H., Jr. (1991). *Varieties of prayer: A survey report.* Philadelphia: Trinity Press International.

Poloma, M. M., & Pendleton, B. F. (1988). Religious domains and general well-being. *Social Indicators Research, 22,* 255–276.

Poloma, M. M., & Pendleton, B. F. (1989). Exploring types of prayer and quality of life: A research note. *Review of Religious Research, 31,* 46–53.

Poloma, M. M., & Pendleton, B. F. (1991). The effects of prayer and prayer experiences on measures of general well-being. *Journal of Psychology and Theology, 19,* 71–83.

Schachter-Shalomi, Z. (1993). On mystical-empirical Jewish prayer—a "rap." In *Paradigm shift: From the Jewish Renewal teachings of Reb Zalman Schachter-Shalomi.* Ed. by E. Singer. Northvale, NJ: Jason Aronson.

Sherkat, D. E., & Reed, M. D. (1992). The effects of religion and social support on self-esteem and depression among the suddenly bereaved. *Social Indicators Research, 26,* 259–275.

Sherrill, K. A., Larson, D. B., & Greenwold, M. (1993). Is religion taboo in gerontology?: Systematic review of research on religion in three major gerontology journals, 1985–1991. *American Journal of Geriatric Psychiatry, 1,* 109–117.

Sinetar, M. (1997). Who speaks? In B. Shield & R. Carlson (Eds.), *For the love of God: Handbook for the spirit*, rev. ed. (pp. 159–165). Novato, CA: New World Library.

Smart, N. (1996). *Dimensions of the sacred: An anatomy of the world's beliefs.* Berkeley: University of California Press.

Snyder, C. R. (2000). The past and possible futures of hope. *Journal of Social and Clinical Psychology, 19,* 11–28.

Strawbridge, W. J., Shema, S. J., Cohen, R. D., Roberts, R. E., & Kaplan, G. A. (1998). Religiosity buffers effects of some stressors on depression but exacerbates others. *Journal of Gerontology: Social Sciences, 53B,* S118–S126.

Surwillo, W. W., & Hobson, D. P. (1978). Brain electrical activity during prayer. *Psychological Reports, 43,* 135–143.

Thomas, L. E. (1991). Dialogues with three religious renunciates and reflections on wisdom and maturity. *International Journal of Aging and Human Development, 32,* 211–227.

Thomas, L. E. (1992). Identity, ideology and medicine: Health attitudes and behavior among Hindu religious renunciates. *Social Science and Medicine, 34,* 499–502.

Thomas, L. E., & Chambers, K. O. (1989). Phenomenology of life satisfaction among elderly men: Quantitative and qualitative views. *Psychology and Aging, 4,* 284–289.

Tillich, P. (1957). *Dynamics of faith.* New York: Harper & Row.

Tobin, S. S. (1991). Preserving the self through religion. In *Personhood in advanced old age: Implications for practice* (pp. 119–133). New York: Springer.

Tobin, S. S. (1993). So what? *The Gerontologist, 33,* 439.

Twerski, A. J. (1992). *Growing each day.* Brooklyn, NY: Mesorah Publications, Ltd.

Wach, J. (1944). *Sociology of religion.* Chicago: University of Chicago Press.

Witter, R. A., Stock, W. A., Okun, M. A., & Haring, M. J. (1985). Religion and subjective well-being in adulthood: A quantitative synthesis. *Review of Religious Research, 26,* 332–342.

Next Steps in Understanding the Prayer/Health Connection

Kenneth F. Ferraro

R esearch on prayer and health is emerging as a vibrant arena of inquiry, and Levin's chapter (this volume) offers a masterful review of this topic. In the process, he articulates what it means to think epidemiologically about prayer and the prayer/health link, especially for older people. He reviews the relevant research, documents the limitations of the literature, and offers a prognosis for better understanding the prayer/health connection.

Although research on prayer and health is attracting considerable scientific interest, one could argue that study of the topic—and religion and health, more generally—faces a period of scientific lag. Most previous studies that include some measurement of religious behavior have few or no measures of prayer. The emphasis has been on denominational affiliation and attendance at religious services. There is, therefore, a profound need to collect data to answer the emergent questions about the prayer/health connection. Levin's essay, and hopefully my response to it, will help identify some of the next logical steps for research on this topic.

PREPARE THE WAY

Levin's chapter helps one understand the possible reasons for a link between prayer and health. It is a rich essay, and several strengths are worthy of mention. First, Levin develops his essay by embracing a variety of religious expressions. Much of the literature on religion and aging has focused on Christianity. Levin draws from this literature, but also points to works by others that focus on other forms of religious experience. Second, he makes some astute observations on the epistemology of knowledge on religion and health. He notes that much of the research on religion and health is largely a gerontological literature. By contrast, much of the empirical literature on prayer is not. For example, most of the work on intercessory prayer has come from medicine, especially cardiology. This is important because much of the former is based on community samples, while the latter is based on clinical samples—the implications of which are very important. Third, this essay is vintage Levin, for it applies the epidemiologic paradigm to religion. One may not think of prayer as a "behavioral host-factor exposure variable," but Levin has carefully applied the epidemiologic perspective to the study of prayer, and he has done it in a way that makes the next steps in this research clear and intriguing.

Levin praises the work of Poloma (e.g., Poloma & Pendleton, 1989), who has single-handedly done more than anyone else to advance the scientific study of prayer in the past two decades. The basis of all science is measurement, and Poloma has led the way in measuring types of prayer (Poloma & Gallup, 1991). It may be said that prayer is like carbon—there is one essential element, but it takes many different forms. Poloma has pioneered the development of a taxonomy for the many forms of prayer.

In a series of works from 1988 to 1991, Poloma and colleagues noted how vacuous it was to attempt to study prayer and well-being by relying on a single-item measure of the frequency of prayer. She worked with Pendleton and Gallup to do something about it. They developed measures of different types of prayer and then tested for a measurement structure among the items (Poloma & Pendleton, 1988, 1989). They found that there were four major types of prayer—ritual, conversational, petitionary, and meditative—and documented their prevalence in American society. Unfortunately, few people acted on Poloma's typology, but I think we now realize that she was ahead of her time and the extant data sets. We are finally beginning to see others measuring types of prayer to extend this line of inquiry (Ladd & Spilka, 2002).

Levin's essay on prayer, love, and transcendence is organized around basic questions such as "what," "who," "where," "when," "how," and "why." I will focus on one question: "What's next?" More specifically, I ask: What are the next steps for enhancing our study of the prayer/health connection?

WORDS VS. DEEDS

It has long been recognized that there are profound differences between what people say and what they do (Deutscher, 1973). The same issue applies to the study of prayer inasmuch as most studies rely on *reports* of prayer. The measurement of prayer is an especially difficult task. Poloma has helped us to see the dimensions of the concept and provided instruments to capture each dimension. At the same time, prayer has no "objective referent" for scientific measurement. A person may claim that he or she prays for 30 minutes per day, but is there a way to verify this? Observation might help for public or vocal prayer, but observation does little for measuring silent prayer or meditation.

The likely consequence of the difference between words and deeds is a social desirability effect. Religious or spiritual people are likely to overestimate their prayer life. Since prayer is virtuous for these people, there might be an amplification of reports of prayer. By contrast, people who reject religion and/or spiritual matters would likely underestimate prayer reports. For them, prayer may be seen as something for the weak. Thus, even when they pray, it may not be reported. For example, accounts from the September 11 tragedy at the World Trade Center indicate many calls to God for help, including from persons who would not describe themselves as religious. Would this be reported as prayer?

Beyond potential social desirability bias, there are also the definitional differences due to culture or religious orientation. Stated differently, what counts as prayer? Does reading a book on prayer count as prayer? Does attending a prayer meeting count? Does a relaxing, perhaps meditative, walk by a stream count? The point is that many people report that they pray, but we know little about the types of prayer being reported. Research needs to define types of prayer and to query subjects about those types. Unfortunately, the measures on most of the publicly-archived surveys are general reports of prayer—what we might call omnibus prayer reports. We need more studies like those of Poloma and her colleagues that question respondents about specific types of prayer (Poloma & Gallup, 1991). Indeed, it is common for areas of inquiry to move from the general or omnibus measures to more specific measures as a sign of scientific maturity. Research on prayer has been slow to mature, but there are signs of recent progress (Ladd & Spilka, 2002).

PERCEIVED EFFECTIVENESS OF PRAYER

Related to the measurement of the act of prayer, it would be useful to learn more about whether people *value* prayer. Levin notes how prayer can motivate: "communion may instill the motivation requisite to act diligently." We need more research on how prayer translates—or fails to translate—into behavior. At the same time, however, we know very little about what people think will result from prayer. There may be huge differences across religions in the perceived efficacy of prayer. For some religions, prayer has little to do with moving God to act, but more with accepting what God has "predestined." For other belief systems, prayer is seen as the means to move God to action; many belief systems blend the two approaches. The point is that we know very little about the perceived efficacy of prayer, and it may be the key to shaping both *how* and *how much* people pray.

Belief in the value of prayer could be measured in a variety of ways. To begin, one might ask about answered prayer: "Have you ever had a specific prayer answered? If yes, when was the last such experience?" One could extend this line of inquiry to find out about the motivation to pray: "Was this a need for you or someone else?" In addition, it may be useful to know if the person has experienced, or even expects, answers to prayers for miracles. People who report the manifestation of miracles may have higher expectations and, hence, more petitionary will. Beyond questions focusing on the experience of answered prayer, it would be helpful to also assess agreement with statements about the efficacy of prayer and any conditions necessary for prayer to "work."

BRINGING THE SOCIAL BACK IN

Homans' (1964) presidential address to the American Sociological Association four decades ago offered a plea for bringing the social back into social science. It is my sense that research on prayer, as well as prayer and health, still needs this clarion call. Prayer has almost always focused on what may be called solitary prayer, but prayer is frequently not a solitary endeavor, especially among religious persons.

Consider the common distinction between organizational and nonorganizational religious behavior (Mindel & Vaughan, 1978)—also described as public vs. private, formal vs. informal, and institutional vs. noninstitutional. When prayer is categorized in such schema, it is almost always identified as a nonorganizational or private matter. Although that is a reasonable conclusion for some religions and some types of prayer, it is naïve to assume that prayer is exclusively in the private domain. Each of the four types of prayer identified by Poloma and Pendleton (1989) can be either solitary or social. Ritual prayer (e.g., Lord's prayer) may be solitary or social. Conversational and meditative prayer may most likely be classified as solitary, but these may also be socially structured, whether in prayer meetings or internet chat rooms. Petitionary prayer clearly manifests itself in solitude (e.g., personal requests) or in social gatherings (e.g., vigil for a social cause).

Perhaps the arena where prayer is almost always regarded as solitary is the study of intercession on health. Byrd's (1988) study of intercession for 393 patients in a coronary care unit was a randomized, double-blind design and revealed beneficial effects of prayer. Each patient in the experimental group was assigned from "three to seven intercessors." It was not disclosed whether the intercessors prayed in groups or in solitude. Might social intercession have different effects than solitary intercession? Moreover, 57 patients rejected participation in the study. Although patients did not know to which group they were assigned, they knew they were assigned. What about the patients who declined participation? Might intercession work better *on* those who believe in its value than for those who do not? Interestingly, a study by Harris et al. (1999) used subjects without their informed consent (after approval from their Institutional Review Board). Even without the pre-screening, their results were consistent with those reported by Byrd: intercession helped cardiac-care patients.

Variants of these studies reveal the complex social nature of intercession. For example, Avilles et al. (2001) studied intercession and cardiovascular disease progression after hospital discharge. Their study was unique, however, because they had both individual and group intercessors. They found no difference in the effect of intercessory prayer, but did not analyze differences between individual and group intercessors. Might the treatment have varied by whether the intercession was individual or group? As stated previously, each type of prayer can be socially structured or in solitude. It would be helpful to know which the case is, even in studies of intercession. It would also be useful to know if intercessor behavior changes as a result of progress reports on the patient. In short, prayer does not occur in a social vacuum.

MECHANISMS FOR THE PRAYER/HEALTH LINK

Whereas the link between prayer and health can take many forms, it would be helpful to see research give explicit attention to the mechanisms involved. There is also evidence to suggest that the mechanisms may be unique for the outcomes considered. For instance, ritual prayer may be the type that is least likely to influence most health outcomes, but it may be helpful for others. Ritual prayer and the recitation of religious prose or poetry may not affect heart disease prevalence, but may lower the risk of dementia. By contrast, conversational prayer and meditative prayer may reduce heart disease through "divine social support." Conversational, contemplative prayer may be an antidote for the "hurry syndrome" of modern societies, thereby promoting overall health. Moreover, as Levin points out, these types of prayer focus on transcendence, which may help one to keep worldly troubles (i.e., stressors) in perspective.

Considering the role of contemplative prayer, Figure 3.1 depicts what may be called a salubrious prayer cycle. As Levin points out in his chapter, "psychophysiological and neurophysiological models exist which seek to make sense of effects of transcendence on the body." In the salubrious prayer cycle, persons who spend time in meditation are more likely to also engage in conversational prayer. Although conversational prayer may contain elements of praise and adoration, it also typically entails entreaties for change. These requests or petitions can be for one's self or for others. Self-petition may not be as likely to lead to meditative prayer, but petition for others—intercession—may be the impetus toward meditative prayer. There are several hypotheses from such a heuristic model of a prayer cycle, but the key premise is that persons engaged in a *diverse* set of prayer experiences are more likely to reap health benefits.

Finally, researchers examining mechanisms for the prayer/health link also need to be aware of the possibility of reverse causality. While prayer may affect health, it is also possible that poor health may lead to prayer. Research on religious consolation reveals that some health and personal problems may, indeed, spur religious activity (Ferraro & Kelley-Moore, 2000; Idler, 1987). In order to better understand the association between prayer and health, longitudinal data will prove most helpful for discerning which mechanisms are operant.

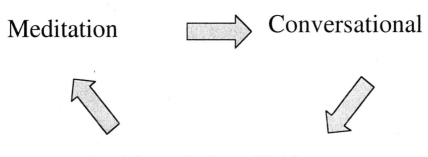

FIGURE 3.1 Salubrious prayer cycle.

FOUR STEPS FOR PRAYER RESEARCH

A recurrent theme of the contributors to this volume is that we need to know more about the role that prayer plays in the connection between religion and well-being in adulthood. Levin's chapter greatly helps us to understand this connection by applying an epidemiologic perspective to the study of prayer. To advance the literature on prayer and health, I have outlined four steps that should aid future research:

• clarify what is meant by prayer, especially reports of prayer
• examine the role of perceived efficacy of prayer
• consider the social dimensions of prayer
• study specific mechanisms by which prayer may influence health and well-being.

The extant research shows that prayer matters, but progress on these four fronts should help uncover the dynamic relationship between prayer and health over the life course.

ACKNOWLEDGMENTS

Support for this research was provided by a grant from the National Institute on Aging (AG01055).

REFERENCES

Aviles, J. M., Whelan, S. E., Hernke, D. A., Williams, B. A., Kenny, K. E., O'Fallon, W. M., & Kopecky, S. L. (2001). Intercessory prayer and cardiovascular disease progression in a coronary care unit population: A randomized controlled trial. *Mayo Clinic Proceedings, 76,* 1192–1198.

Byrd, Randolph C. (1988). Positive therapeutic effects of intercessory prayer in a coronary care unit population. *Southern Medical Journal, 81,* 826–829.

Deutscher, I. (1973). *What we say/what we do; Sentiments and acts.* Glenview, IL: Scott, Foresman.

Ferraro, K. F., & Kelley-Moore, J. (2000). Religious consolation among men and women: Do health problems spur seeking? *Journal for the Scientific Study of Religion, 39,* 220–234.

Harris, W. S., Gowda, M., Kolb, J. W., Strychacz, C. P., Vacek, J. L., Jones, P. G., Forker, A, O'Keefe, J. H., & McCallister, B. D. (1999). A randomized, controlled trial of the effects of remote, intercessory prayer on outcomes in patients admitted to the coronary care unit. *Archives of Internal Medicine, 159,* 2273–2278.

Homans, G. C. (1964). Bringing men back in. *American Sociological Review, 29,* 809–818.

Idler, E. L. (1987). Religious involvement and the health of the elderly: Some hypotheses and an initial test. *Social Forces, 66,* 226–238.

Ladd, K. L., & Spilka, B. (2002). Inward, outward, and upward: Cognitive aspects of prayer. *Journal for the Scientific Study of Religion, 41,* 475–484.

Mindel, C. H., & Vaughan, C. E. (1978). The multidimensional approach to religiosity and disengagement. *Journals of Gerontology, 33,* 103–108.

Poloma, M. M., & Gallup, G. H., Jr. (1991). *Varieties of prayer: A survey report.* Philadelphia: Trinity Press International.

Poloma, M. M., & Pendleton, B. F. (1988). Religious domains and general well-being. *Social Indicators Research, 22,* 255–276.

Poloma, M. M., & Pendleton, B. F. (1989). Exploring types of prayer and quality of life: A research note. *Review of Religious Research, 31,* 46–53.

Commentary

Prayer and the Elderly: Exploring a "Gerontological Mystery"

Margaret M. Poloma

L evin (this volume) has raised a number of important issues in his informative and challenging paper on "Prayer, Love, and Transcendence," a topic he refers to as a "gerontological mystery." While gerontology has led the way in researching the effects of religion on health, it has favored the use of church attendance, a "public" measure of religiosity, as its religiosity measure of choice. As Levin has noted, private and non-organizational indicators, including prayer and religious experiences, have been largely neglected. When prayer has been used as a religiosity measure in research, the most common indicator has been frequency of prayer. Those few researchers who have struggled to conceptualize, measure, and unlock the mystery of prayer, have done so with little if any specific focus on the issues related to aging and religion.

As someone who has sought to demonstrate the complexity of prayer, wrestling with questions about what people do and what they experience during prayer, Levin's stimulating and provocative article posed a challenge. I decided to revisit the 1985 Akron Area Survey (AAS), the original survey through which I sought to measure varieties of prayer and to determine its effects on various well-being measures, to explore prayer's efficacy on the well-being of seniors in the sample. The AAS (Poloma & Pendleton, 1991a) included a battery of questions on religious beliefs and practices not available in the Gallup national data set used by Poloma and Gallup (1991), promising to be a better data set to explore a model for prayer tested for this article. The results of the 1988 national study corroborated the basic findings of the Akron area study on prayer, suggesting that this Midwestern city corresponded to the "national profile" at the time. See Poloma & Gallup (1991); Poloma & Pendleton (1991a, 1991b, 1990, 1989) for details on the two samples. Unlike earlier analyses of the effects of private prayer on general well-being, this article focuses on the senior subsample and includes corporate as well as private measures of prayer.

The model guiding this reanalysis of the AAS data emerged during discussion of Levin's chapter at the 2001 Penn State social structures conference. There seemed to be a consensus that the practice of prayer can be described as personal (private) or corporate (institutional). Furthermore prayer can be active, involving particular forms and activities, or it can be receptive or experiential. The typology that emerged and the one explored in this chapter is fourfold: personal and active prayer (measured by forms of private prayer), corporate and active (measured by church attendance), personal and receptive (measured by religious experiences during prayer), and corporate and receptive (measured by religious experiences during church services).

Two tables using AAS data are presented here for interpretation and discussion, the first providing a bivariate analysis of relevant variables and the second testing the four-fold multivariate model. The top half of Table 3.1 contains a correlation matrix for select variables (including age) for the entire sample ($N = 562$). Since age was shown to be positively related to all the religious indicators (but not the well-being measures), a separate correlation matrix was developed for a subsample of respondents over age 55 ($n = 160$) that can be found on the bottom half of Table 3.1. The subsample of seniors was then used in the regression analysis found in Table 3.2 to test for the effects of the four categories of prayer—personal/active; corporate/active; personal/receptive; and corporate receptive—on four measures of well-being.

REVIEWING THE MEASURES

Well-Being Measures

The AAS collected information on four measures of subjective perceptions of well-being: happiness, general life satisfaction, existential well-being, and negative affect. *Happiness* was measured by a single item: "How happy are you?" *Life satisfaction* is an index formed by using items from semantic differential scales with values ranging from one to seven, asking the respondents to evaluate how "miserable/enjoyable,"

TABLE 3.1   Bivariate Correlations for Prayer and Well-Being Items

Total Sample N = 562

	1	2	3	4	5	6	7	8	9	10	11
1 Age	1.00	.04	.05	.07	-.06	.22**	.25**	.17**	.18**	.14*	.13*
2 Happiness		1.00	.61**	.43**	.35*	.17**	.16**	.06	.20**	.17**	.12*
3 Lifesat			1.00	.53**	-.40*	.16*	.16*	.09	.20*	.24*	.17*
4 Existwb				1.00	.24*	.30**	.32**	.24**	.33**	.30**	.32**
5 Negaffect					1.00	.07	.06	.07	.01	-.04	.00
6 Colloqpray						1.00	.72**	.63**	.58**	.48**	.48**
7 Mentalpray							1.00	.62**	.72**	.50**	.61**
8 Freqpray								1.00**	.57**	.52**	.47**
9 Prayexp									1.00	.49*	.64**
10 Attend										1.00	.50**
11 Churchexp											1.00

* $p < .01$; ** $p < .001$

Senior Sample (55+) n = 160

	1	2	3	4	5	6	7	8	9	10
1 Happiness	1.00									
2 Lifesat	.66**	1.00								
3 Existwb	.51**	.57**	1.00							
4 Negaffect	-.40**	-.44**	-.32**	1.00						
5 Colloqpray	.21**	.25**	.37**	-.01	1.00					
6 Mentalpray	.20**	.21**	.38**	-.01	.70**	1.00				
7 Freqpray	.05	.06	.27**	-.02	.53**	.67**	1.00			
8 Prayexp	.20**	.18	.33**	-.02	.49**	.50**	.43**	1.00		
9 Attend	.13	.19*	.25**	-.13	.28**	.33**	.39**	.31**	1.00	
10 Churchexp	.05	.13	.35**	.01	.33**	.60**	.35**	.66**	.36**	1.00

$* p = < .01; ** p = < .001$

TABLE 3.2   Multiple Regression Equations (Senior Sample: n = 160)

	I Happiness (beta)	II Life Satisfaction (beta)	III Existential Well-Being (beta)
Private Prayer Measures			
Colloquial Prayer	.14	.15	.27**
Prayer Experiences	.13	.10	.19*
	Adj. R^2 = .04*	Adj. R^2 = .05	Adj. R^2 = .15**
Corporate Prayer Measures			
Church Attendance	−.01	.10	.10
Church Experiences	.14	.10	.31**
	Adj. R^2 = .01	Adj. R^2 = .00	Adj. R^2 = .13**
Private and Corporate Measures			
Colloquial Prayer	.07	.12	.34**
Prayer Experiences	.26	.08	.07
Church Attendance	.20	.06	.11
Church Experiences	.24	.05	.09
	Adj. R^2 = .04	Adj. R^2 = .01	Adj. R^2 = .20**

* p = < .05; ** p = < .001

"disappointing/rewarding," "boring/interesting," and "satisfying/dissatisfying" respondents generally found their life. *Existential well-being* was an index composed of two questions, with Likert-like responses of strongly agree, agree, disagree, strongly disagree: "I feel a sense of well-being about the direction my life is headed" and "I believe there is some real purpose for my life." *Negative affect,* conceptualized as "depressed mood" in some studies, was measured by a set of items from the CES-D scale. Respondents were asked to describe on a scale from one to seven "how frequently during the past year have you felt": "depressed," "lonely," "sad," "tense," and "fearful." (For further information on and discussion of the AAS dataset, see Poloma and Pendleton, 1991a, 1991b, 1990, 1989.)

Prayer Measures

Private Prayer. A filter question measuring the frequency of prayer, with responses ranging from "never" to "several times a day," was used to screen the 90% of respondents who prayed at least on occasion from those who never prayed. Those who prayed were then asked a series of questions asking what they did when they prayed, revealing four factors with an Eigenvalue greater than 1, which the researchers labeled *colloquial prayer, meditative prayer, petitionary prayer,* and *ritual prayer* (Poloma & Pendleton, 1991). The bivariate analysis will employ only the first two prayer forms (factors with stronger Eigenvalues yielding indices with alphas greater than .80). *Colloquial prayer* is a more discursive and general form of prayer that includes talking to God in one's own words, praying for the world, offering prayers of thanksgiving, requesting guidance, and praying for forgiveness of sin (alpha = .85). *Meditative prayer* is seemingly more intuitive and thoughtful, including praying in adoration, listening for God's voice, thinking about God, and sitting in the presence of God (alpha = .82). Respondents who prayed were also asked five questions intended to measure religious experiences during prayer, including experiencing God's peace, presence, new insight into scripture, answer to specific prayer requests, and divine leading to engage in a specific action. The alpha for the prayer experience scale was .87.

Corporate prayer was measured by a single item inquiring about the frequency of church attendance, which then served as a filter separating the 86% who attended church at least once in the past year from those who had not attended. Those who reported attending church were then asked a series of five questions similar to those asked about private prayer experiences. The alpha for the five item index measuring corporate/receptive prayer was .77.

FINDINGS

Bivariate Analysis

As expected, the bivariate analysis demonstrated statistically significant correlations between religiosity measures and age, with older respondents being more religious than younger respondents. None of the correlations between age and the four measures of well-being were found to be significant. In reviewing the correlations for the entire sample and the subsample of seniors, only a few different patterns could be found between the correlations for the entire sample and the subsample of seniors on items relating to the relationship between prayer and well-being. As expected, private prayer forms and experiences demonstrate statistically significant relationships with three of the four well-being measures in both the sample and subsample. (No statistically significant relationship was found for *negative affect* and religiosity in either the total or partial samples or in bivariate or multivariate equations.)

A noteworthy finding is that *frequency of prayer* failed to produce a statistically significant bivariate relationship in either sample with three of the four well-being measures. Only existential well-being, the index measuring meaning and purpose in life, was found to have a moderate positive relationship with frequency of prayer. (Given this finding, frequency of prayer was dropped as a measure of private/active prayer in the multivariate equations.)

Also worthy of note are the differences found in the relationship for corporate prayer and corporate prayer experiences and the well-being measures. While church attendance and church experiences both show significant bivariate relationships with happiness in the full sample, no statistically significant correlations were found between the corporate prayer measures and happiness in the elderly sample. Both religious experience in the corporate church setting and church attendance demonstrate significant relationships with *life satisfaction* for the total sample, but only church experience is significant in the senior sample. These differences suggest that the role different dimensions of religiosity play in affecting well-being may differ throughout the life course. This thesis is supported by Peacock and Poloma's (1999) article that charted several dimensions of religiosity across the life course. Using the 1988 Gallup dataset (see Poloma & Gallup, 1991), Peacock and Poloma found there was a general increase of religiosity across the lifespan, but that the increase was not a linear one. For most religiosity indicators, decreases were found after age 25 that were recouped by age 45, with still greater gains for those over 55. It was with these findings in mind that those 55 and over were selected as the senior sample used in this analysis.

Multivariate Analysis

In order to determine which facets of prayer have the greatest impact on self-reports of well-being by the elderly, the prayer measures representing the four-fold prayer taxonomy (personal/active, corporate active, personal/receptive, and corporate receptive) were regressed against the three well-being measures (happiness, life satisfaction, and existential well-being). Since none of the correlations for *negative affect* and the prayer measures were found to be statistically significant, only the remaining three general measures of well-being are included in the multiple regression analyses presented in Table 3.2. After examining the bivariate correlations and reviewing the individual items, the colloquial prayer index was selected as the *personal/active* prayer indicator for the regression equations. The prayer experience index that tapped subjective responses to the act of praying was used to measure the *personal/receptive* prayer category. A single-item question inquiring about church attendance served to represent *collective/active* prayer, while collective/receptive prayer was measured by the church experience index.

Three columns can be found in Table 3.2, with each presenting the results from a set of multiple regression equations exploring the role that prayer has on subjective perceptions of well-being for the elderly subsample. Personal prayer (colloquial and experiences) and then corporate prayer (attendance and experiences) were regressed against *happiness*. Although personal prayer explained 4% of the variance, neither beta in the model was statistically significant. The second equation regressing happiness against active and receptive measures of corporate prayer failed to pass the test of significance. The third equation in which happiness was regressed against personal and corporate prayer items (active and receptive) in a single regression model also failed the significance test (although the beta for prayer experiences was statistically significant). The results of the first set of multiple regression equations failed to cast new light on the relationship between prayer categories and happiness beyond the bivariate relationships found in Table 3.1.

The same three-step procedure was followed using *life satisfaction* as the dependent variable. Only the equation in which life satisfaction was regressed against private prayer items was statistically significant (with an adjusted R^2 of .03) but neither beta was statistically significant. Once again the analysis failed to unravel the tangled web of the effects of prayer on subjective perceptions of well-being.

The results for *existential well-being* are somewhat more promising. When existential well-being was regressed against the two measures of private prayer, 15% of the variance was explained, with both colloquial prayer (beta = .27) and prayer experiences (beta = .19) contributing to the explained variance. The equation for corporate prayer was also statistically significant, with an adjusted R^2 of .13. Religious experiences during the church services (beta = .31) proved to be more important than church attendance in accounting for existential well-being scores. Combining the private and corporate indices in the final model increased the amount of explained variance to 20%. Colloquial prayer (beta = .34) was the only statistically significant predictor of a greater meaning and purpose in life. In light of the earlier two steps, which found prayer experience and church experience to be statistically related to existential well-being scores, it is likely that problems with colinearity may have suppressed the effects religious experience has on existential well-being.

DISCUSSION AND CONCLUSIONS

If one were to view the results presented here as a half-empty cup, the concluding discussion would focus on the failure of this analysis to unravel the mystery of prayer. For the most part the analysis was unable to demonstrate which prayer measures best predict subjective perceptions of well-being for the elderly. Although the bivariate correlations consistently demonstrated significant relationships between most religiosity measures (including the complex phenomenon we call prayer) and well-being, multivariate analysis failed to tease out important details behind the simple findings. The important questions that Levin posed as "how" and "why" issues remain unanswered, suggesting that measures need further testing and that future research needs to go beyond cross-sectional surveys. It should also be noted that even if this model had been tested successfully, lethal questions could have been raised about the sample itself—a dated product of the 1980s suffering from well-known aging, cohort, and period effects.

In choosing to present the results of this endeavor as a cup that is half full, it can be argued that important findings have been offered in support of Levin's astute observations. When applying the prayer model to existential well-being, the significant findings affirm the importance of prayer—and especially prayer experiences—in constructing a meaningful and purposive worldview. As Levin (p. 21) states: "Feeling and experiencing the sense of relationship with God and tradition engendered by collective and private prayer can provide *meaning* to life."

The bivariate findings presented also provide a base from which to launch a response to Levin's challenge to explore the mechanisms of prayer and health (p. 19). Most importantly, single-item measures of church attendance and frequency of prayer have proved inadequate for the task. Frequency of prayer demonstrated a bivariate relationship ($r = .27$) with only one of the four well-being measures (existential well-being). Church attendance was correlated with only life satisfaction ($r = .19$) and existential well-being ($r = .25$) in the senior sample.

Prayer remains somewhat of a mystery, with private and corporate dimensions interacting with active and receptive features to shroud the process. Relying on the old single items of prayer frequency and church attendance will not unlock dynamics of religiosity's impact on health and well-being. Researchers would do well to heed the flag of caution that Levin has raised about any mindless use of frequency of prayer or church attendance as sole measures of religiosity in well-being studies.

Rather than limiting religiosity measures to those traditionally used, more attention must be given to the study of religious experience. As Levin notes in grappling with the "why" question in relating prayer to healing/health, experiencing a sense of a relationship with God appears to provide meaning to life (p. 21), which is often manifested as a perceived intimate relationship with the divine. The findings of the full regression model for existential well-being, as already discussed, also suggest that religious experiences during church services may be far more significant than the act of "going to church."

Prayer experience measures, whether personal or corporate, can provide vital information about those moments of transcendence that may be efficacious for greater healing and health. Given the fact that seniors have been consistently found to be more religious than younger cohorts, this age cohort offers the promise of a rich field for further explorations of the mystery of prayer.

REFERENCES

Peacock, J. R., & Poloma, M. M. (1999). Religiosity and life satisfaction across the life course. *Social Indicators Research, 48,* 321–349.

Poloma, M. M., & Gallup, G. H., Jr. (1991). *Varieties of prayer: A survey report.* Philadelphia: Trinity Press International.

Poloma, M. M., & Pendleton, B. F. (1991a). *Exploring neglected dimensions of religion in quality of life research.* Lewiston, NY: Edwin Mellen Press.

Poloma, M. M., & Pendleton, B. F. (1991b). The effects of prayer and prayer experiences on measures of general well-being. *Journal of Psychology and Theology, 19,* 71–83.

Poloma, M. M., & Pendleton, B. F. (1990). Religious domains and general well-being. *Social Indicators, 22,* 255–276.

Poloma, M. M., & Pendleton, B. F. (1989). Exploring types of prayer and the quality of life. *Review of Religious Research, 31,* 46–53. Reprinted in Francis, L. J. (Ed.) *Perspectives on prayer: A reader.* City, UK: Fowler Wright.

CHAPTER 4

Empirical Advances in the Psychology of Religion and Coping

Kenneth I. Pargament and Gene G. Ano

"In times of crisis religion usually comes to the foreground" (Johnson, 1959, p. 82). As this quote by psychologist and pastor Paul Johnson suggests, there is a close connection between religion and the most critical times of life. Perhaps this should not be altogether surprising; for thousands of years the religions of the world have prescribed religious coping, that is, specific ways of understanding and dealing with life's trials and tribulations that are related to the sacred. Much more recently, there has been a sharp increase in the study of these methods of religious coping and their implications for health and well-being.

In this chapter, we would like to summarize recent advances in research in the area of religion and coping. It should be emphasized from the outset that our approach will not be exhaustive nor, hopefully, exhausting. Instead, we will highlight several of the advances in the field through illustrations of promising new research and findings. For a more heavily referenced review, see Harrison, Hays, Koenig, Eme-Akwari, & Pargament, 2001). As a prelude to these advances, we would like to review some of the underlying assumptions of religion and coping theory.

UNDERLYING ASSUMPTIONS OF RELIGION AND COPING THEORY

Assumption 1: Religion Expresses Itself in Many Ways in Times of Stress

Traditionally, psychologists have tended to stereotype religion as passive and defensive. Religion has been stigmatized as an avoidant form of coping, a form of denial, a passive defense mechanism, and a way to avoid dealing with life's problems by handing them over to an imaginary god. While we can certainly find examples of people using religion as a means of denial, as a passive form of defense, as a psychological crutch, or as the last resort to untenable situations, we can also find many examples of people using religion adaptively to actively cope with and tackle life's problems of pain and suffering head on. In fact, empirical research has demonstrated that religiousness is generally more closely and consistently associated with active than passive forms of coping. But the key point is that religion is not merely passive and defensive; it comes in many shapes and sizes.

Assumption 2: The Way Religion Expresses Itself in Crisis Depends Upon a Host of Factors: Personal, Social, Situational, and Cultural

Religious coping does not come out of nowhere. Religious problem-solving strategies emanate from a more general orienting system that is comprised of well-established traits, beliefs, practices, attitudes, goals, and values. Particular situations may also trigger religious coping, especially those situations that push individuals beyond the capacity of their personal and social resources. For example, in a study of religious coping among college students, Ano (2003) found that personality, situational, and other religious factors significantly predicted particular types of religious coping strategies, even after statistically controlling for other important predictor and demographic variables. In addition, religious coping is shaped by cultural factors (Kula, in press; McReady & Greeley, 1976). For instance, in a study of religious coping among 200 people in Turkey one week following the great earthquake of 1999, 63% attributed the earthquake to a punishing God, a figure far greater than we find among people in the United States following major natural disasters (Kula, in press).

Assumption 3: Religious Coping has Implications for People Spiritually, Psychologically, Socially, and Physically

Religion can serve a variety of purposes. It has been connected to psychological goals, such as anxiety reduction, personal control, self-development, and the search for meaning, comfort, or peace. Religion has been associated with social ends, such as the pursuit of relational intimacy, interpersonal connectedness, and social unity. It has been linked to physical functions, such as healthier behavioral practices, the physiological relaxation response, and improved immunological functioning. And perhaps the most crucial function of religion is its spiritual purpose—transcendence, to know God, however that knowledge may be pursued and however that God may be perceived. Because religion serves a variety of functions, social scientists need to be aware of the multi-dimensional implications of religious coping.

Assumption 4: Religious Coping Can be Helpful or Harmful

Religious coping is not automatically beneficial. It may be helpful or harmful. Just as religious coping may help the recently paralyzed victim of a terrible accident to cope by focusing upon the love of God and expressing that love toward others, religious coping may prevent the person with a curable disease from seeking medical treatment because it demonstrates a lack of faith in God. The psychology of religion and coping does not offer easy answers about the value of religious coping. Simplistic explanations should give way to more refined questions about the extent to which various religious coping methods are well integrated with the individual's needs, goals, situations, and social context.

Assumption 5: The Effects of Global Religious Orientation Variables on Outcomes Are Mediated Through More Proximal Religious Variables

Global religious measures such as average frequency of church attendance, frequency of prayer, self-rated levels of religiosity, or even religious orientation tell us little about how people express their faith in the midst of difficult life situations. What aspects of participation in religious services are helpful, if any? If a person prays frequently, how is he praying and what is he praying for? Do the prayers have a cathartic effect, such as prayers of lamentation, or do they help the individual gain a sense of control, such as prayers of supplication? If another individual describes herself as "very religious," does she believe that God is intimately involved in her life and that no problem is too great for God to handle? Religious coping methods are specific manifestations of religion in difficult times. Working collaboratively with God to solve a problem, seeking spiritual support from others, reappraising a situation as an opportunity for spiritual growth—forms of religious coping such as these are directly and functionally related to the situation at hand. As a result, such concrete embodiments of religion should be closely related to the outcome of that situation. The effects of global religious orientational variables on outcomes are mediated through religious variables that are more proximal to the situation. A number of studies, in fact, offer support for this mediating model (e.g., Ano & Roesch, in press; Loewenthal, MacLeod, Goldblatt, Lubitsh, & Valentine, 2000; Nooney & Woodrum, 2002). For example, using path analytic strategies, Ano and Roesch found that the effects of religious orientation on depression were mediated by situation-specific religious attributions and religious coping methods. Nooney and Woodrum (2002), working with data from the 1998 General Social Survey, found that the effects of church attendance on depression were mediated through church-based social support and the effects of prayer on depression were mediated through religious coping.

Assumption 6: Religious Coping Cannot be Fully Reduced to Psychological, Social, or Physical Dimensions

From Leuba to Freud, many social scientists have attempted to explain religion in purely psychological or social terms. And yet, it could be argued, at least on conceptual grounds, that there is something special or even unique about religion. After all, no other human phenomenon has the sacred as its focal point. However, in addition to this theoretical rationale, a case can be made (and will be made shortly), based upon empirical research, that spirituality represents another significant dimension of life, one that makes distinctive contributions to health and well-being.

Assumption 7: The Study of Religious Coping Calls for Multiple Methods and Tools

Because of the complex nature of religious coping, no single research method can adequately capture its full essence. There is no single character of religious coping. Experiments, surveys, correlational analyses, naturalistic observations, case studies, narrative approaches, and qualitative interviews all have important roles to play in our efforts to learn more about the various modes of religious expression. We cannot afford methodological arrogance or elitism when it comes to the study of religious life. Religious life is far too complex to be examined with exclusivistic epistemological tools. Only by broadening our methodological tools and simultaneously sharpening our focus on proximal religious variables can we come to a more comprehensive understanding of religious coping methods in specific critical life situations.

Assumption 8: Whether It is Part of the Solution or Part of the Problem, Religion Can be More Fully Interwoven into Efforts to Help People

For some individuals, religious beliefs, practices, and traditions are an integral part of their daily functioning. When they seek out professional help, they don't leave their religious coping resources behind. But clinicians are typically reluctant to address religious issues in the context of their professional relationships. When religious issues are raised, clinicians may switch the focus to more familiar topics or reduce religion to presumably more basic psychological processes (e.g., anger at God translates into anger at father). If religion is not addressed, clinicians may assume (at times incorrectly) that religious issues are not important. Yet we know that clients are interested in spiritually-sensitive treatment, and we know that religion is, in fact, associated with physical and mental health. Thus, practitioners face the challenge of understanding and addressing religious issues from their clients' perspectives and integrating these issues into their professional helping relationships.

These are some of the key assumptions that underlie the theory of religion and coping. Since 1997, several of these assumptions have received additional empirical attention, which has resulted in an expanding knowledge of religious coping. Let us turn now to some of these recent advances that have taken place in the study of religion and coping.

RESEARCHERS ARE GETTING CLOSER TO RELIGIOUS LIFE

In the past ten years, researchers have examined national survey data that reveal clear and significant links between religion and mental and physical health. Important as these findings are, they rest on the briefest, most global indices of religion, such as denomination, frequency of church attendance, frequency of prayer, self-rated religiousness, and self-rated spirituality. Measuring religion in this fashion yields about as much information as a physician conducting a physical would get by asking a patient to rate his or her physical health on a one to five scale. When significant results have emerged from this body of research, the question that repeatedly follows is: "What is it about religion that can explain these results?" We won't be able to answer this question until we get closer to religious experience.

One of the reasons we like the metaphor of coping for the psychology of religion is that it forces us to examine religious experience more closely. Coping involves an attempt to make sense of, deal with, and manage stressful life circumstances in a specific situational context. Studying religion from a coping framework reifies this otherwise abstract phenomenon and allows us to see how particular people use religion concretely in specific life situations and contexts. It forces us to step out of our sheltered academic environments and step into the experience of real people facing real life problems. By doing so, we are able to challenge our own presuppositions and biases about religion. Psychologists who study religion and coping are making some promising strides in getting closer to religion. Let us give a few examples.

First, we are assessing religious coping in finer detail. Overgeneralized single items that ask "To what degree have you involved your religious beliefs and practices in the ways you have coped with your illness" are insufficient. Such methods merely examine *how much* religion is accessed. Because religion is a complex phenomenon, it is also important to examine the *who* (benevolent God, punishing God), *what* (spiritual, interpersonal), *when* (during acute or major stressors, for how long), *where* (in church congregations, privately), and *why* (to find meaning, to gain control, to achieve life transformation) of religious coping. Working with a sample of medically ill elderly patients and a sample of college students coping with a variety of life stressors, my colleagues and I (K.I.P.) identified 17 religious coping methods through factor analysis that illuminate the complexity and diversity of religious coping (Pargament, Koenig, & Perez, 2000). These religious coping strategies serve a variety of functions and include various ways of reframing the stressor, seeking spiritual and religious support, religious problem solving, religious forgiveness, purification and conversion, and spiritual and interpersonal discontent. Furthermore, higher order factor analyses revealed that these coping methods could be grouped into positive religious coping activities that reflect a secure relationship with God and religious community, and negative religious coping activities that reflect a struggle with God, with one's faith, and with one's religious community (Pargament, Smith, Koenig, & Perez, 1998).

Second, we are beginning to work with people in the midst of their problems. Retrospective accounts of religious coping, like retrospective accounts generally, have their limitations (Stone et al., 1998). As a result, researchers have begun to assess religious coping longitudinally across various points in time. For example, Keefe et al. (2001) examined religious coping among 35 patients suffering from rheumatoid arthritis. Over 30 consecutive days, participants in the study were asked to keep structured daily diaries that measured their daily spiritual experiences, daily religious and spiritual pain coping and pain coping efficacy, and daily pain, daily mood, and daily perceived social support. This alternative method of measuring religious coping allowed the investigators to examine fluctuations in religious coping over time and provided another way of getting a closer look at religious coping. And the results were interesting. Participants who reported more religious and spiritual coping efficacy also reported less joint pain, less negative mood, more positive mood, and greater general social support. It is also important to note that the authors found significant variability in religious coping scores from day to day over the course of the month, indicating that religious coping was not simply a stable personality disposition; it was sensitive to changing times and circumstances. Continuous studies that measure variations in religious coping from day to day such as this provide a clearer window into the process of religion and its diverse impacts on people struggling through extreme moments.

Third, we are now seeing efforts to integrate religious coping into the larger framework of people's lives. In one line of study, researchers are beginning to measure the involvement of religion and religious coping over the individual's life history (see George, this volume). For example, Hays, Meador, Branch, and George (2001) developed a measure of lifetime religious and spiritual experience and examined its utility in explaining later life health. They predicted that greater religious involvement and "exposure" to religiousness over one's lifetime would be associated with more health benefits. A stratified, random sample of cognitively intact elderly community residents participated in semi-structured and structured interviews assessing demographic characteristics and various domains of lifetime history of religious and spiritual experiences. The results of the study indicated that people who reported more assistance and guidance from God and greater religious social support over the lifespan engaged in healthier behaviors. In contrast, greater history of religious conflict throughout the lifespan was associated with higher levels of depression. Similarly, in another study, 406 patients from various community mental health facilities who were diagnosed as having a persistent mental illness completed surveys assessing various demographic, religious coping, and mental health variables (Tepper, Rogers, Coleman, & Malony, 2001). The results of the study indicated that a greater number of years that religious coping had been used as well as a greater proportion of overall coping time devoted to religion were predictive of less severe psychological symptoms and better overall mental health. Although these studies are limited by their cross-sectional design, they represent an initial attempt to examine the prevalence and impact of religious coping through people's lives.

In another line of study, researchers are examining religious coping as a part of people's life stories or narratives. For example, Ganzevoort (1998, 2001) highlighted the need for a multidimensional approach toward religious coping and advocated a narrative reformulation of religious coping that considers the authorship, story, audience, and underlying purpose of the narrative. Ganzevoort's approach considers the dynamic process of religious coping and weaves the story lines of religion together with other prominent life themes, such as identity, gender, context, transitions, and coherence, in an attempt to illuminate the potential reciprocal influences between religion and other life processes. Particularly noteworthy is the interesting and innovative way Ganzevoort has bridged qualitative and quantitative methods in some of his work by cluster analyses of story themes and examinations of their intercorrelations. For example, in a case study, Ganzevoort (1998) conducted a rigorous structure analysis of a narrative interview with a sexually abused man and examined the intercorrelations among story themes to understand the idiosyncratic meanings and functions of religion in the individual's life. He found that the individual gave religion more than one place and function in his story and concluded that the meaning of religion should be seen as a constellation of differentiated meanings in the various story lines. Other researchers are also taking a closer look at religious coping by listening to the stories people have to tell. For example, Pendleton, Cavalli, Pargament, and Nasr (2002) conducted interviews with 23 children diagnosed with cystic fibrosis. Through interviews and examinations of children's drawings, she found that, consistent with Fowler's theory, many children expressed a steadfast, unchallengeable belief that God would act on their requests. This work is particularly exciting because it sets the stage for further studies of religious coping among children, a population relatively neglected in this area of research. Although the generalizability of such findings is limited, these studies provide alternative and innovative methods for examining religious coping.

Getting closer to religious experience makes our jobs as researchers more challenging. Remaining in our sheltered academic environments with our own biases and assumptions has its advantages, at least for us. But getting closer to religious experience has benefits for both us and the people we serve. In doing so, we are learning that religion is richer and more complex than we initially imagined. And most importantly, we believe we are moving toward a more accurate, comprehensive understanding of religious life.

SACRED OBJECTS ARE CENTRAL
TO RELIGIOUS COPING

Events impact people not only psychologically, socially, and physically, but also spiritually. For instance, many women who have been sexually abused as children suffer damage not only to their sense of themselves and their relations with other people, but to their feeling of being loved and accepted by God, the conviction that they have a greater purpose in life, and the knowledge that they are linked to a larger spiritual community. As one survivor put it: "Our God seems to have abandoned us, and the sacred seems untouchable" (Flaherty, 1992, p. 28).

Sacred objects include not only God, but also any aspect of life that takes on spiritual character and significance by virtue of its association with the divine. Durkheim (1915) wrote: "By sacred things one must not understand simply those personal beings which are called gods or spirits; a rock, a tree, a pebble, a piece of wood, a house, in a word anything can be sacred" (p. 52). Several classes of objects can be viewed, represented, or experienced as sacred: material objects (crucifix, drugs), time and space (the Sabbath, churches), events and transitions (Bar Mitzvah, death), cultural products (music, literature), people (saints, cult leaders), psychological attributes (the self, meaning), social attributes (caste, patriotism), and roles (marriage, parenting, work).

Pargament and Mahoney (2002)) have hypothesized that people are particularly motivated to preserve and protect those aspects of life they hold sacred from various threats or violations. In support of this hypothesis, we have found that couples who view their marriages as sacred engage in more constructive problem-solving activities when they face conflict (Mahoney et al., 1999). Individuals who view the environment as sacred are also more likely to act in ecologically friendly ways (Tarakeshwar, Swank, Pargament, & Mahoney, 2001).

And yet, sacred objects cannot always be protected. When a sacred aspect of life is harmed or violated, people may be particularly vulnerable to distress, for we are talking about events that are more than traumas or major life stressors; words like these cannot do justice to the spiritual character of these experiences. As Elkins (1995) writes: "some violations and betrayals . . . wound so deeply that they can only be called abuses to the soul" (p. 91).

Our research group has conducted a series of studies that has examined the impact of perceptions of spiritual loss and desecration on subsequent physical and mental health. The results have been consistent (Magyar, Pargament, & Mahoney, 2000; Mahoney et al., 2002). For example, in a study of college students in Ohio and New York City after the 9/11 terrorist attacks, students who perceived the terrorists as desecrating sacred values were more likely to report greater depression, anxiety, and symptoms of post-traumatic stress disorder (Mahoney et al., 2002). Furthermore, they were more likely to support extreme retaliation measures, such as dropping a nuclear bomb on the terrorists or the use of biological weapons. Thus, we are learning that appraisals of sacred threat, loss, and violation have powerful effects; people take strong steps in coping to protect their most sacred values from harm.

RELIGIOUS COPING HAS LONG-TERM EFFECTS

In 1997, the majority of studies on religious coping and mental health outcomes used cross-sectional methods. Although the results of these studies revealed important relationships between religious coping and mental health, we could not determine what was causing what. Was religious coping leading to better outcomes or were people who experienced better adjustment simply more likely to report greater use of particular religious coping strategies? Similarly, when certain forms of religious coping were associated with greater distress, were such religious coping strategies resulting in distress or were people who were experiencing greater distress simply more likely to turn to religion for help? Recent methodological advances have helped to clarify the picture.

Within the past few years, several investigators have examined religious coping longitudinally and have demonstrated that religious coping significantly predicts changes in mental health over time (e.g., Ai, Dunkle, Peterson, & Bolling, 1998; Alferi, Culver, Carver, Arena, & Antoni, 1999; Krause, 1998; Tix & Frazier, 1998). Let us highlight two studies. Tix and Frazier examined religious coping among patients and their loved ones dealing with the stress of kidney transplant surgery. Two hundred thirty-nine patients and 179 significant others completed questionnaires assessing demographic, coping, religious coping, and psychological adjustment variables at three months post-surgery.

Hierarchical regression analyses indicated that religious coping was generally associated with better adjustment concurrently and over time at three and twelve months post-surgery among both patients and their significant others. Similarly, Ai et al. examined religious coping among a sample of 151 coronary bypass surgery patients. Participants completed questionnaires measuring demographic variables, health conditions, spiritual coping, social support, and psychological adjustment immediately after surgery and at one-year follow-up. Results of the study indicated that religious coping with the surgery, particularly private prayer, was associated with decreased depression and general distress one year post-surgery.

Although these studies did not use comprehensive measures of religious coping (i.e., positive and negative forms), their longitudinal methods helped to clarify the temporal linkages between religious coping and adjustment. Studies such as these suggest that religious coping leads to some relatively long-term changes in mental health. To put it another way, what people do concretely with their faith in the face of difficult situations has some significant consequences that last over time. Although these effects might be explained by other variables, it is important to note that each of these studies controlled for demographic variables and other potential explanations.

THE EFFECTS OF RELIGIOUS COPING
GO BEYOND MENTAL HEALTH

Because psychological well-being is the criteria of greatest interest to psychologists, most of the research in this area has focused on mental health outcomes. However, it is important to recognize that other groups or professionals do not place such value on mental health. Physicians and other medical professionals are mostly interested in physical health. For others, particularly the religiously minded, spirituality is the most important criterion. To complicate matters further, some critics have raised concerns that the improvements in mental health associated with religious coping might be purchased at the price of spiritual well-being or physical health. To test such contentions, researchers in the last few years have developed studies that incorporate a broader range of criteria, including psychological, social, physical, and spiritual outcomes.

As one illustration, some colleagues and the senior author recently examined the effects of religious coping on various outcomes among a sample of 577 medically ill, elderly patients who had been hospitalized for a variety of ailments (Pargament, Koenig, Tarakeshwar, & Hahn, in press). At baseline, religious coping was assessed via interviews with the patients in the hospital. Patients were then tracked over a two-year period and changes in their psychological functioning, physical health, and spiritual well-being were assessed. In addition to controlling for baseline health status, we were able to control for demographic variables, mental health status, selective attrition, and selective mortality in all of the analyses.

Results of the study showed that religious coping was associated with changes in outcomes from each domain. For example, with respect to the psychological outcomes, religious coping was associated with stress-related growth, changes in depression, changes in quality of life, and greater cooperativeness in the interview. Regarding physical health criteria, religious coping was related to changes in subjective health, cognitive status, and functional physical status of the patients over the two-year period. In terms of spiritual outcomes, religious coping was linked to feelings of closeness with God, the sense of closeness to one's church, and self-rated feelings of spiritual growth. As will be noted shortly, whether religious coping had positive or negative implications for these outcomes depended on the specific form of religious coping.

These findings suggest that religious coping has implications not only for psychological functioning, but for other important criteria as well, such as physical and spiritual health and well-being. Thus, in many instances, we may find complementary changes across psychological, physical, and spiritual outcome domains. However, there are some important exceptions to this rule. For example, when we examined specific forms of religious coping in the sample of medically ill patients, we found that demonic reappraisals had mixed implications for different outcomes. That is, patients who believed the devil was at work in their illness showed higher levels of spiritual well-being, but reported poorer functional physical status, and exhibited a greater risk of dying over the following two years. Thus, some benefits of religious coping may be purchased at the price of other important criteria, which leads us to the next advance that has occurred in the psychology of religion and coping.

SOME FORMS OF RELIGIOUS COPING ARE HARMFUL

In our study of the medically ill, elderly patients, we had an unexpected finding. Over the two-year period of the study, 176 of the patients died. As a result, we were able to examine whether the religious coping measures predicted mortality (Pargament, Koenig, Tarakeshwar, & Hahn, 2001). Using Cox regression analyses, we controlled for potentially confounding variables, such as baseline illness severity, mental health status, and demographic variables, and found that one form of religious struggles, negative religious coping methods that reflect a dissatisfying relationship with God, were associated with a significantly greater risk of dying over the two-year period. More specifically, people who felt abandoned by God, who questioned God's love for them, and who felt that the devil was at work in their illness displayed a 19 to 28% increased risk of dying. While a number of studies have shown that church attendance is associated with lower mortality rates (see McCullough, Hoyt, Larson, Koenig, & Thoresen, 2000), the positive religious coping strategies in this study were not associated with a reduced risk of dying. Interestingly, this is, as far as we know, the first study that has demonstrated that particular forms of religious expression are associated with a greater risk of mortality.

Other studies have also demonstrated that religious struggles with God may have harmful effects. In addition to obvious threats to spiritual functioning, these types of religious struggles have been associated with declines in mental health and physical health. For example, in cross-sectional studies employing questionnaires, anger to God, feeling punished by God, and feeling abandoned by God have been associated with more anxious and depressed mood among college students (Exline, Yali, & Lobel, 1999; Pargament, Zinnbauer et al., 1998) and greater psychological distress among victims of the 1993 floods in the Midwest United States (Smith, Pargament, Brant, & Oliver, 2000). In one longitudinal study of religious coping, among a sample of 96 medical rehabilitation patients, negative religious coping, particularly anger at God, was associated with poorer psychological adjustment at admission and at four months follow-up, and with poorer physical recovery at four months follow-up (Fitchett, Rybarczyk, DeMarco, & Nicholas, 1999). Studies such as these suggest that religious struggles with God have negative implications for different people across a wide range of criteria.

Other forms of religious struggle, such as religious doubts and interpersonal religious conflicts, have also been linked to signs of distress. For example, more religious doubts were associated with greater anxiety and negative affect among church members (Pargament, Zinnbauer et al., 1998), more depressed affect and less positive affect among a national sample of Presbyterian members, elders, and clergy (Krause, Ingersoll-Dayton, Ellison, & Wulff, 1999), and less happiness and life satisfaction in a national sample of adults (Ellison, 1991).

Negative church interactions have also been tied to greater psychological distress among clergy and elders in the Presbyterian church (Krause, Ellison, & Wulff, 1998) and lower self-esteem, greater anxiety, and more negative mood among college students and church members (Pargament, Zinnbauer et al.).

These findings have been a bit surprising because countless anecdotes and theological teachings attest to the potential benefit of religious struggles. For instance, exalted religious figures from Moses to Buddha to Jesus have gone through their own religious struggles only to come out on the other side strengthened and refined. Theories of faith development also stress the value of religious struggles in terms of the "dark night of the soul" (Fowler, 1987). However, in empirical studies such as these mentioned here, religious struggles are linked to despair, declines in physical functioning, and even death. Perhaps the key to the benefits of religious struggles has to do with whether or not such struggles can be resolved. Some recently conducted analyses suggest this contention may indeed be the case (Pargament, Koenig et al., in press).

Working with our sample of medically ill patients who survived over the 2-year period, we compared four groups of patients to see if any particular group was at greater risk for declines in mental health, physical health, and spiritual well-being. The first group represented individuals who apparently were unable to resolve their religious struggles with God within the 2-year period; they reported negative religious coping at baseline and follow-up (Chronic). The next two groups involved people who experienced religious struggles temporarily: those who reported negative religious coping at baseline but not at follow-up, and those who reported negative religious coping at follow-up but not at baseline (Acute). The final group included individuals who reported no negative religious coping at baseline or follow-up (None). Results of the study showed that individuals who were unable to resolve their religious struggles with God (the Chronic group) experienced significantly greater declines than the other groups in quality of life and, to a marginal degree, functional independent status and mood. Patients who experienced religious struggles temporarily and those who did not experience them at all during the study did not face similar risks. Thus, individuals who were unable to resolve their religious struggles over time were at greater risk for poorer health.

Findings such as these suggest that health professionals need to be sensitive to religious struggles among people suffering from medical illness. Because of the deleterious effects of chronic religious struggles, interventions that help people resolve their struggles seem called for.

Referral to a pastor, chaplain, or religiously trained practitioner may be necessary for assisting people to walk through their "dark nights of the soul" before such dark nights become "dark years." While further studies are needed to determine whether the resolution of spiritual struggles can promote growth, it is evident from a growing body of literature that negative forms of religious coping can have harmful effects. Thus, researchers and practitioners need to be just as sensitive to the possible pitfalls of religion as they are to its salubrious potential.

FACTORS THAT MODERATE THE LINKS BETWEEN RELIGIOUS COPING AND OUTCOMES HAVE BEEN IDENTIFIED

Recent studies have demonstrated that religious coping takes different forms among different religious groups and cultures. For instance, within Christian populations, factor analyses have yielded two higher order factors of religious coping: positive and negative (Pargament, Smith et al., 1998). However, analyses with other religious traditions and cultures have yielded different results. Dubow, Pargament, Boxer, and Tarakeshwar (2000) interviewed a sample of Jewish adolescents and adults to generate a religious coping measure that was sensitive to culturally-specific methods with Judaism. They administered the measure to a sample of Jewish adolescents and conducted a factor analysis. Three factors emerged: two positive and negative religious coping factors similar to those in the Christian samples, and a third factor that represents the importance of Jewish communal and ethical involvement in dealing with stressors. Similarly, Tarakeshwar, Pargament, and Mahoney (in press) developed a measure of religious coping methods specific to Hindus through interviews with a community sample as well as a literature review. Gathering data from a sample of Hindus in the United States, Tarakeshwar et al. (in press) identified three kinds of religious coping factors. Positive religious coping was subdivided into two separate factors. The first factor involved a God-focused coping strategy characterized by turning to God for love, guidance, and strength, and the second factor involved a spiritually-focused coping method characterized by a search for spiritual connection, spiritual reawakening, yoga, and meditation. The third factor involved a negative religious coping strategy that, interestingly, included bad karma, a concept not evident in the Christian or Jewish traditions of religious coping.

While religious coping differs *among* major religious traditions, the links between religious coping and outcomes vary *within* religious traditions as well. First, within the Christian tradition, religious coping may be more helpful to some denominations than others. For example, Alferi et al. (1999) examined religious coping among a sample of 49 Evangelical and Roman Catholic Hispanic women recently diagnosed with breast cancer. Participants filled out questionnaires assessing demographic variables, religious coping, and emotional distress before surgery, after surgery, and at three, six, and twelve months follow-up. Results of the study indicated that religious coping was more helpful for Evangelicals than Roman Catholics; higher levels of religious coping predicted less distress for the Evangelical women, but greater distress for the Roman Catholic women. Tentatively, the authors suggested that the Evangelical women's focus on faith and acceptance during this crisis may have been more helpful for them than the emphasis on confession, judgment, and absolution from guilt among the Catholic women. However, we must be cautious about drawing the simple conclusion that Evangelical Protestants are "better off" than Roman Catholics. In another study, Kooistra and Pargament (1999) examined religious doubting in a sample of 267 parochial school adolescents. Participants completed measures of demographic variables, religious doubting, family environment, life events, and emotional distress. The researchers found that one form of religious coping, religious doubts, was more strongly correlated with distress among Protestant Dutch Reformed adolescents than Roman Catholic adolescents. Thus, the different findings from these studies suggest that the connections between religious coping and outcomes are neither simple nor straightforward. Involvement in any religious denomination is likely to be associated with distinctive advantages and disadvantages, depending upon the context of the situation and the outcome variables measured.

Second, religious coping appears to have stronger effects for people who are more religious. In two studies involving a national sample of Presbyterian members, elders, and clergy in the United States, positive religious coping and church-based emotional support were more strongly related to positive affect and less depression for clergy than for elders, and for elders than for members (Krause et al., 1998; Pargament, Tarakeshwar, et al., 2001). Conversely, when people reported using negative religious coping strategies and experiencing negative church interactions, individuals who were more religious also tended to suffer greater consequences, as evidenced by stronger relations to depression and less positive affect among clergy and elders. Extrapolating from these findings to the study noted earlier on religious struggles as a predictor of mortality (Pargament, Koenig, et al., in press), people with a life history of deeper religious involvement may be especially vulnerable to the risks of negative religious coping. Overall, these findings suggest that religious coping can be a "double-edged sword." People who orient themselves more closely to religion may derive greater benefits from their religious involvement since their faith is more fully integrated into their self-definitions and social roles. On the other hand, negative religious coping may be particularly disconcerting to more religiously committed people because questions and conflicts are being raised about resources, roles, and values that are so central to their lives.

Third, religious coping appears to be especially helpful to people experiencing more stressful situations that push them beyond the capacity of their immediate personal and social resources. These are the conditions that underscore the limitations of humanity and seem to call for more ultimate solutions (Krause, 1998; Wink & Dillon, 2001). In such circumstances, religion may be more compelling, as evidenced by more recent findings that supplement earlier studies attesting to the importance of religion in dire times. For example, Krause (1998) conducted a study of religious coping using longitudinal survey data from a nationwide sample of about 500 older adults living in dilapidated neighborhoods. Logistic regression analyses revealed that, over a four-year period, people who made more use of religious coping methods were better protected from the deleterious effects of the more deteriorated neighborhoods. Thus, over time, religious coping helped buffer the effects of the more stressful living conditions on self-reported health.

RESEARCHERS HAVE NOT EXPLAINED RELIGIOUS COPING AWAY

A number of researchers are currently examining possible mediators of the relationship between religion and health, in an attempt to explain the mechanisms by which religion works. For example, can the relationship between church attendance and lower rates of mortality be explained by the social support members receive from the church, the sense of meaning derived from religious doctrines, the healthier lifestyles practiced by church members, or even the peace and tranquility elicited by the worship music? Explaining how religion works at the psychological and social levels is part of our jobs as researchers and practitioners. However, there is an important difference between explaining religion and explaining religion away.

From Durkheim to Leuba to Freud to Ellis, many social scientists have asserted that religion is merely an expression of more basic psychological, social, or physiological processes. More recently, one mainstream psychologist articulated a similar point of view: "The psychological processes by which religion affects subjective well-being and psychological and physical health are interesting and important, and research on them is easily justified—but they have very little to do with religion per se, and there is nothing that necessarily leads from an interest in these processes to a focus on religion" (Funder, 2002, p. 214). Such contentions represent an attempt to explain religion away. However, in order to develop an accurate knowledge base, we need to be careful of the "religion is nothing but . . ." fallacy.

Reductionistic claims about religion have not been supported by empirical research. In numerous studies, religion emerges as a significant predictor of outcomes even after controlling for other important predictors. For example, in the Tix and Frazier (1998) study of kidney transplant patients and their loved ones, religious coping predicted life satisfaction even after controlling for general coping dimensions, such as cognitive restructuring, internal control, and social support. In a study of religious coping among a sample of 92 hospice caregivers, Mickley, Pargament, Brant, and Hipp (1998) distinguished religious appraisals (e.g., appraising the dying process as a benevolent religious act, perceiving dying as a punishment from God) from nonreligious appraisals (e.g., defining dying as an opportunity for growth, blaming the doctors or loved one). Participants responded to measures of religious and nonreligious appraisals, general and religious outcomes, depression, anxiety, and purpose in life. Hierarchical regression analyses revealed that religious appraisals significantly predicted meaning in life, anxiety and depression, and spiritual well-being, even after the effects of nonreligious appraisals were statistically controlled. Working with a sample of 150 family members of loved ones undergoing coronary artery bypass surgery, Pargament et al. (1999) found that religious problem-solving strategies for gaining control (e.g., collaborative, deferring, self-directing coping) were uniquely associated with coping efficacy, anxiety and depression, and spiritual well-being after partialling out the effects of nonreligious methods of coping (e.g., planning, suppression, venting of emotions). It is important to stress that, in these studies, religious coping consistently predicted significant amounts of variance in measures of health and well-being above and beyond the effects of other important predictors.

Furthermore, George, Ellison, and Larson (2002) conducted an extensive review of research on the relationship between religious involvement and mental and physical health. In their review, they also investigated a variety of psychosocial mediators. They concluded that: "Conventional theories about the social and psychological antecedents of health and longevity have not fully elucidated the processes under-lying the link between religion and health" (p. 199). Thus, empirical studies suggest that religion may not be fully reduceable to presumably more basic processes (Pargament, 2002a). The most parsimonious explanation of these findings may be that religion has direct and unique effects on physical health and mental health. Religion repre-sents a significant dimension of life that stands on its own ground.

Of course, as additional research examines more comprehensive mediators of the relationship between religion and health, we may see decreasing effects of religion. However, it is highly unlikely that religion will be "explained away." Although religion interacts with other basic processes, there is extensive theoretical and empirical rationale to sug-gest that religion is a distinctive dimension.

PSYCHORELIGIOUS INTERVENTIONS ARE IN PROGRESS

The goals of psychology do not end with description and explanation. We are also interested in applying our knowledge in ways that benefit people and their communities. In the domain of religion, clinicians are now beginning to develop psychoreligious interventions that draw on religious coping resources or address religious struggles in coping. It is unclear yet whether interventions that integrate a religious dimension are, in fact, more effective than traditional psychological interventions (see McCullough, 1999). Let us describe some recent developments of psychoreligious treatments and highlight some of the complexities that arise in this important area of research.

First, because religion is an integral part of many people's lives, people may automatically incorporate spiritual resources into secular interven-tions that are not explicitly religious in nature. In one treatment-outcome study, Mark Rye and I (K.I.P.) developed a six-week group-based for-giveness intervention program for college women who felt they had been wronged in a romantic relationship (Rye & Pargament, 2002). Two types of forgiveness interventions were developed: religious and secular. In the religiously integrated group, interventions were explic-itly rooted in religious language and practices and group leaders active-ly encouraged participants to draw upon religious/spiritual resources, whereas group leaders did not refer to religious/spiritual resources in the secular forgiveness group. A third group that received no inter-vention was included as a control condition. Participants varied in their religiousness, but were moderately religious overall. Each participant was randomly assigned to one of the three groups.

Results of the study showed that both forgiveness interventions were more effective than the no-treatment control condition, as evidenced by improvements on measures of forgiveness and existential well-being at one week posttest and six weeks follow-up. However, there were no significant differences between the religious and secular forgiveness interventions, indicating that both groups were equally effective. Although the effectiveness of the two interventions could have varied as a function of the personal religiousness of the participants, analyses indicated that religiousness did not moderate the impact of the two interventions. Subsequent content analyses of the most common strategies participants used to help them forgive revealed that participants in both groups ranked religious/spiritual approaches (e.g., "asking God for help or support to forgive" and "praying for the person who wronged me") as two of the three most common strategies. Thus, it appears that the secular forgiveness intervention was not, in fact, completely secular. And yet, researchers and practitioners cannot insist that individuals avoid religious involvement within and outside of treatment in order to ensure secular integrity. As a result, it may be quite difficult to "control" for the religious element of treatment in order to assess its effects.

Second, psychoreligious interventions may be helpful to some people in certain situations, but unhelpful to other people in different situations. In another study, Cole and Pargament (1999) compared the effectiveness of a spiritually oriented group intervention with a cognitive-behavioral group therapy for adults coping with cancer. The spiritually focused intervention integrated spiritual issues and assisted participants in drawing upon religious resources while addressing four existential themes that have been shown to be pertinent to this population: control, identity, relationships, and meaning. Results of the study showed that the spiritually integrated intervention was more effective than the secular treatment in sustaining the well-being of the participants over time. Whereas participants in the cognitive-behavioral treatment group declined in their mental health over the course of the study, participants in the spiritually focused group maintained their level of mental health before and after treatment.

However, when this study was replicated in a sample of adults suffering from cardiac syncope (fainting disorder), different results were found (Cole, Pargament, & Brownstein, 2000). Whereas the spiritually integrated intervention proved more effective in the sample of cancer patients, the secular treatment proved more effective among patients with cardiac syncope, as evidenced by greater decreases in anxiety in the cognitive-behavioral treatment than the spiritually focused intervention.

When we juxtapose the findings of these two studies, the results seem to suggest that the spiritually focused treatment may be more helpful to people dealing with more uncontrollable illnesses. This idea is consistent with previous research that has shown that certain spiritual resources may help people find meaning and develop strength when faced with uncontrollable stressors (see Park, Cohen, & Herb, 1990). In our studies, patients with cancer faced a far more uncertain, uncontrollable future than patients with syncope, whose illnesses were relatively easily controlled by pacemakers or defibrillators. The findings from these studies suggest that, like other psychological interventions, spiritually oriented treatments may need to be tailored to particular groups of people dealing with particular problems in particular contexts. Our evaluations of spiritually integrated interventions will need to consider this notion and incorporate this level of complexity and sophistication.

Despite the complexities that arise in evaluating the effectiveness of psychoreligious interventions, spiritual components still appear to have some therapeutic value. In a relevant study, Wachholtz (2002) recently compared two forms of meditation: in one condition, participants selected a secular mantra (e.g., I am loved, people love me), in the second condition, participants selected a spiritual mantra (e.g., God is love, God loves me). Both groups of participants received identical training and practiced their meditation techniques over a three-week period. A third group of participants was given relaxation training as a control condition. Psychological functioning was assessed before and after the training, and pain tolerance was measured during meditation through a cold pressor task which assessed how long participants were able to keep their hand in a bucket of ice water. The results were striking. In comparison to the secular meditation and relaxation groups, the spiritual meditation group experienced significantly greater declines in state anxiety and significantly greater increases in spiritual well-being. Furthermore, participants in the spiritual meditation group exhibited significantly greater pain tolerance, as they were able keep their hands in the ice water an average of 45 seconds longer than participants in the other two groups. Although these findings need to be replicated, they suggest that some of the beneficial effects of various meditation practices may be tied to their spiritual character.

CONCLUSIONS

There has been a growing interest in the psychology of religion and coping over the past ten years. This recent interest has resulted in a burgeoning theoretical and empirical body of knowledge of a traditionally neglected and misunderstood phenomenon. Significant empirical advances in the psychology of religion and coping indicate that religion can no longer be perceived as merely a neurotic attempt to deal with human finiteness or a passive defense against reality, nor can it be reduced to other basic psychological, social, or physiological processes. We are moving beyond such preconceived notions about religion toward a more accurate, comprehensive understanding of religion as a complex phenomenon that has both advantages and disadvantages (Pargament, 2002b). Nevertheless, questions still far outnumber answers. Let us conclude our discussion by highlighting some of the exciting new directions for research in the psychology of religion and coping.

First, we should investigate religious coping among members of different cultures and religious traditions. Researchers are beginning to examine religious coping methods that are specific to particular religious traditions, such as Hummel's (1999) analysis of religious consolation among Lutherans in the United States, but this type of study should be extended to other cultures and religions, including non-Western traditions. Fortunately, we are beginning to see some research on religious coping within Israel, Scandinavia, the Netherlands, Poland, Czechoslovakia, and India, which supports the potential for some exciting comparative results.

Second, we need to learn more about the role of religion in personal transformations, what has been called "quantum change" (Miller & C'de Baca, 2001). Much of the theory and research in the psychology of religion and coping has focused on the conservational functions of religion, the role religion plays in helping people preserve, protect, and sustain their objects of greatest significance. But we also know that religion can, at times, serve as a catalyst for life-altering changes in underlying goals, values, and lifestyles. Researchers should take a serious look at religion's capacity for promoting life transformations.

Third, we should examine particular methods of religious coping in greater detail with more comprehensive measures of spiritual outcomes. There is already a burgeoning interest in forgiveness, but we can also learn a great deal more about other specific religious coping methods, such as religious confession and religious rites of passage (e.g., confirmations, Bar/Bat Mitzvah, weddings, and funerals). In addition, the effects of such religious coping strategies on other spiritual outcomes (e.g., spiritual maturity, commitment to faith, religious stewardship, and spiritual security) should be considered.

Fourth, we should investigate religion and religious coping among some relatively neglected groups. For example, most of the research on religious coping has been conducted with adult populations, but religious coping has its roots in early childhood and extends throughout the lifespan. It is time to learn more about the developmental aspect of religious coping and how religious coping evolves over the course of an individual's lifetime (Kimble, McFadden, Ellor, & Seeber, 1995). Many questions arise. Do religious coping methods change at different phases of life? Are certain forms of religious coping especially helpful to certain groups, such as the elderly? Are there identifiable lifespan patterns or trajectories of religious coping?

Finally, we are beginning to move from knowledge to application by developing, implementing, and evaluating the effectiveness of different types of religious and spiritually integrated treatments. But there are some fascinating unanswered questions. Are religiously integrated approaches to change as helpful to people as traditional psychological interventions? Are they more helpful for more religious clients? If so, how do we develop approaches to change that are sensitive to diverse religious values and traditions?

Although we are leaving you with more questions than answers, we hope you find the questions as exciting as we do. While we doubt that religion will be "explained away," we hope that interest in the scientific study of religion will continue to grow, promoting further opportunities for research and scholarship. We are engaged in a wonderful odyssey together as fellow sojourners in search of empirical knowledge and wisdom about religion—the most distinctively human phenomenon of all.

AUTHOR NOTE

Portions of this paper were originally presented at the XIVth Conference of the International Association for Psychology of Religion, Soesterberg, The Netherlands.

REFERENCES

Ai, A. L., Dunkle, R. E., Peterson, C., & Bolling, S. F. (1998). The role of private prayer in psychological recovery among midlife and aged patients following cardiac surgery. *The Gerontologist, 38,* 591–601.

Alferi, S. M., Culver, J. L., Carver, C. S., Arena, P. L., & Antoni, M. H. (1999). Religiosity, religious coping, and distress: A prospective study of Catholic and Evangelical Hispanic women in treatment for early-stage breast cancer. *Journal of Health Psychology, 4,* 343–356.

Ano, G. G. (2003). Correlates of religious struggles: An exploratory study. Unpublished masters thesis. Bowling Green State University, Bowling Green, OH.

Ano, G. G., & Roesch, S. C. (in press). Testing an attribution and coping model of stress: Religion as an orienting system. *Journal of Psychology and Christianity.*

Cole, B., & Pargament, K. I. (1999). Re-creating your life: A spiritual/psychotherapeutic intervention for people diagnosed with cancer. *Psychooncology, 8,* 395–407.

Cole, B., Pargament, K. I., & Brownstein, S. (2000, August). *A cognitive-behavioral group intervention for cardiac syncope.* Paper presented at the annual meeting of the American Psychological Association, Washington, DC.

Dubow, E. F., Pargament, K. I., Boxer, P., & Tarakeshwar, N. (2000). Initial investigation of Jewish early adolescents' ethnic identity, stress, and coping. *Journal of Early Adolescence, 20,* 418–441.

Durkheim, E. (1915, J. W. Swain, Trans.). The elementary forms of the religious life. New York: Free Press.

Elkins, D. N. (1995). Psychotherapy and spirituality: Toward a theory of the soul. *Journal of Humanistic Psychology, 35,* 78–98.

Ellison, C. G. (1991) Religious involvement and subjective well-being. *Journal of Health and Social Behavior, 32,* 80–99.

Exline, J. J., Yali, A. M., & Lobel, M. (1999). When God disappoints: Difficulty forgiving God and its role in negative emotion. *Journal of Health Psychology, 4,* 365-379.

Fitchett, G., Rybarczyk, B. D., DeMarco, G. A., & Nicholas, J. J. (1999). The role of religion in medical rehabilitation outcomes: A longitudinal study. *Rehabilitation Psychology, 44,* 1–22.

Flaherty, S. M. (1992). *Women, why do you weep? Spirituality for survivors of childhood sexual abuse.* New York: Paulist Press.

Fowler, J. W. (1987). *Faith development and pastoral care.* Philadelphia: Fortress Press.

Funder, D. C. (2002). Why study religion? *Psychological Inquiry, 13,* 213–214.

Ganzevoort, R. R. (1998). Religious coping reconsidered, part two: A narrative reformulation. *Journal of Psychology and Theology, 26,* 276–286.

Ganzevoort, R. R. (2001). Religion in rewriting the story: Case study of a sexually abused man. *International Journal for the Psychology of Religion, 11,* 45–62.

George, L. K., Ellison, C. G., & Larson, D. B. (2002). Explaining the relationships between religious involvement and health. *Psychological Inquiry, 13,* 190–200.

Harrison, M. O., Hays, J. C., Koenig, H. G., Eme-Akwari, A. G., & Pargament, K. I. (2001). The epidemiology of religious coping: A review of recent literature. *International Journal of Psychiatry, 13,* 86–93.

Hays, J. C., Meador, K. G., Branch, P. S., & George, L. K. (2001). The spiritual history scale in four dimensions (SHS-4): Validity and reliability. *The Gerontologist, 41,* 239-249.

Hummel, L. M. (1999). *A kind of religious coping: A theological and empirical analysis of consolation in the Lutheran tradition.* Unpublished doctoral dissertation, Boston University, Boston.

Johnson, P. E. (1959). *Psychology of religion.* Nashville: Abingdon Press.

Keefe, F. J., Afflect, G., Lefebvre, J., Underwood, L., Caldwell, D. S., Drew, J., Egert, J., Gibson, J., & Pargament, K. I. (2001). Living with rheumatoid arthritis: The role of daily spirituality and daily religious and spiritual coping. *Journal of Pain,* 101–110.

Kimble, M. A., McFadden, S. H., Ellor, J. W., & Seeber, J. (Eds.). (1995). *Aging, spirituality and religion: A handbook.* Minneapolis, MN: Fortress Press.

Kooistra, W., & Pargament, K. I. (1999). Predictors of religious doubting among Roman Catholic and Dutch Reformed high school students. *Journal of Psychology and Theology, 27,* 33–42.

Krause, N. (1998). Neighborhood deterioration, religious coping, and changes in health during late life. *The Gerontologist, 38,* 653–664.

Krause, N., Ellison, C. G., & Wulff, K. M. (1998). Church-based emotional support, negative interaction, and psychological well-being: Findings from a national sample of Presbyterians. *Journal for the Scientific Study of Religion, 37,* 725–741.

Krause, N., Ingersoll-Dayton, B., Ellison, C. G., & Wulff, K. M. (1999). Aging, religious doubt, and psychological well-being. *The Gerontologist, 39,* 525–533.

Kula, N. (in press). Earthquake and religious coping. *Journal of Faculty Divinity.* Corum-Gazi University, Turkey.

Loewenthal, K. M., MacLeod, A. K., Goldblatt, V., Lubitsh, G., & Valentine, J. D. (2000). Comfort and joy? Religion, cognition, and mood in Protestants and Jews under stress. *Cognition and Emotion, 14,* 355–374.

Magyar, G. M., Pargament, K. I., & Mahoney, A. (August, 2000). *Violation of the sacred: A study of desecration among college students.* Paper presented at the annual meeting of the American Psychological Association, Washington, DC.

Mahoney, A. M., Pargament, K. I., Ano, G., Lynn, Q., Magyar, G. M., McCarthy, S., Pristas, E., & Wachholtz, A. (2002, August). *The devil made them do it: Demonization and desecration of the 9/11 terrorist attacks.* Paper presented at the annual meeting of the American Psychological Association, Chicago.

Mahoney, A., Pargament, K. I., Jewell, T., Swank, A. B., Scott, E., Emery, E., & Rye, M. (1999). Marriage and the spiritual realm: The role of proximal and distal religious constructs in marital functioning. *Journal of Family Psychology, 13,* 321–338.

McCullough, M. E., Hoyt, W. T., Larson, D. B., Koenig, H. G., & Thoresen, C. E. (2000). Religious involvement and mortality: A meta-analytic review. *Health Psychology, 19,* 211–222.

McCullough, M. E. (1999). Research on religion-accommodative counseling: Review and meta-analysis. *Journal of Counseling Psychology, 46,* 92–98.

McReady, W. C., & Greeley, A. M. (1976). *The ultimate values of the American population (Vol. 23).* Beverly Hills: Sage.

Mickley, J. R., Pargament, K. I., Brant, C. R., & Hipp, K. M. (1998). God and the search for meaning among hospice caregivers. *The Hospice Journal, 13*, 1–17.

Miller, W. R., & C'de Baca, J. (2001). *Quantum change: When epiphanies and sudden insights transform ordinary lives.* New York: Guilford Press.

Nooney, J., & Woodrum, E. (2002). Religious coping and church-based social support as predictors of mental health outcomes: Testing a conceptual model. *Journal for the Scientific Study of Religion, 41*, 359–368.

Pargament, K. I. (2002a). Is religion nothing but . . . ? Explaining religion versus explaining religion away. *Psychological Inquiry, 13*, 168–171.

Pargament, K. I. (2002b). The bitter and the sweet: Evaluating the costs and benefits of religiousness. *Psychological Inquiry, 13*, 168–181.

Pargament, K. I., Cole, B., VandeCreek, L. Belavich, T., Brant, C., & Perez, L. (1999). The vigil: Religion and the search for control in the hospital waiting room. *Journal of Health Psychology, 4*, 327–341.

Pargament, K. I., Koenig, H. G., & Perez, L. M. (2000). The many methods of religious coping: Development and initial validation of the RCOPE. *Journal of Clinical Psychology, 56*, 519–543.

Pargament, K. I., Koenig, H. G., Tarakeshwar, N., & Hahn, J. (2001). Religious struggle as a predictor of mortality among medically ill elderly patients: A two year longitudinal study. *Archives of Internal Medicine, 161*, 1881–1885.

Pargament, K. I., Koenig, H. G., Tarakeshwar, N., & Hahn, J. (in press). Religious coping methods as predictors of psychological, physical, and spiritual outcomes among medically ill elderly patients: A two-year longitudinal study. *Journal of Health Psychology.*

Pargament, K. I., & Mahoney, A. (2002). Spirituality: The discovery and conservation of the sacred. In C. R. Snyder & S. J. Lopez (Eds.), *Handbook of positive psychology* (pp. 646–659). New York: Oxford University Press.

Pargament, K. I., Smith, B. W., Koenig, H. G., & Perez, L. (1998). Patterns of positive and negative religious coping with major life stressors. *Journal for the Scientific Study of Religion, 37*, 710–724.

Pargament, K. I., Tarakeshwar, N., Ellison, C. G., & Wulff, K. M. (2001). Religious coping among the religious: The relationship between religious coping and well-being in a national sample of Presbyterian clergy, elders, and members. *Journal for the Scientific Study of Religion, 40*, 497–513.

Pargament, K. I., Zinnbauer, B. J., Scott, A. B., Butter, E. M., Zerowin, J., & Stanik, P. (1998). Red flags and religious coping: Identifying some warning signs among people in crisis. *Journal of Clinical Psychology, 54*, 77–89.

Park, C., Cohen, L. H., & Herb, L. (1990). Intrinsic religiousness and religious coping as life stress moderators for Catholics versus Protestants. *Journal of Personality and Social Psychology, 59*, 562–574.

Pendleton, S. M., Cavalli, K. S., Pargament, K. I., & Nasr, S. Z. (2002). Religious/spiritual coping in childhood cystic fibrosis: A qualitative study. *Pediatrics, 109*, 1–11.

Rye, M. S., & Pargament, K. I. (2002). Forgiveness and romantic relationships in college: Can it heal the wounded heart? *Journal of Clinical Psychology, 58,* 419–441.

Smith, B. W., Pargament, K. I., Brant, C., & Oliver, J. M. (2000). Noah revisited: Religious coping by church members and the impact of the 1993 midwest flood. *Journal of Community Psychology, 28,* 169–186.

Stone, A. A., Greenberg, M. A., Kennedy-Moore, E., & Newman, M. G. (1991). Self-report, situation-specific coping questionnaires: What are they measuring? *Journal of Personality and Social Psychology, 61,* 648–658.

Tarakeshwar, N. (2002). Measures of Hindu religious dimensions: Development and initial evidence of reliability and validity. Unpublished doctoral dissertation, Bowling Green State University, Bowling Green, Ohio.

Tarakeshwar, N., Pargament, K. I., & Mahoney, A. (in press). Religious coping and mental health of Hindus in the United States. *Journal of Community Psychology.*

Tarakeshwar, N., Swank, A. B., Pargament, K. I., & Mahoney, A. (2001). The sanctification of nature and theological conservatism: A study of opposing religious correlates of environmentalism. *Review of Religious Research, 42,* 387–404.

Tepper, L., Rogers, S. A., Coleman, E. M., & Malony, H. N. (2001). The prevalence of religious coping among persons with persistent mental illness. *Psychiatric Services, 52,* 660–665.

Tix, A. P., & Frazier, P. A. (1998). The use of religious coping during stressful life events: Main effects, moderation, and mediation. *Journal of Consulting and Clinical Psychology, 66,* 411–422.

Wachholtz, A. (2002). *Comparing the effects of spiritual meditation with secular meditation and relaxation training.* Unpublished master's thesis. Bowling Green State University, Bowling Green, Ohio.

Wink, P., & Dillon, M. (2001). Religious involvement and health outcomes in late adulthood. In T. G. Plante, & A. C. Sherman (Eds.), *Faith and health* (pp. 75–106). New York: Guilford Press.

Commentary

Religious Coping in Later Life

Susan H. McFadden

n the late 1980s, publications appeared from two research programs that laid the foundation for current thinking about older adults' religious coping. Harold Koenig and his colleagues reported on a study in which they asked older people how they had "managed, coped, or kept themselves on an even keel" (Koenig, George, & Siegler, 1988, p. 304) during the best and worst times of their lives. Their respondents replied with a wide variety of coping responses but by far the most frequently mentioned were religious. In the same year that paper appeared, Koenig, Smiley and Gonzales (1988) published an important book that examined religious beliefs and behaviors in relation to older people's mental and physical health. Interestingly, this book included one paragraph citing Kenneth Pargament's work on religious coping styles (Pargament et al., 1988). At that time, Pargament's "Project on Religion and Coping" primarily focused on adults of all ages who participated in midwestern religious congregations, but it soon became clear that his emerging conceptualization of a psychology of religion and coping had important applications to older people, especially given what Koenig's group was learning about religion and aging.

Pargament's organizing metaphor for his psychology of religion and coping—the life journey—is familiar to gerontologists. He conceptualizes learned behaviors, personality traits, values, interpersonal relationships, and religion as "orienting systems" that guide people in difficult times (Pargament, 1997). These orienting systems can point toward solutions to problems that produce health and wholeness, but they can also direct people to respond maladaptively. Pargament has consistently noted that religious coping can produce negative as well as positive outcomes. For example, in an essay on religious coping among older persons, he suggested that frightening, punitive images of God are woven into some people's personal life histories (Pargament, Van Haitsma, & Ensing, 1995); later research found that medically ill older people were at greater risk of mortality when they held such negative God-images (Pargament, Koenig, Tarakeshwar, & Hahn, 2001).

In addition to the observation that religion can both support and work against effective coping, another important theme in Pargament's work concerns the need to understand religious coping as expressed by individuals experiencing particular life circumstances in specific contexts. His book on the psychology of religious coping contains five appendices that catalog research on a variety of reciprocally interactive factors—personal, situational, and contextual—that affect religious coping (Pargament, 1997). Studies of personal predictors have examined age, gender, race, type of religiousness, social status, education, and personality. Situational factors affecting older people's coping include being homebound, chronically ill, and going through complicated surgery. Finally, church attendance, type of religious affiliation, and geographic location are examples of contextual predictors. Add to these three multi-faceted domains the fact that human lives unfold in time, producing a variety of "trajectories of religiosity" (Ingersoll-Dayton, Krause, & Morgan, 2002, p. 61) as well as occasion-to-occasion intraindividual variability in older people's religious beliefs (Kim, Nesselroade, & Featherman, 1996), and we have a very complex, even humbling, challenge for those who seek to understand how older people's religious faith (or lack of faith) operates in situations that threaten well-being and call for some kind of coping response.

Because this brief chapter cannot review all of these diverse influences on older adults' religious coping, it focuses on three issues that represent advances in thinking about religious coping since Pargament, Koenig, and their colleagues first brought their work to public attention in the late 1980s. The first concerns the effects of religious affiliation on coping. Many researchers once treated religion generically, but today they are increasingly aware of the influence of the values and worldviews of particular religious faiths on people's interpretations of suffering and their subsequent coping responses. Second, in addition to denominational identity, the nature of the local congregation has important implications for older adults' coping. Increasingly, those who study religion and aging are identifying aspects of congregational life that vary among faith communities and affect the lives of elders. Finally, by examining congregational programs and outreach ministries, we begin to see more clearly the diversity of religious older people's life circumstances. Some are healthy and active, participating fully in the life of the faith community. Others are homebound or living in long-term care. These persons—especially those suffering from dementia—have often been absent from discussions of late life religiosity. For example, the first volume of *Aging, Spirituality, and Religion: A Handbook* (Kimble, McFadden, Ellor, & Seeber, 1995) contained only a few, brief references to dementia. The second volume, however, has four chapters entirely focused on dementia and the needs of caregivers (Kimble & McFadden, 2003). As Pargament states (this volume), we need to extend the study of religion and coping to "relatively neglected groups."

RELIGIOUS AFFILIATION

Religious affiliation contributes to the formation of the orienting system that people employ in times of trouble or threat. For example, a study of Jewish, Catholic, and Protestant nursing home residents found that religious affiliation affected decisions about life-prolonging treatments, with Jewish residents being most likely to request these treatments (Ejaz, 2000). The sacred writings and traditions of these faiths shaped frail elders' interpretations of suffering at the end of life and the bridge to death. Another study examined spiritual life histories (Hays, Meador, Branch, & George, 2001) and showed that in contrast to mainline Protestants, Catholics, and Jews, fundamentalistic/pietistic Protestants had a stronger sense that God helped them; they also scored higher on a measure of lifetime social support in religious settings. Cicirelli's (2002) research on older adults' views of death also compared people affiliated with mainline Protestant denominations with those associated with fundamentalist or evangelical Protestantism. Using an attachment theoretical approach, Cicirelli observed that fundamentalist and evangelical Protestants, primarily African Americans, viewed God as an attachment figure and their "intense personal relationship with God" (p. 243) affected how they coped with fears about death and the difficulties of everyday life. They had few doubts that God loved them and would welcome them in the afterlife. In contrast, older adults from mainline Protestant denominations were less likely to express strong emotional connections to God and had greater uncertainty about what might lie beyond death.

Although common images of older religious persons emphasize their constancy, late life changes in religious affiliation do occur. In *The Psychology of Religion and Coping*, Pargament (1997) compared religious conversion with religious switching. In the former, an individual responds to difficult life circumstances by transforming the goals of religious life (e.g., what salvation means) as well as the means to obtain those goals (e.g., practices of a particular religious denomination). Religious switching involves no change in definition of the goal of religious life, but the way to reach that goal does change, as when a person decides that Catholicism no longer conveys the kind of meaning found in evangelical Protestantism. Although conversion is usually considered by psychologists of religion to be a young person's experience, Koenig reported that significant changes in religious faith "may be common among older adults as they experience health changes, social losses, and struggle with issues involving control and dependency" (1994, p. 423). In his study of 276 men in the Durham VA Mental Health Survey, 31% reported conversion after age 50.

When the usual style of religious coping fails to resolve life crises, people may experience conversion, religious switching, or increased religiosity within the same denomination. Alternatively, some older persons reject religious beliefs and practices, sometimes as a result of disillusionment with denominational polity or the behaviors of leaders and members of a particular faith community (Ingersoll-Dayton et al., 2002). These are all forms of what Pargament (1997) calls religious transformation. He also observes that people sometimes respond to crises by holding onto—or conserving—religious beliefs and values. Using four case studies of frail elders in crisis, Devor and Pargament (2003) illustrated how coping through religious transformation or conservation could have positive or negative outcomes. These case studies were drawn from Devor's work at the Danielsen Institute at Boston University, where theologically trained psychology interns learn to work with frail elders coping emotionally and spiritually with the challenging situations and contexts of late life. Although this program of home visitation is unusual for psychologists, clergy and members of local congregations have long practiced this kind of care.

THE LOCAL CONGREGATION

Faith traditions offer ways of interpreting suffering as well as support for public rituals and private behaviors that enable people to cope with tribulation. Religions and their various denominational subcategories convey images of God and God's response to human troubles. Some emphasize an emotional relationship with God and emotional expressions of religiosity, while others orient more toward intellectual understandings of God and God's work in the world. Theological positions developed over the centuries may not be comprehended or appreciated by people who call themselves religious, but beliefs about good and evil, sin and forgiveness, suffering and redemption permeate hymns, scripture readings, sermons, public prayers, and adult classes—all activities of local congregations.

Although religious coping is often conceptualized on an individual level, it has an important institutional component as shown in research on the salutary effects of religious attendance by older people (see Idler, this volume). The exact mechanisms of the relationship between religion and late life health are unclear, but social support from clergy and fellow congregants is believed to play an important role. A study that examined emotional and spiritual support from church members, along with emotional support from clergy, found that spiritual support from fellow congregants had the greatest effect on positive religious coping. Spiritual support occurred when members shared their religious experiences, helped one another to live faithfully, and showed others how to know God better (Krause, Ellison, Shaw, Marcum, & Boardman, 2001). This could take the form of a person from the faith community visiting an older person in the hospital and describing personal experiences of growing closer to God through prayer.

Older people are often very loyal to their local faith communities where for many years they have both given and received spiritual support. They develop deep emotional attachments to the particular institutions where they have experienced many of the key markers of human development. However, this kind of love for one's local religious community may be problematic because negative experiences at the congregational level can be devastating (Krause, Ellison, & Wulff, 1998; Nooney & Woodrum, 2002). For example, some older adults feel abandoned by clergy and congregational leaders who focus time, energy, and resources on ministries with children, families, and young adults. In other words, the religious institution itself can be the locus of distressing experiences that call for religious coping. An elderly person who has been a lifelong, faithful member of a congregation might experience a crisis of faith not only in God but in the faith community if, when the person is ill, bereaved, or facing some other trauma, no fellow congregant offers spiritual support and the clergy express no interest or concern.

Although local congregations have the potential to offer considerable support for religious coping, sometimes a lack of attention to the need for continued religious development leaves people without sufficient resources to face the exigencies of aging. In her book about the role of religion in older adults' lives, sociologist Susan Eisenhandler

(2003) described "reflexive" faith—religious beliefs and values that have never been critically examined. Eisenhandler observed that many of the people she interviewed needed a "reflective" faith that would intentionally engage with theological questions and religious traditions. This approach to faith, which is often nurtured in small study groups within congregations, could help aging persons hold onto a sense of meaning and purpose in life while coping with failing health, deaths of loved ones, dementia diagnoses and the like. Too often, however, leaders of faith communities assume that older people's religious lives are fully formed and closed to change. Using Pargament's terminology, one can interpret Eisenhandler as saying that when the challenges of aging call for religious transformation, the local congregation may be unprepared to take that journey with the elder. Eisenhandler questioned whether the faith communities of the persons she interviewed would rise to the challenge of nurturing a more reflective faith that could support them through the unique experiences of being old in America today.

On the other hand, many local congregations do offer holistic support to older adults. For example, some provide parish nurses (Djupe & Westberg, 1995), religious education (Simmons, 1995), and intergenerational programs that integrate attention to physical, emotional, intellectual, social, and spiritual needs of elders. Many congregations train laypeople to visit homebound and institutionalized members (Seeber, 2003) and offer a variety of services to caregivers (Richards, 2003). Some run adult day centers and others sponsor housing for older adults (Netting, 1995). Clergy offer a variety of forms of pastoral caregiving and counseling (Ellor, 2003; Kimble, 1995; Knutson, 2003; Rost, 2003), attending to issues ranging from addiction (Albers, 2003) to depression experienced by residents of long-term care facilities (MacKinlay, 2003). It has long been noted that African-American congregations offer a wide range of support services to their elderly members, including direct financial aid and advocacy with social service agencies, in addition to more traditional kinds of informal caregiving (Taylor & Chatters, 1986; Wimberly, 2003).

The types of support that a congregation offers for coping with the many challenges of aging depend upon its size, location, denomination, and finances—variables most often studied by sociologists. Interestingly, before he began publishing his work on religious coping, Pargament proposed and tested a multidimensional model of "congregational climate" (Pargament, Silverman, Johnson, Echemendia, & Snyder, 1983). Congregational climate is composed of psychosocial variables (e.g., support for autonomy, sense of community, intrinsic or extrinsic religiosity) that mediate between the characteristics of the institution and the individual attributes of members. A comparison of small black Protestant congregations, small white Protestant congregations, moderate-sized Protestant congregations, and large white Catholic congregations produced some fascinating observations of differences that were in large part confirmed in the national study of American religions conducted by Roof and McKinney (1987). Researchers today might find it fruitful to return to Pargament et al.'s (1983) model of congregational climate to test its prediction of support for religious coping by older persons.

FRAILTY AND DEMENTIA

As Pargament and his colleagues have repeatedly stated, religious coping occurs when individuals meet specific life situations within particular contexts. For many older people, forms of religious coping rest upon a foundation built over many years of repeated acts of prayer and meditation, participation in religious ritual, and engagement with the life of a local congregation. What happens, however, when an older person is torn away from that foundation? For example, a person who has begun every day with quiet, solitary meditation and a strong cup of coffee may experience a profound disruption of religious coping upon moving to a long-term care facility with rigid schedules and communal dining. Likewise, elders in long-term care who can no longer attend religious services in their own faith communities may experience deep spiritual loss when worship takes place in a dining hall where people walk in and out with food trays. These problems point to the significant role of chaplains in long-term care (Friedman, 1995). Chaplains contribute in a variety of ways to the quality of life of those who live and work in these facilities. Two important aspects of their work lie in nurturing connections between residents and their local congregations and in educating clergy and laypeople about continued possibilities for religious coping even among the frail and demented.

Alzheimer's disease has been called the "theological disease" (Keck, 1996, p. 15). It confronts human beings with their own mortality, weakness, and dependency and it radically tests the foundations of religious coping. Religious coping has been described primarily as an individual response to times of trial, but how does the person with dementia engage in religious coping? One way is to be surrounded by people who uphold the personhood of the one with dementia (Kitwood, 1997) and honor the "faded self" (Post, 1995, p. 21) by keeping memory of that individual alive within the faith community (Sapp, 1997). For example, many chaplains note the ability of people with dementia to participate in worship through songs, corporate prayers, and sacraments even when they are mostly mute and seemingly unresponsive to their environments. Persons in whom the disease has not progressed so far can benefit not only from corporate worship, but also from private devotions and pastoral care that convey continued meaning, support, and acceptance.

In the coming years, with rising numbers of persons receiving the dreaded diagnosis ever earlier, it will be important to discern the possibilities for religious coping when the mind can no longer hold onto coherent thoughts. In these circumstances, religious coping may be seen primarily as a transactional experience in which clergy, chaplains, and laypeople find ways to elicit feelings of love, comfort, and "blessed assurance" associated with religious beliefs and practices.

CONCLUSION

Thanks to the research conducted by Koenig, Pargament and their colleagues in the last quarter century, we know a great deal more today about older adults' religious coping. Religious coping can enable older people to conserve long-held beliefs and practices, though sometimes coping results in religious transformation. Either way, the outcome may be positive and supportive of well-being, or negative and deleterious to physical and mental health.

Psychologists generally focus upon the individual in their studies of religious coping but Pargament, a clinician with deep roots in community psychology, has always insisted that we need to pay attention to the situations that call for coping and the contexts in which this happens. The physical, mental, emotional, social, and spiritual challenges that inevitably accompany the aging process produce many situations that require some kind of coping response. Often these difficult situations accumulate and become chronic in an older person's life. Beliefs about the meaning of their lives and their deaths, the practices they employ to feel connected to the sacred, and the ways they know and understand God are all shaped to some degree by religious affiliation. However, it is important to note that the theology, history, and polity of the various religious denominations are expressed concretely in local congregations. Thus the contexts of religious coping have multiple layers.

At the local level, older people receive a variety of kinds of support for positive religious coping. As we have seen, faith communities offer formal and informal services to assist older adults as they journey through the last stage of life. In addition, worship services, opportunities for fellowship, prayers and hymns, the pastor's greeting at the door, and even the flowers on the altar, can be resources for religious coping. When people enter the realm of frailty and dementia, the faith community is often there to offer continuing support. Religious coping then necessarily becomes communal, as persons of faith advocate for the frail person and act as conduits for transcendent love and acceptance.

REFERENCES

Albers, R. H. (2003). Pastoral care of the aged afflicted by addiction. In M. A. Kimble & S. H. McFadden (Eds.), *Aging, spirituality and religion: A handbook* (Vol. 2, pp. 224–238). Minneapolis, MN: Fortress Press.

Cicirelli, V. G. (2002). *Older adults' views on death.* New York: Springer Publishing.

Devor, N. G., & Pargament, K. I. (2003). Understanding religious coping with late-life crises. In M. A. Kimble & S. H. McFadden (Eds.), *Aging, spirituality, and religion: A handbook* (Vol. 2, pp. 195–205). Minneapolis, MN: Fortress Press.

Djupe, A. M., & Westberg, G. (1995). Congregation-based health programs. In M. A. Kimble, S. H. McFadden, J. W. Ellor, & J. J. Seeber (Eds.), *Aging, spirituality, and religion: A handbook* (pp. 325–334). Minneapolis, MN: Fortress Press.

Eisenhandler, S. A. (2003). *Keeping the faith in late life.* New York: Springer Publishing.

Ejaz, F. K. (2000). The influence of religious and personal values on nursing home residents' attitudes toward life-sustaining treatments. *Social Work in Health Care, 32*(2), 23–39.

Ellor, J. W. (2003). The role of spiritual assessment in counseling older adults. In M. A. Kimble & S. H. McFadden (Eds.), *Aging, spirituality and religion: A handbook* (Vol. 2, pp. 286–298). Minneapolis, MN: Fortress Press.

Friedman, D. A. (1995). Spiritual challenges of nursing home life. In M. A. Kimble, S. H. McFadden, J. W. Ellor, & J. J. Seeber (Eds.), *Aging, spirituality, and religion: A handbook* (pp. 362–373). Minneapolis, MN: Fortress Press.

Hays, J. C., Meador, K. G., Branch, P. S., & George, L. K. (2001). The spiritual history scale in four dimensions (SHS-4): Validity and reliability. *The Gerontologist, 41,* 239–249.

Ingersoll-Dayton, B., Krause, N., & Morgan, D. (2002). Religious trajectories and transitions over the life course. *International Journal of Aging and Human Development, 55,* 51–70.

Keck, D. (1996). *Forgetting whose we are: Alzheimer's disease and the love of God.* Nashville, TN: Abingdon Press.

Kim, J. E., Nesselroade, J. R., & Featherman, D. L. (1996). The state component in self-reported worldviews and religious beliefs of older adults: The
MacArthur Successful Aging Studies. *Psychology and Aging, 11,* 396–407.

Kimble, M. A. (1995). Pastoral care. In M. A. Kimble, S. H. McFadden, J. W.
Ellor, & J. J. Seeber (Eds.), *Aging, spirituality, and religion: A handbook* (pp.
131–147). Minneapolis, MN: Fortress Press.

Kimble, M. A., & McFadden, S. H. (Eds.). (2003). *Aging, spirituality and religion:
A handbook* (Vol. 2). Minneapolis, MN: Fortress Press.

Kimble, M. A., McFadden, S. H., Ellor, J. W., & Seeber, J. J. (Eds.). (1995).
Aging, spirituality, and religion: A handbook. Minneapolis, MN: Fortress Press.

Kitwood, T. (1997). *Dementia reconsidered: The person comes first.* Philadelphia:
Open University Press.

Knutson, L. D. (2003). Pastoral care of elders and their families. In M. A.
Kimble & S. H. McFadden (Eds.), *Aging, spirituality and religion: A handbook* (Vol. 2, pp. 206–223). Minneapolis, MN: Fortress Press.

Koenig, H. G. (1994). *Aging and God: Spiritual pathways to mental health in midlife
and later years.* New York: Haworth Pastoral Press.

Koenig, H. G., George, L. K., & Siegler, I. C. (1988). The use of religion and
other emotion-regulating coping strategies among older adults. *The
Gerontologist, 28,* 303–310.

Koenig, H. G., Smiley, M., & Gonzales, J. A. P. (1988). *Religion, health, and
aging: A review and theoretical integration.* New York: Greenwood Press.

Krause, N., Ellison, C. G., Shaw, B. A., Marcum, J. P., & Boardman, J. D. (2001).
Church-based social support and religious coping. *Journal for the Scientific
Study of Religion, 40,* 637–656.

Krause, N., Ellison, C. G., & Wulff, K. M. (1998). Church-based emotional support, negative interaction and psychological well-being: Findings from a
national sample of Presbyterians. *Journal for the Scientific Study of Religion,
37,* 725–741.

MacKinlay, E. (2003). Pastoral care for depression in long-term care residents.
In M. A. Kimble & S. H. McFadden (Eds.), *Aging, spirituality and religion:
A handbook* (Vol. 2, pp. 255–267). Minneapolis, MN: Fortress Press.

Netting, F. E. (1995). Congregation-sponsored housing. In M. A. Kimble, S. H.
McFadden, J. W. Ellor, & J. J. Seeber (Eds.), *Aging, spirituality, and religion:
A handbook* (pp. 335–349). Minneapolis, MN: Fortress Press.

Nooney, J., & Woodrum, E. (2002). Religious coping and church-based social
support as predictors of mental health outcomes: Testing a conceptual
model. *Journal for the Scientific Study of Religion, 41,* 359–368.

Pargament, K. I. (1997). *The psychology of religion and coping: Theory, research, practice.* New York: Guilford.

Pargament, K. I., Kennel, J., Hathaway, W., Grevengoed, N., Newman, J., &
Jones, W. (1988). Religion and the problem-solving process: Three styles
of coping. *Journal for the Scientific Study of Religion, 27,* 90–104.

Pargament, K. I., Koenig, H. G., Tarakeshwar, N., & Hahn, J. (2001). Religious
struggle as a predictor of mortality among medically ill elderly patients: A
two year longitudinal study. *Archives of Internal Medicine, 161,* 1881–1885.

Pargament, K. I., Silverman, W., Johnson, S., Echemendia, R., & Snyder, S. (1983). The psychosocial climate of religious congregations. *American Journal of Community Psychology, 11,* 351–381.

Pargament, K. I., Van Haitsma, K. S., & Ensing, D. S. (1995). Religion and coping. In M. A. Kimble, S. H. McFadden, J. W. Ellor, & J. J. Seeber (Eds.), *Aging, spirituality, and religion: A handbook* (pp. 47–67). Minneapolis, MN: Fortress Press.

Post, S. G. (1995). *The moral challenge of Alzheimer disease.* Baltimore: Johns Hopkins University Press.

Richards, M. (2003). Caring for the caregiver. In M. A. Kimble & S. H. McFadden (Eds.), *Aging, spirituality and religion: A handbook* (Vol. 2, pp. 180–192). Minneapolis, MN: Fortress Press.

Roof, W. C., & McKinney, W. (1987). *American mainline religion: Its changing shape and future.* New Brunswick, NJ: Rutgers University Press.

Rost, R. A. (2003). Issues of grace and sin in pastoral care with older adults. In M. A. Kimble & S. H. McFadden (Eds.), *Aging, spirituality and religion: A handbook* (Vol. 2, pp. 239–254). Minneapolis, MN: Fortress Press.

Sapp, S. (1997). Memory: The community looks backward. In D. K. McKim (Ed.), *God never forgets: Faith, hope and Alzheimer's disease* (pp. 38–54). Louisville, KY: Westminster John Knox Press.

Seeber, J. J. (2003). Volunteer ministries with older adults. In M. A. Kimble & S. H. McFadden (Eds.), *Aging, spirituality and religion: A handbook* (Vol. 2, pp. 168–179). Minneapolis, MN: Fortress Press.

Simmons, H. C. (1995). Religious education. In M. A. Kimble, S. H. McFadden, J. W. Ellor, & J. J. Seeber (Eds.), *Aging, spirituality, and religion: A handbook* (pp. 218–232). Minneapolis, MN: Fortress Press.

Taylor, R. J., & Chatters, L. M. (1986). Church-based informal support among elderly Blacks. *The Gerontologist, 26,* 637–642.

Wimberly, A. E. S. (2003). Congregational care in the lives of black older adults. In M. A. Kimble & S. H. McFadden (Eds.), *Aging, spirituality and religion: A handbook* (Vol. 2, pp. 101–120). Minneapolis, MN: Fortress Press.

Commentary

Religion, Coping, and Health

A. Sandra Willis

P argament and Ano (this volume) offer important guiding assumptions for the evolving conceptualization and further empirical study of religion within a coping framework. They review contemporary research conducted in a variety of contexts and using a variety of methods. Pargament states that religion may serve many purposes associated with psychological and social goals as well as with physical functioning. Based on multidisciplinary research of the past 25 years, it appears that religiosity, including beliefs, practices, and religion-focused coping, may positively influence many aspects of human behavior and experience throughout the lifespan.

Evidence for the salutary influence of religious affiliation and practices on quality of life has been reported by researchers in the areas of morbidity and mortality (Hummer, Rogers, Nan, & Ellison, 1999; McCullough, Hoyt, Larson, Koenig, & Thoreson, 2000), coping with illnesses (Jenkins & Pargament, 1988; Koenig, Pargament, & Nielsen, 1998), substance use (Pardini, Plante, & Sherman, 2001; Wallace & Williams, 1997; Willis, Wallston, & Johnson, 2001), among others. For Israeli cancer patients in the early stages of malignant melanoma, religious involvement was negatively related to emotional distress (anxiety, depression, anger, tension, confusion), while positively associated with active cognitive coping, when controlling effects of demographic and disease-related factors (Baider et al., 1999). However, these researchers reported that measures of health-related quality of life and social support were unrelated to religious involvement.

RELIGION AND HEALTH IN THE ELDERLY

A number of studies of elderly individuals have documented the beneficial effects of religiosity on health, adaptation, and life-satisfaction (Hunsberger, 1985; Idler, 1987; Idler & Kasl, 1992; Krause, 1998; Levin, 1994; Levin, Markides, & Ray, 1996; Levin, Taylor, & Chatters, 1994; Markides, 1983; Morse & Wisocki, 1988); a few studies report negative associations (Wilcock et al., 1998) or lack of significant associations (Pargament & Park, 1996). Wink and Dillion (2001) used longitudinal data, spanning early to late adulthood, of a sample of relatively healthy women and men living in California. They explored the nature of the relationships between religiosity and physical and mental health: Is the positive impact observed in previous cross-sectional research due to an effect based in late adulthood or can the effect be predicted from religiosity throughout adulthood? Analyses revealed no evidence for a direct relationship between the importance of religion and physical health with two exceptions: Religious women were more optimistic about their health in late adulthood than nonreligious women and religious men reported less bodily pain than nonreligious men. Characteristics of the sample, primarily participants' relative good health and regional differences in a number of factors including religion/spirituality and lifestyle, may help explain results of these analyses and gauge comparability to data collected in other studies.

Interestingly, Wink and Dillion (2001) did find significant interaction effects of religion and physical health on mental health factors of happiness and life satisfaction. Nonreligious, elderly Californians in poor physical health were more likely to experience unhappiness and dissatisfaction with life than the religious individuals in the sample. The same pattern was observed in data collected 15 years earlier in middle adulthood. Wink and Dillion suggest that "Although one should be cautious in making causal inferences, it appears to us that the positive relation between religion and mental health in times of adversity goes beyond the mere possibility that psychologically healthy individuals acquire faith in times of stress" (p. 102). Indeed, the longitudinal research of Pargament and others reveals enduring patterns of using positive religious coping strategies consistently over time in a variety of health-related areas: engaging in health-enhancing behavior (Hays, Meador, Branch & George, 2001), less distress and depression following coronary bypass surgery (Ai, Dunkle, Peterson, & Bolling, 1998), better overall mental health (Tepper, Rogers, Coleman, & Malony, 2001), and a variety of positive outcomes across physical, psychological, and spiritual domains in elderly patients who had been hospitalized (Koenig et al., 1998).

RELIGION IS SOMETIMES HARMFUL, OFTEN HELPFUL

Pargament (1997, and this volume) is careful to point out that religion may be harmful as well as helpful. Religious coping may take the form of maladaptive mechanisms that distract the individual from accurate perception of life events and their roles within them. It is possible that some forms of religious coping may compete with or prevent proactive behaviors aimed at reducing or eliminating stress. In some cases, religion is a significant part of content or context of potentially problematic cognitions and behaviors, such as distorted thinking, guilt, self-blame, poor self-esteem, fostering and venting fear about the presence of evil in the world. Negative coping, struggle or movement away from religious resources in response to adversity, (Brief RCOPE, Carver, 1997; Pargament, Koenig, & Perez, 2000; Pargament, Smith, Koenig, & Perez, 1998) in multiple myeloma patients facing bone marrow transplants was associated with adverse quality of life outcomes (Sherman, Simonton, Plante, Moody, & Wells, 2001).

For many people regardless of age, religion seems to be an adaptive feature of social and personal life (see Plante & Sharma, 2001, for review). Researchers from a variety of disciplines, including psychology, sociology, religion, and medicine have found fairly strong relationships between religion variables and variables associated with development and mental and physical health. In children and adolescents, religious involvement may enhance development of self-esteem and reduce substance use and delinquent behaviors (Plante & Pardini, 2000; Wallace & Williams, 1997; Willis et al., 2001). Plante, Saucedo, and Rice (2001) investigated religious coping and well-being and speculated that religious coping might be helpful with individuals experiencing significant trauma, though it might be unrelated to handling moderate daily hassles. Prayer and church attendance were beneficial coping mechanisms for families of children with disabilities (Bennet, Deluca, & Allen, 1995). Religious coping was reportedly adaptive for Salvadoran immigrants leaving their homeland to escape civil war (Plante, Manuel, Menendez, & Marcotte, 1995), and for elderly poor residents of dilapidated housing (Krause, 1998).

RELIGION, COPING, AND RESEARCH

If people who believe in God, attend church services, pray, and use religious coping strategies are healthier—mentally and physically—how can we explain this phenomenon? A great many factors could be at work as mediators and moderators of religiosity effects. As Pargament (this volume) argues, global religious orientation is mediated by more proximal variables. Which of these factors are most potent? Is it possible to determine the relative contributions of religious factors and related social and personal factors?

I agree with Pargament's (1997, and this volume) assumption that religious factors cannot be fully reduced to psychological, social, or physical dimensions, though I think it is valuable to attempt to do so in basic and applied research. Presuming religious beliefs, behaviors, and experiences may be accurately measured (see Sherman & Simonton, 2001; Hill & Hood, 1999) within naturalistic contexts, one is challenged to detect and interpret the complex multivariate interactions that exist in phenomena of this kind. Furthermore, the complexity varies with individual differences in ways that involve seemingly inextricable blends of biological temperament; social-environmental experience, individual beliefs, values and life philosophy; and social, material and personal resources available to the individual, among others.

Given the apparent significance of religion in many areas of health and well-being, including the association with health-enhancing behavior during early adulthood that functions to optimize the quality of life in later adulthood, there are so many ways to direct religion and health research. As Pargament advocates and practices "getting closer to religion," research should include a focus on the authentic experience of religion, which may include personal history within the church—the extent to which religious affiliation and practices may be habitual based on social development directed by parents or mindfully self-directed for intrinsic value.

Using coping as a focal point for the study of religion, one may consider exposure to socially-ritualized behavior, doctrine-based beliefs, and personal beliefs related to meaning in life. A system of belief that emphasizes the presence of an omnipotent, loving being and the importance of giving, empathy, and forgiveness in personal relationships may enhance the well-being of individuals and the quality of their interpersonal relationships, thereby teaching a style of interaction that provides the giver as well as those in need with enhanced optimism, positive affect, and coping. Positive cognitive and affective components of expectations may influence appraisal of stress and types of coping strategies used to handle adversity in life. The faith community may foster and maintain social interactions that provide emotional and instrumental support for efficacious coping.

IN CONSIDERATION OF COPING

While religion and spirituality have been conceptualized as a passive style of coping by some researchers (e.g., McCrae & Costa, 1986), others suggest that certain types of religion or activities within a religious community function as active coping mechanisms (Folkman & Lazarus, 1980; Stanton & Franz, 1999; Willis, 2001). Similarly, religious commitment, instead of being viewed as an externally focused, powerless coping style, has been related to internal locus of control (Jackson & Coursey, 1988), personal competence (self-efficacy), and initiative in problem-solving (Carver, Sheier, & Weintraub, 1989; Pargament, 1997). On the other hand, aspects of religious belief such as "waiting for God to show me the way" do seem to exemplify passive coping. Dunkel-Schetter, Feinstein, Taylor, and Falker (1992) reported factor analyses in which items such as "hoping for a miracle," and "leaving it in God's hands" fell into a passive coping category.

What coping strategies are used by persons of faith? The Strength of Religious Faith Scale (Plante & Boccaccini, 1997) was used to assess use of prayer, attendance to religious services, and other forms of religious involvement, and the Brief COPE (Carver, 1997) and the Ways of Religious Coping Scale (Boudreaux, Catz, Ryan, Amaral-Melendez, & Brantley, 1995) were used to measure 14 coping strategies and internal/private and external/social religious coping. Following the use of religious coping, those high in faith were more likely to use positive reframing, planning, and active coping, and to seek instrumental and emotional support rather than using passive and maladaptive emotional coping mechanisms (Willis et al., 1999; Willis, Wallston, & Johnson, 2001; also see Table 4.1).

To learn more about religiosity, individual differences in coping strategies, and tobacco-related health behavior, data were collected from adolescent/young adult populations ($N = 325$; ages 16–23) from Alabama, California, Iowa, Tennessee, and Washington, DC to form a sample diverse in race and denominational affiliation (Willis et al., 1999; Willis et al., 2001). Adolescents' and young adults' initiation in and maintained use of tobacco are of great concern (Chassin, Presson, Pitts, & Sherman, 2000): These behaviors may compromise health in the short- and long-term. Smoking habits begun during youth may continue throughout the lifespan and influence quality of life during middle and late adulthood.

A number of researchers reported an inverse relationship between religiosity variables and substance use and abuse (Foshee & Hollinger, 1996; Kunz & Giesbrecht, 1999; Patlock-Peckham, Hutchinson, Cheong,

TABLE 4.1   Differences in Coping Strategies Among Religious and Agnostic Young Adults

	Protestant ($n = 142$)		Catholic ($n = 114$)		Agnostic ($n = 29$)		
	M	SD	M	SD	M	SD	F (p)
Active Coping	3.36	.65	3.08	.69	3.17	.74	5.55 (.004)
Positive Reframing	3.01	.79	2.73	.76	2.70	.83	4.47 (.012)
Acceptance	3.14	.63	2.94	.64	3.21	.65	4.16 (.017)
Turning to Religion	3.20	.81	2.61	.93	1.74	1.03	37.68 (.001)
Instrumental Support	3.01	.85	3.09	.76	2.57	1.05	4.23 (.015)
Denial	1.37	.63	1.68	.71	1.45	.63	6.73 (.001)
Substance Use	1.26	.58	1.46	.70	1.53	.88	3.83 (.023)

Note. Brief COPE response format 1–4 scale: 1 indicates "I usually don't do this at all," 4 indicates "I usually do this a lot."

& Nagoshi, 1998; Pullen, Modrcin-Talbott, West, & Muenchen, 1999), suggesting that religion may offer a protective effect. Are religious youths less likely to use tobacco than nonreligious youths? If they do smoke, might they begin later and smoke less often? I found that agnostic young adults (79.3%) were significantly more likely to have tried smoking, χ^2 (2, $N = 284$) = 6.45, $p = .04$, than Protestants (55.3%) and Catholics (64%). Agnostics ($M = 14.65$ years of age, $SD = 1.9$) began smoking significantly earlier than Protestants ($M = 16.21$, $SD = 2.19$) and Catholics ($M = 16.31$, $SD = 2.9$). Agnostics were heavier smokers than Protestants, smoking 26.48 cigarettes a month on average, compared to Protestants' 6.3 cigarettes; however Catholics smoked nearly 20 cigarettes/month (variance within all groups was high). Similarly, 65% of Protestant smokers had attempted to stop using tobacco as opposed to 48.2% of Catholics and 50% of agnostics (Willis, 2000).

Of a number of sources of individual differences in beliefs, perception of control over health status, affect, optimism, and perceived susceptibility to health risk, the strongest predictors of tobacco use (not using) were the religious ones: strength of faith (Santa Clara Strength of Faith Scale, Plante & Boccaccini, 1997), God health locus of control (Multidimensional Health Locus of Control Scale, Wallston, Wallston, & DeVellis, 1978; Wallston et al., 1999; Willis et al., 2001), and turning to religion (internal and external) as a coping mechanism (Brief COPE, Carver 1997; Religious Ways of Coping Scale, Boudreaux et al., 1995). Regression analyses revealed that religious coping accounted for

TABLE 4.2   Coping Predictors of Tobacco-related Behavior in Religious and Agnostic Young Adults

	Protestant	Catholic	Agnostic
Ever Tried Smoking	Religion (–.16) Humor (.16) Emotional Support (–.15) Positive Reframing (–.14)	Acceptance (.36*) Humor (.21) Religion (–.18)	None
Age at First Use of Tobacco	Self-Distraction (.34*)	Self-Blaming (–.27)	None
Frequency of Smoking	None	Emotional Support (.26) Denial (.25)	Positive Reframing (–.46)
Ever Tried Quitting	Self-Distraction (.29) Positive Reframing (.25)	Venting (.27)	Positive Reframing (–.54)

$p < .05$; * $p < .01$

most of the variance in tobacco use among young adults. In other words, the effect of faith on tobacco use seems to be mediated by religious coping and, to a lesser extent, by perception of control over health status (Willis et al., 2001). Table 4.2 shows other coping strategies related to tobacco use among Protestant, Catholic, and agnostic individuals.

CONCLUSIONS

Pargament has taken the road less traveled by his contemporaries, a road some still consider impassable (even with a prayer). For more than two decades he has acted as a guide on this road for many others, a sizeable number of whom are his graduate students who have devoted themselves enthusiastically to continued discovery and rigorous study of religion and coping. Pargament's careful work and balanced interpretation of research findings have helped allay some of the doubts expressed about the appropriateness and value of religious variables to the study of psychology. Pargament's work rises to the rigor demanded by skeptics and conversely helps moderate popular media appeals to accept glowing, overgeneralized claims about the health-enhancing effects of religion. These research findings need not be applied prematurely, before we have good reason—evidence from varied method and context—to believe that these applications will be efficacious. Moreover, Pargament's concept of religion as coping offers a framework that provides researchers with guidance in a sea of proximal variables, approaches, and methods, to help us learn more about the authentic experience of religion and its relationship with health and well-being.

REFERENCES

Ai, A. L., Dunkle, R. E., Peterson, C., & Bolling, S. F. (1998). The role of private prayer in psychological recovery among midlife and aged patients following cardiac surgery. *The Gerontologist, 38,* 591–601.

Baider, L., Russak, S. M., Perry, S., Kash, K., Gronert, M., Fox, B., et al. (1999). The role of religious and spiritual beliefs in coping with malignant melanoma: An Israeli sample. *Psycho-Oncology, 8,* 27–35.

Bennet, T., Deluca, D. A., & Allen, R. W. (1995). Religion and children with disabilities. *Journal of Religion and Health, 34,* 301–311.

Bennett, P., Norman, P., Moore, L., Murphy, S., & Tudor-Smith, C. (1997). Health locus of control and value for health in smokers and nonsmokers. *Health Psychology, 16*(2), 179–182.

Boudreaux, E., Catz, S., Ryan, L., Amaral-Melendez, M., & Brantley, P. J. (1995). The ways of religious coping scale: Reliability, validity, and scale development. *Assessment, 2,* 233–244.

Carver, C. S. (1997). You want to measure coping but your protocol's too long? Consider the Brief COPE. *International Journal of Behavioral Medicine, 4,* 92–100.

Carver, C. S., Scheier, M. F., & Weintraub, J. K. (1989). Assessing coping strategies: A theoretically based approach. *Journal of Personality and Social Psychology, 56,* 267–283.

Chassin, L., Presson, C. C., Pitts, S. C., & Sherman, S. J. (2000). The natural history of cigarette smoking from adolescence to adulthood in a midwestern community sample: Multiple trajectories and their psychosocial correlates. *Health Psychology, 19,* 223–231.

Dunkel-Schetter, C., Feinstein, L. G., Taylor, S. E., & Falker, R. L. (1992). Patterns of coping with cancer. *Health Psychology, 11,* 79–87.

Folkman, S., & Lazarus, R. S. (1980). An analysis of coping in a middle-aged community sample. *Journal of Health and Social Behavior, 21,* 219–239.

Foshee, V. A., & Hollinger, B. R. (1996). Maternal religiosity, adolescent social bonding, and adolescent alcohol use. *Journal of Early Adolescence, 16,* 451–469.

Hays, J. C., Meador, K. G., Branch, P. S., & George, L. K. (2001). The spiritual history scale in four dimensions (SHS-4): Validity and reliability. *The Gerontologist, 41,* 239–249.

Hill, P. C., & Hood, R. W., Jr. (Eds.). (1999). *Measures of religiosity.* Birmingham, AL: Religious Education Press.

Hummer, R. A., Rogers, R. G., Nam, C. B., & Ellison, C. G. (1999). Religious involvement and U.S. adult morality. *Demography, 36,* 272–285.

Hunsberger, B. (1985). Religion, age, life satisfaction, and perceived sources of religiousness: A study of older persons. *Journal of Gerontology, 40,* 615–620.

Idler, E. (1987). Religious involvement and the health of the elderly: Some hypotheses and an initial test. *Social Forces, 66,* 226–238.

Idler, E., & Kasl, S. (1992). Religion, disability, depression, and the timing of death. *American Journal of Sociology, 97,* 1052–1079.

Jackson, L. E., & Coursey, R. D. (1988). The relationship of God control and internal locus of control to intrinsic religious motivation, coping and purpose in life. *Journal for the Scientific Study of Religion, 27,* 399–410.

Jenkins, R. A., & Pargament, K. I. (1988). Cognitive appraisals in cancer patients. *Social Science and Medicine, 26,* 625–633.

Koenig, H. G., Pargament, K. I., & Nielsen, J. (1998). Religious coping and health status in medically ill hospitalized older adults. *Journal of Nervous and Mental Disease, 186,* 513–521.

Krause, N. (1998). Neighborhood deterioration, religious coping, and changes in health during late life. *The Gerontologist, 38,* 653–664.

Kunz, J. L., & Giesbrecht, N. (1999). Gender, perceptions of harm, and other social predictors of alcohol use in a Punjabi community in the Toronto area. *Substance Use and Misuse, 34,* 403–419.

Levin, J. S. (1994). Investigating the epidemiologic effects of religious experience. In J. Levin (Ed.), *Religion in aging and health* (pp. 3–17). Thousand Oaks, CA: Sage.

Levin, J. S., Markides, K., & Ray, L. (1996). Religious attendance and psychological well-being in Mexican Americans: A panel analysis of three generations data. *Gerontologist, 36,* 454–463.

Levin, J. S., Taylor, R., & Chatters, L. (1994). Race and gender differences in religiosity among older adults: Findings from four national surveys. *Journal of Gerontology: Social Sciences, 49,* S137–S145.

Markides, K. (1983). Aging, religiosity, and adjustment: A longitudinal analysis. *Journal of Gerontology, 38,* 621–625.

McCrae, R. R., & Costa, P. T. (1986). Personality, coping and coping effectiveness in an adult sample. *Journal of Personality, 54,* 385–405.

McCullough, M. E., Hoyt, W. T., Larson, D. B., Koenig, H. G., & Thoreson, C. (2000). Religious involvement and mortality: A meta-analytic review. *Health Psychology, 19*(3), 211–222.

Morse, C., & Wisocki, P. (1988). Importance of religiosity to elderly adjust-ment. *Journal of Religion and Aging, 4,* 15–26.

Pardini, D., Plante, T. G., & Sherman, A. (2001). Strength of faith and its asso-ciation with mental health outcomes among recovering alcoholics and addicts. *Journal of Substance Abuse Treatment, 19,* 347–354.

Pargament, K. I. (1997). *The psychology of religion and coping: Theory, research, prac-tice.* New York: Guilford.

Pargament, K. I., Koenig, H. G., & Perez, L. M. (2000). The many methods of religious coping: Development and initial validation of the RCOPE. *Journal of Clinical Psychology, 56,* 519–543.

Pargament, K. I., & Park, C. L. (1996). Merely a defense? The variety of reli-gious means and ends. *Journal of Social Issues, 51,* 13–32.

Pargament, K. I., Smith, B. W., Koenig, H. G., & Perez, L. (1998). Patterns of positive and negative religious coping with major life stressors. *Journal for the Scientific Study of Religion, 37,* 710–724.

Patlock-Peckham, J. A., Hutchinson, G. T., Cheong, J., & Nagoshi, C. T. (1998). Effect of religion and religiosity on alcohol use in a college student sam-ple. *Drug and Alcohol Dependence, 49,* 81–88.

Plante, T. G., & Boccaccini, M. T. (1997). The Santa Clara strength of religious faith questionnaire. *Pastoral Psychology, 45*(5), 375–387.

Plante, T. G., Manuel, G., Menendez, A., & Marcotte, D. (1995). Coping with stress among Salvadoran immigrants. *Hispanic Journal of Behavioral Sciences, 17,* 471–479.

Plante, T. G., & Pardini, D. A. (2000, August). Religious denomination affilia-tion and psychological health: Results from a substance abuse population. In A. S. Willis (Chair), *Health and religious denomination affiliation.* Symposium conducted at the annual meeting of the American Psychological Association, Washington, DC.

Plante, T. G., Saucedo, B., & Rice, C. (2001). The association between religious faith and coping with daily stress. *Pastoral Psychology, 49,* 291–300.

Plante, T. G., & Sharma, N. K. (2001). Religious faith and mental health out-comes. In T. G. Plante & A. C. Sherman (Eds.), *Faith and health* (pp. 240–261). New York: Guilford Press.

Pullen, L., Modrcin-Talbott, M.A., West, W.R., & Muenchen, R. (1999). Spiritual high vs high on spirits: Is religiosity related to adolescent alcohol and drug abuse? *Journal of Psychiatric Mental Health Nurse, 6,* 3–8.

Sherman, A. C., & Simonton, S. (2001). Assessment of religiousness and spir-ituality in health research. In T. G. Plante & A. C. Sherman (Eds.), *Faith and health* (pp. 139–163). New York: Guilford Press.

Sherman, A. C., Simonton, S., Plante, T. G., Moody, V. R., & Wells, P. (2001). Patterns of religious coping among multiple myeloma patients: Associations with adjustment and quality of life. *Psychosomatic Medicine, 63,* 124.

Stanton, A. L., & Franz, R. (1999). Focusing on emotion: An adaptive coping strategy? In C. R. Snyder (Ed.). *Coping: The psychology of what works* (pp. 90–118). New York: Oxford University Press.

Tepper, L., Rogers, S. A., Coleman, E. M., & Malony, H. N. (2001). The prevalence of religious coping among persons with persistent mental illness. *Psychiatric Services, 52*, 660–665.

Wallace, J. M., & Williams, D. R. (1997). Religion and adolescent health-compromising behavior. In J. Schulenberg & J. L. Maggs (Eds.), *Health risks and developmental transitions during adolescence.* (pp. 444–468). New York: Cambridge Press.

Wallston, K. A., Malcarne, V., Flores, L., Hansdottir, I., Smith, C. A., Stein, M. J., et al. (1999). Does God control your health? The God Locus of Health Control scale. *Cognitive Therapy and Research, 23*(2), 131–142.

Wallston, K. A., Wallston, B. S., & DeVellis, R. (1978). Development of the Multidimensional Health Locus of Control (MHLC) scale. *Health Education Monographs, 6,* 161–170.

Wilcock, A., Van Der Arend, H., Darling, K., Scholz, J., Siddaly, R., Snigg, C., & Stephens, J. (1998). An exploratory study of people's perceptions and experiences of well-being. *British Journal of Occupational Therapy, 61,* 75–82.

Willis, A. S. (2000, August). Religious denomination, outlook, and coping among young adult tobacco users. In A. S. Willis (Chair), *Health and religious denomination affiliation.* Symposium conducted at the annual meeting of the American Psychological Association, Washington, DC.

Willis, A. S. (2001, August). Religion and problematic behavior. In T. G. Plante & A. C. Sherman (Chairs), *Health and faith.* Symposium conducted at the annual meeting of the American Psychological Association, San Francisco, CA.

Willis, A. S., Wallston, K. A., & Johnson, K. R. S. (2001). Tobacco and alcohol use among young adults. In T. G. Plante & A. C. Sherman (Eds.), *Faith and health* (pp. 213–239). New York: Guilford Press.

Willis, A. S., Wallston, K. A., Smith, M. S., Plante, T. G., Johnson, K. R. S., Christenbery, T., Reeves, J. E., & Dutton, G. (1999, June). *Religious faith and health locus of control predict smoking behaviors in adolescents.* Poster presented at the annual meeting of the American Psychological Society, Denver, CO.

Wink, P., & Dillon, M. (2001). Religious involvement and health outcomes in late adulthood. In T. G. Plante & A. C. Sherman (Eds.), *Faith and health* (pp. 75–106). New York: Guilford Press.

CHAPTER 5

Religion, Forgiveness, and Adjustment in Older Adulthood

Giacomo Bono and Michael E. McCullough

The concept of forgiveness illustrates the tremendous differences between the personal and social priorities of U.S. adults and the scientific agenda of mainstream social science. In 1991, Poloma and Gallup reported on a nationally representative sample of U.S. adults who were asked, "Which do you usually do when you feel that someone has deliberately done something wrong to you?" These respondents were given a variety of possible response options to choose. Among these options, 48% of respondents reported that they "tried to forgive," and 45% reported that they "try to overlook it" when someone intentionally hurts them. Only 14% reported that they try to "hold onto resentment" and a mere 8% reported that they "try to get even." If these self-reports are to be taken at face value, then it is safe to conclude that more people prefer forgiveness and similarly constructive responses to interpersonal transgressions over negative responses such as holding a grudge or seeking revenge. This clear preference stands in contrast to the scientific priorities given to revenge and forgiveness among social scientists. A search of PsycInfo abstracts revealed 803 articles from 1900–1990 that included the words "revenge," "retaliation," "retribution," or their derivatives, whereas only 171 studies included the words "forgiveness," "forbearance," or its derivatives.

Despite this historical imbalance, the gap between the priorities of U.S. adults and the scientific work on forgiveness vs. revenge has begun to narrow. Indeed, research on forgiveness grew considerably during the 1990s, and this progress has continued into the 21st century. Recent work has identified social-psychological antecedents to forgiveness (Exline & Baumeister, 2000; Fincham, 2000; Finkel, Rusbult, Kumashiro, & Hannon, 2002; McCullough, Bellah, Kilpatrick, & Johnson, 2001; McCullough, Worthington, & Rachal, 1997; McCullough et al., 1998), personality processes underlying forgiveness (McCullough, 2001; McCullough & Hoyt, 2002), the temporal process by which forgiveness unfolds (McCullough, Fincham, & Tsang, 2003), the process by which reasoning about forgiveness develops as people age (Enright, Santos, & Al-Mabuk, 1989; Mullet & Girard, 2000); the effects of forgiveness on physiological outcomes (Berry & Worthington, 2001; Witvliet, Ludwig, & Vander Laan, 2001), and the clinical benefits of forgiveness interventions (for reviews see Enright & Coyle, 1998; Worthington, Sandage, & Berry, 2000).

Recently, scholars have also turned to examining the relationships between religion and forgiveness (McCullough & Worthington, 1999; Rye et al., 2000; Tsang, McCullough, & Hoyt, in press). In this chapter, we propose that religion and forgiveness are connected in a way that is particularly relevant to the concerns of the present volume: We propose that (a) social and psychological changes that occur as people age create changes in religiousness and changes in the value people place on forgiveness, and that (b) these changes help explain the complex links between religiousness, forgiveness, and adjustment. Many aging processes might be useful for explaining why people become more religious as they age, or more forgiving as they age, or why the links of religion and forgiveness with health and adjustment might become stronger as people age, but we will explore one explanation in detail. Specifically, we draw heavily from the work of Laura Carstensen and her colleagues (e.g., Carstensen, Isaacowitz, & Charles, 1999) and suggest that age-related associations of religiousness and forgiveness reflect, at least in part, superordinate changes in socioemotional concerns that occur as people age.

From these propositions, and the existing data, we wish to suggest that the value of forgiveness as a resource for preserving social and emotional well-being, perhaps even along with physical health, will become especially poignant as people enter older adulthood. The present chapter provides a brief background of forgiveness in the psychological literature; outlines theoretical and empirical links between religion, forgiveness, and aging; describes research linking forgiveness to physical health as well as mental health; and raises arguments for the unique role of forgiveness in adjustment to aging. Finally, the chapter closes with conclusions about the role of forgiveness in well-being and recommendations for future research.

WHAT IS FORGIVENESS? CHARACTERISTICS OF TRANSGRESSION RESPONSES, PERSONS, AND SOCIAL UNITS

To date, researchers have not agreed on a unanimous definition of forgiveness, although there are also many points of agreement. Enright, Freedman, and Rique (1998) considered forgiveness "a willingness to abandon one's right to resentment, negative judgment, and indifferent behavior toward one who unjustly injured us, while fostering the undeserved qualities of compassion, generosity, and even love toward him or her" (pp. 46–47). Exline and Baumeister (2000) defined forgiveness as the "cancellation of a debt" by "the person who has been hurt or wronged." (p. 133). McCullough, Pargament, and Thoresen (2000) proposed what they hoped could suffice as a consensual definition. Their definition emphasizes the changes a victim undergoes when he or she has forgiven a transgressor: Forgiveness is an intraindividual, prosocial change toward a perceived transgressor that is situated within a specific interpersonal context.

McCullough et al. (2003) have even used a multilevel modeling conceptualization of longitudinal growth to operationalize forgiveness specifically as a complex of prosocial changes in one's basic interpersonal motivations toward a transgressor. Indeed, they have even suggested that, with longitudinal data in which an individual's motivations toward someone who has offended them are assessed at multiple time points, it is possible to distinguish between forgiveness (change over time) and forbearance (i.e., degree to which a person is tolerant or lenient and able to refrain from responding destructively immediately following a transgression). They also showed that forbearance and forgiveness appear to have different psychological substrates.

But to understand forgiveness better for the purposes of this chapter, it is helpful to distinguish among the three senses in which the term "forgiveness" can be used (McCullough & Witvliet, 2002). Forgiveness can be defined as a response (as described in the above paragraph), a personality disposition, and as a characteristic of social units. At the level of the psychological functioning of a transgression recipient, McCullough and his colleagues (1997, 1998) recognize forgiveness as the convergence of three distinct but related motivational systems. Specifically, they defined forgiveness as a suite of transgression-related motivational changes toward a transgressor in which revenge- and avoidance-related motivations subside, and motivations toward benevolence or goodwill increase or re-emerge (McCullough et al., 1997). Moreover, McCullough and colleagues contend that forgiveness functions as a result of increases in empathy for a transgressor. Essentially, forgiveness occurs when victims are able to act not on motivations inspired by their initial experience of righteous indignation and hurt-perceived attack, but on a desire to restore community, or at least a stance of goodwill, with their transgressors.

As a personality disposition, forgiveness reflects a trait-like tendency to forgive others across a variety of interpersonal transgressions. Most investigators who have examined forgiveness as a personality disposition have relied solely on self-reports of general tendencies to forgive typical transgressions (Mauger et al., 1992; Mullet, Houdbine, Laumonier & Girard, 1998) or hypothetical transgressions (Berry, Worthington, Parrott, & O'Connor, 2001; Hebl & Enright, 1993; Tangney, Fee, Reinsmith, Boone, & Lee, 1999). By contrast, McCullough and Hoyt (2002) estimated people's dispositions toward avoidance, revenge, and benevolence motivations across several transgressions (both actual and fictional) and then explored the relationships of these trait-like measures of forgiveness with the traits in the so-called "Big Five" or "Five Factor" personality taxonomy (e.g., McCrae & Costa, 1987). Results showed that stable, trait-like individual differences accounted for 22–36% of the variance in people's endorsements of avoidance, revenge, and benevolence in response to an array of transgressions. In particular, "Agreeableness" predicted lower revenge motivation and greater benevolence motivation, while "Neuroticism" predicted greater avoidance motivation and lower benevolence motivation.

As a quality of social units—marriages, for example (Fincham, 2000)—forgiveness resembles attributes similar to trust, intimacy, or commitment. A variety of relational factors have been found to be responsible for forgiveness. Not surprisingly, people are more inclined to forgive transgressors for less severe offenses (Boon & Sulsky, 1997). They are also more likely to forgive committed versus less-committed relationship partners (Finkel et al., 2002; McCullough et al., 1998) and apologetic versus unapologetic transgressors (Bono & Crano, 2002; Darby & Schlenker, 1982; Girard & Mullet, 1997; Weiner, Graham, Peter, & Zmuidinas, 1991). Moreover, people are more prone to forgive if they attribute less responsibility and intentionality to the transgressor (Bono, 2002; Bradfield & Aquino, 1999; Fincham, 2000).

RELIGION, FORGIVENESS, AND AGING: IS THERE A CONNECTION?

We continue our exploration of forgiveness with three observations. First, we note that among adults, religiousness appears to increase with age. To draw one example from the large population of studies on this point, Taylor and Chatters (1989) examined the associations of seven single-item measures of religiousness with age among over 2,000 Black American adults. For the women, scores on all seven measures were significantly and positively associated with age. For men, scores on six of the measures were significantly and positively associated with age. Similar age differences have been noted in samples from other nations as well (e.g., Tiwari, Mathur, & Morbhatt, 1980). Although some scholars have wondered if these age differences might be caused exclusively by period or cohort effects, the best evidence to date, which was drawn from a nationally representative longitudinal study of married adults, indicated that the influence of religion on daily life increased continuously throughout the life cycle (Argue, Johnson, & White, 1999), even after controlling for potential period and cohort effects.

Our second observation is that people who are older tend, on average, to be more forgiving and less vengeful than are younger people. This observation is very much in line with research conducted on a Dutch sample by Van Lange, Otten, De Bruin, and Joireman (1997). They found that higher percentages of older adults (i.e., approximately 82%) can be classified as having "prosocial" interpersonal orientations, as opposed to individualistic or competitive interpersonal orientations, compared to younger adults (i.e., approximately 56% of the adults under age 30). Empirical research has confirmed that willingness to forgive varies as a function of age, with young children generally being least willing to forgive and older adults being most willing (Enright et al., 1989; Girard & Mullet, 1997; Mullet et al., 1998; for a review see Mullet & Girard, 2000). For example, Mullet et al. (1998) examined the links between four aspects of people's attitudes toward forgiveness among a sample of French adults aged 18–90 years. The first two of these aspects—(a) a global measure of the extent to which people endorse revenge in lieu of forgiveness, and (b) a measure of the extent to which people let their personal feelings or social circumstances interfere with forgiving, were negatively associated with age. When younger adults forgive it tends to be motivated by personal and social considerations (e.g., because they are in a good mood, because family or friends think they should forgive, or because the consequences of the harm have been cancelled in some way). On the other hand, older persons tend to forgive mainly because of strong convictions that forgiveness should be practiced unconditionally (Girard & Mullet, 1997).

Our third observation is that people with religious and spiritual interests tend to report being, on average, slightly more forgiving and slightly less prone to vengeance than less religious/spiritual people.

The fact that forgiveness plays a central role in Jewish, Christian, Islamic, Confucian, Buddhist, and Hindu thought (Calian, 1981; Herford, 1964; Phillips, 1986; Solomon, 1986) certainly indicates a widespread belief that forgiveness is spiritually and perhaps psychologically or socially beneficial. The world's major Abrahamic religions (i.e., Judaism, Christianity, and Islam) endorse forgiveness even as a behavior by which people can emulate God. Beyond simply exhorting people to forgive each other (at least members of the in-group), religions encourage compassion and empathy—emotions that foster forgiveness (McCullough et al., 1997)—and they model forgiving actions through scripture and ritual (Pargament & Rye, 1998). Indeed, all of these components of religious meaning systems may promote forgiveness (Tsang, McCullough, & Hoyt, in press).

The first research to identify a positive relationship between religious involvement and forgiving was carried out three decades ago. Rokeach (1973) reported findings based on surveys of college students and adults (Rokeach, 1969; Tate & Miller, 1971) indicating that people who scored high on self-report measures of church attendance, self-rated religiousness, and intrinsic and extrinsic motivation for religious involvement—as measured by Allport and Ross's (1967) Religious Orientation Inventory—assigned being "forgiving" a relatively high priority in their value systems. Follow-up research by Shoemaker and Bolt (1977) supported and extended these findings by demonstrating that religious people (in this case, Christian students) also tend to endorse the belief that highly religious people *should* place a high value on forgiveness. Later research, which added measures of feeling close to God and amount of personal prayer, also found a positive relationship between religiousness and attitudes toward forgiveness (Poloma & Gallup, 1991). In fact recently, researchers employed the Schwartz and Bilsky (1995) cross-cultural values survey and hypothetical offense scenarios on a wide sample of almost 400 young and older adults of various ethnicities and corroborated this notion by finding significant positive associations between forgiveness judgments and self-rated measures of having a spiritual life and being devoted to religious beliefs (Bono, 2002).

Subsequent research on self-reported practices regarding religious involvement and forgiving behavior revealed consistent results. With Gallup data from a nationally representative sample of 1,030 U.S. adults, Poloma and Gallup (1991) found positive relationships between measures of self-reported religiousness (e.g., importance of religion, church membership, church attendance, prayer experiences) and forgiving behaviors when offended. Analyzing the same data set, Gorsuch and Hao (1993) found that individuals who reported themselves as having higher personal religiousness (but not religious conformity) also claimed to have more motivation for forgiving others and fewer reasons for not forgiving transgressors (e.g., resentment and desire to see harm come to transgressors), compared to people lower in personal religiousness. Other researchers demonstrated a positive relationship between the disposition to be forgiving (as measured by the Forgiveness of Others Scale) and measures of spiritual coping resources in both clinical and non-clinical samples (Mauger, Saxon, Hamill, & Pannell, 1996).

Complementary research conducted by Enright, Santos, and Al-Mabuk (1989) revealed a positive relationship between religious involvement and moral reasoning about forgiveness. These researchers presented children, adolescents, and adults with two interpersonal dilemmas from the Defining Issues Test (Rest, 1979); administered Allport, Gillespie, and Young's (1953) Religious Belief Scale; and followed up with interview questions aimed at measuring judgments of the propriety of forgiveness in the dilemmas they read. The participants' responses were then analyzed vis-à-vis a six-stage model of reasoning about forgiveness, which Enright et al. developed out of Kohlberg's (1976) moral reasoning model. Results showed that people high in religious beliefs had more sophisticated moral reasoning regarding forgiveness (at least in terms of the Enright-Kohlberg model) than did less religious people. In particular, they were more likely to view forgiveness as being motivated by the recognition of all persons as unconditionally deserving of care and respect rather than viewing forgiveness as being motivated by pressure from other people, the value of maintaining social harmony, or the need to adhere to legal or religious authorities.

All of the research linking religion to forgiveness that we have described above indicates that people who are more religious tend to highly value forgiveness, believe that they should be forgiving, claim to be forgiving people, and believe that others should be forgiving out of the recognition of all people's common worth. Research on the association of religious involvement with measures of actual forgiveness behavior toward specific transgressions, however, has been inconsistent enough that we should pause to consider whether religious people actually are more forgiving in response to single, real-life transgressions. Using the Enright Forgiveness Inventory (Subkoviak, Enright, & Wu, 1992), a transgression-specific measure of forgiveness, Rackley (1993) found no association between religious involvement and forgiveness of one's spouse for a particular transgression. Similarly, with a sample of adults and their parents, Subkoviak et al. (1995) found only a modest overall association between personal religiousness and the extent to which people forgave a specific transgression ($r = .09$).

McCullough and Worthington (1999) called this tendency for religiousness to be associated positively with global assessments of one's own values regarding forgiveness or disposition to be forgiving, but only trivially correlated with forgiveness responses to single, specific transgressions the *religion-forgiveness discrepancy*. They proposed that the religion-forgiveness discrepancy could be attributed to any of four possible causes: social desirability pressures among religious people to be more forgiving, problems with aggregation and specificity in the measurement of the two variables which may mask their relationship, measurement error due to recall or encoding biases, and the distal influence of religion being overridden by more proximal conditions associated with transgression-specific forgiveness.

More recent research has sought to resolve these psychometric issues and explain the observed discrepancy. Tsang et al. (in press) found that when self-reports of forgiveness are based on transgressions that are recalled under restrictive procedures (i.e. forcing participants to recall specific types of transgressions from within specific types of relationships) as well as aggregated across multiple transgressions, positive correlations emerge between religiousness and transgression-specific forgiveness (with religion accounting for approximately 4% of the variance in forgiveness). Therefore, studies with improved methods seem to support the proposition that religious individuals are, in general, slightly more forgiving than are less religious people, even though this association is not terribly strong (Cohen, 1988).

At present, the data make a fairly compelling case that both religiousness and forgiveness increase with age. Moreover, it appears that forgiveness and religion themselves are associated. Is this merely a coincidence, or is it possible that common developmental phenomena produce increases in religious concerns *and* increased valuing of forgiveness as people approach older adulthood? We suspect that the latter may be the case.

RELIGIOUSNESS, FORGIVENESS, ADJUSTMENT, AND AGING: CARSTENSEN'S THEORY OF SOCIOEMOTIONAL SELECTIVITY

Carstensen's work on socioemotional selectivity theory (1991, 1993, 1995; Carstensen et al., 1999) may explain why concerns about both religion and forgiveness emerge in older adulthood and, as we will discuss presently, why forgiveness may turn out to be especially functional for older individuals. Many investigators have noted that social contact declines during older adulthood (Lang & Carstensen, 1994). Although some have interpreted this trend as evidence for a general pattern of cognitive, psychological, and social disengagement, others including Carstensen and colleagues now posit that such changes are voluntary, resulting from changes in the salience of social goals. Essentially, when time is perceived as open-ended (i.e., during early adulthood), future-oriented goals and knowledge acquisition are of primary concern, but when time is perceived as limited (i.e., during older adulthood, as the end of life looms ever larger), present-oriented goals and emotional aspirations become predominant.

Therefore, as people gradually become older, social partners are chosen for their emotional value and social interactions are regulated in a way that optimizes emotional outcomes. Moreover, individuals become more vested in the relationships they seek to maintain, and the narrowing of contacts occurs not with spousal, family, or close relationships but rather with acquaintances (Carstensen, 1992). One possible result of this focusing of one's socioemotional investments in a narrower but more meaningful set of interaction partners is that the potential links between the well-being of interpersonal relationships and a person's health and well-being may become stronger as people approach older adulthood.

Could Increased Religiousness in Older Adulthood Reflect Socioemotional Selectivity?

Of course, many have noted that among the many functions that religion can serve is the function of providing people with emotionally satisfying interpersonal and spiritual experiences. In this regard, religious concerns may become accentuated in older adulthood not simply because of a need to come to terms with one's own mortality (e.g., the meaning of life, concerns about the afterlife), but also because the interpersonal contacts that are fostered by interactions in religious settings can, for some, lead to emotionally satisfying *interpersonal* relationships too. Moreover, many investigators have noticed that God can serve the role of attachment figure, providing a relationship of warmth, support, and intimacy (Kirkpatrick, 1999). Insofar as God is perceived as a relational being, a growing desire to experience God through prayer, reading of scripture, and worship may help to satisfy the desire for emotional satisfaction that seems to become a preeminent concern in older adulthood.

Could Increased Forgiveness in Older Adulthood Reflect Socioemotional Selectivity?

For similar reasons, forgiveness may come to be increasingly valued in older adulthood. Since the quality of relationships increases with time (i.e. relationships are chosen more selectively and important close relationships are maintained over more casual ones), forgiveness then poses great implications for the relational health of the elderly. Forgiveness helps salvage relationships, and naturally this quality becomes more important as the quality of relationships increases and the quantity decreases. Each instance of unforgiveness burns bridges that are much more intimately connected to people's lives and social goals, making unforgiveness more costly and forgiveness more precious for older individuals. In older adulthood, individuals may lose the perverse luxury of simply terminating relationships that are troubled and moving on to begin new ones.

Indeed, work on the life review indicates that there may be a direct link between forgiveness and the developmental tasks of people in older adulthood and that such bridge-burning stands at odds with the universal need to comprehend one's past experiences as a coherent story in late life (Butler, Lewis, & Sunderland, 1998). Butler et al. contend that some of the challenges in the life review may be to settle unresolved conflicts, right old wrongs, face one's regrets, make up with long-standing enemies, and reconcile one's close relationships. People who are less successful in this life review may be likely to sink into anxiety, guilt, depression, or even despair as they begin to confront dissolution and death. Thus, forgiveness may well be a prime mechanism for achieving a successful life review and being better prepared for the inevitable end of life. In Eriksonian terms, forgiveness may be a powerful tool for the elderly in realizing integrity over despair (Erikson, 1959). With this in mind, it is worth examining the research that focuses specifically on the benefits of forgiveness to physical health, mental health, and relational-well-being.

FORGIVENESS AND PHYSICAL HEALTH

A decade of research has found religion to be beneficial to health and well-being, and many consider forgiveness to be one reason why this is so (Kaplan, 1992, 1993; Kaplan, Monroe-Blum, & Blazer, 1993; Levin, 1996; Koenig, McCullough, & Larson, 2001). Research that bears at least indirectly on the link between forgiveness and physical health includes a raft of studies that have focused on the harmful effects of sustained hostility and anger on cardiovascular health (Miller, Smith, Turner, Guijarro, & Hallet, 1996; Williams & Williams, 1993). It is possible that the practice of forgiveness may be a key to reducing such sustained hostility (Kaplan, 1992). Though causal relationships between forgiveness and physical health have not yet been established in controlled empirical studies, there are reasons to believe that forgiveness may be beneficial to physical health through both cardiovascular and immunological pathways (see review by Thoresen, Harris, & Luskin, 2000). This is mainly because of the detrimental consequences of chronic anger, hostility, and blaming—concepts related to the forgiveness process. Sustained anger and hostility have been found to predict premature death (Miller et al.). The same is true with blaming others for one's misfortunes (Affleck, Tennen, Croog, & Levine, 1987; Tennen & Affleck, 1990). Furthermore, increasing positive emotional states rather than negative emotional states helps improve immunological and cardiovascular functioning (McCraty, Atkinson, Tiller, Rein, & Watkins, 1995).

More direct evidence that forgiveness may help produce such beneficial outcomes comes from recent research by Witvliet et al. (2001). In their study, participants who were asked to imagine forgiving a real-life offender showed improved functioning on measures of cardiovascular (heart rate, blood pressure) and sympathetic nervous system functioning (skin conductance levels, corrugator electromyogram), compared to those who were asked to imagine not forgiving a real-life offender. Not only did such psychophysiological responses parallel participants' self-reported emotions (i.e., they felt more negative, aroused, angry, sad, and less in control), but those responses also persisted into the postimagery recovery period. Moreover, the researchers argued that because people may intensify their hurtful memories and vengeful thoughts in daily life, such psychophysiological responses may even be more potent during natural reactions to offensive events. They concluded that their results provided a window into what happens to the body during experiences of unforgiveness and that such responses, if chronically exhibited, can severely erode physical health by influencing susceptibility to and progression of disease. Berry and Worthington (2001) also reported an interesting link between forgiveness and cortisol reactivity in response to relationship imagery.

In addition to physiological mechanisms, Thoresen et al. (2000) also suggest several psychosocial mechanisms that might explain the link between forgiveness and physical well-being. They suggest forgiveness may lead to increased optimistic thinking and decreased hopelessness, increased self-efficacy, higher levels of perceived social and emotional support, and, for some, a greater sense of transcendent consciousness and communion with God—all of which might promote physical health.

FORGIVENESS, MENTAL HEALTH, AND WELL-BEING

Excessive defensiveness, blame, and thoughts about revenge characterize a variety of psychopathologies (Greenwald & Harder, 1994). Also, Poloma and Gallup (1991) found in a nationally representative sample that people who are relatively more forgiving enjoy greater satisfaction with life, whereas more vengeful or resentful individuals tend to experience significantly lower levels of life satisfaction. Even the experience of forgiving God has been found to be related to lower anxiety and depressed mood (Exline, Yali, & Lobel, 1999).

Mauger and his colleagues (1992) developed and conducted research with a Forgiveness of Others Scale as well as a Forgiveness of Self Scale—both of which yielded correlations with some of the clinical subscales of the Minnesota Multiphasic Personality Inventory (Hathaway & McKinley, 1946). The latter scale, though, showed stronger correlations with depression, anger, anxiety, and low self-esteem than the former, suggesting that feeling forgiven may be more strongly associated with psychological well-being than is the act of forgiving other people. Similarly, Tangney and her colleagues (1999) found that the tendency to forgive others was also related negatively to symptoms of depression and anger, as well as to lower paranoid ideation and interpersonal sensitivity, while the tendency to forgive oneself was negatively related to depression, paranoid ideation, interpersonal sensitivity, and psychoticism.

Researchers also have investigated relationships between forgiving individual transgressors and various measures of psychological well-being. In a cross-sectional survey of 30 divorced or permanently separated mothers with children aged 10 to 13, Aschleman (1996) found that mothers who had forgiven the fathers for previous transgressions committed against them were more likely than unforgiving mothers to exhibit a greater sense of self-acceptance and purpose in life. They also showed less self-reported anxiety and depressive symptoms. Previous work by Trainer (1981) yielded similar results. Other research has not yielded convincing evidence, demonstrating either weak or nonsignificant correlations between self-reported measures of psychological well-being and forgiveness (Hargrave & Sells, 1997; McCullough et al., 2001;

Subkoviak et al., 1995). Though McCullough et al. (2001) found cross-sectional correlations with life satisfaction, they found no evidence that forgiving actually causes such improvements in an 8-week follow-up period.

In a review of the literature on forgiveness and mental health, McCullough (2001) suggested that the reason only some researchers find evidence of the link is because the link is, in fact, somewhat elusive in most situations. Subjective well-being and mental health are influenced by many psychosocial factors, and individual transgressions may not exert strong direct effects. Also, it is likely that forgiveness of only certain interpersonal transgressions (i.e., those that are serious enough) may buffer people from stress and lead to psychological benefits. This would explain why research by Aschleman (1996) and Trainer (1981)—which involved especially severe events—produced evidence, while other efforts have not. In a similar vein, Subkoviak et al. (1995) suggested that forgiveness may only help adjustment when it concerns transgressions in the context of spousal, romantic, and family relationships. Several researchers contend that future work in this area should focus not on the "main effects" of forgiveness on mental health but should instead examine specific relational contexts (Fincham, 2000; McCullough, 2001). It should be noted that this notion of forgiveness being especially beneficial in the context of serious relationship conflicts has important implications for the elderly, where important relationships increasingly play a central role.

Before discussing such implications and the relevant research linking forgiveness to adjustment in older adulthood, it is worth mentioning the research on forgiveness interventions that have been employed with promising results. This area of research has likewise been growing, with various forms (i.e., individual, group, and psychoeducational therapy) being successfully applied to a variety of clinical and non-clinical subject populations.

One of the first of these interventions was actually an experiment conducted on elderly women who had recently gone through a hurtful interpersonal experience (Hebl & Enright, 1993). These researchers randomly assigned the participants to an 8-week forgiveness intervention group or a discussion-only control group. Results demonstrated that women in the experimental group scored higher in forgiveness and willingness to forgive and that level of forgiveness was related to greater self-esteem, as well as lower levels of depression and anxiety. Extending on this work, Al-Mabuk, Enright, and Cardis (1995) conducted two group intervention studies (one that lasted 2 weeks and one that lasted 6 weeks) with adolescents who felt that they had been inadequately loved by their parents. This intervention, designed to help the participants' forgive their parents, produced increases in self-esteem, reductions in depression and anxiety, improved attitudes towards parents, and greater levels of hope.

Finally, some interventions have revealed long-term benefits. A one-on-one forgiveness intervention with female victims of physical incest (by a male relative) yielded increases in forgiveness, hope, anxiety, and depression for people in the experimental group. Once participants in the wait-list control group went through the same treatment, they showed similar improvements (Freedman & Enright, 1996). Moreover, these improvements remained at a follow-up one year later. Using a similar experimental design on men who had been hurt by their romantic partners' decision to have an abortion, Coyle and Enright's (1997) intervention produced increases in forgiveness and decreases in grief, anger, and anxiety. The wait-list control experienced like improvements, and these benefits remained at follow-up 3 months later.

Worthington et al. (2000) summarized the effects of forgiveness group interventions with a meta-analysis of 12 studies. They found that the interventions were, on average, effective in improving participants' forgiveness scores by 43% of a standard deviation (Cohen's d = .43) over the control group. Furthermore, they observed that more contact was more efficacious for clients than less contact, with interventions of six or more hours in length yielding 76% of a standard deviation (Cohen's d = .76) over the control group and interventions of 4 hours or less in length yielding 24% of a standard deviation more (Cohen's d = .24).

Less formal group involvements, such as religious groups and self-help groups, also appear to help people, in part, by helping them forgive. Wuthnow (2000) reported the results of a national survey of 1,379 Americans who participated in small, typically informal religious groups (e.g., prayer groups, bible study groups, or Sunday School) or self-help groups (e.g., self-help groups, women's groups, men's groups). One of the interesting commonalities that these informal religious and self-help groups seem to share is that they encourage forgiveness. Fully 61% of the respondents reported that their group had helped them forgive. Also, membership in a group that explicitly encouraged forgiveness was related to increases in self-reported successes in overcoming addiction, successes in overcoming guilt, and perceptions of encouragement when feeling discouraged.

FORGIVENESS AND RELATIONAL WELL-BEING

Much of the potential for forgiveness to contribute to well-being may come from its potential for helping people to mend and preserve their supportive, close relationships, and several studies have revealed evidence that forgiveness may be beneficial to relational well-being. This seems especially likely when one considers that the lack of supportive relationships has been linked to a wide variety of psychological and physical diseases (Baumeister & Leary, 1995; House, Landis, & Umberson, 1988). Just as research has uncovered positive links to mental health, several studies have also revealed positive correlations with relational well-being (Nelson, 1993; Rackley, 1993; Woodman, 1991). McCullough and colleagues (1998) also found that the degree to which the partners in approximately 100 heterosexual romantic relationships reported having forgiven each other for two specific transgressions that had occurred in the history of their relationship (the most severe transgression ever and a more recent transgression) was positively associated, not only with their own satisfaction with and commitment to their romantic relationships, but also with their partners' satisfaction and commitment as well. These findings suggest that forgiveness is linked to both the forgiver and the forgiven's reports of relationship quality.

Conversely, other research has demonstrated that endorsing revenge as a conflict resolution strategy is positively related to difficulty maintaining close friendships (Rose & Asher, 1999). The more that the children in this study reported "getting back" at friends in imaginary conflict scenarios, the fewer best friends they had, the more their peers rated them as hostile and less positive, and the less accepted they were by their peers. Though this research was conducted on school children, it is safe to assume that such strategies become increasingly maladaptive as the maintenance of high-quality relationships take precedence. One would expect that adopting this interpersonal coping strategy early on in life could produce a pattern that, if maintained, would allow people to maintain good friends later in life. This indeed poses dim prospects for older individuals, who value close relationships more.

FORGIVENESS AND ADJUSTMENT IN AGING: REFLECTIONS OF SOCIOEMOTIONAL SELECTIVITY?

In fact, given older adults' sharpened focus on maintaining a core network of close, emotionally satisfying relationships, it seems plausible

that forgiveness—which helps people repair breaches in close relationships—will be particularly strongly related to measures of health
and well-being in older adults. One recent study, which is discussed in
detail by another contributor to this volume (Musick, this volume), has
yielded interesting evidence that this is actually the case. Toussaint,
Williams, Musick, and Everson (2001) used national probability data to
examine whether self-reported forgiveness was associated with psychological distress, life satisfaction, and self-rated health for adults in three
age groups: 18–44, 45–64, and 65+. The extent to which respondents
reported a tendency to forgive others who harmed them was positively
correlated with psychological distress for all age groups, even after
controlling for sex, race, education, income, marital status, a variety
of measures of religiousness/spirituality, and even measures of self-
forgiveness, feeling forgiven by God, and attempts to facilitate forgiveness
through asking forgiveness or prayer. The strength of these associations
was found to be stronger for the two older groups than they were for the
group of adults aged 18–44. Moreover, Toussaint et al. (2001) found
that forgiving others was associated uniquely and positively with life satisfaction for adults aged 45–64 and 65+, but not for adults aged 18–44.
Finally, it was only for the oldest group of adults (aged 65+) that forgiveness of others was associated positively with self-rated health. For
adults aged 18–44 and 45–64, the associations of forgiving others with
self-rated health were negligible. Toussaint et al. interpreted this pattern of findings as evidence that forgiveness is ultimately beneficial for
physical and mental health, especially among elderly adults, but that
not all forms of forgiving may be beneficial (e.g., initiating forgiveness,
insincerely forgiving or pseudo-forgiving, or forgiving related to personality characteristics such as neuroticism or low self-esteem).

Other investigators have found evidence that forgiveness is related
to better physical or psychological adjustment in older adulthood
(Hebl & Enright, 1993; Strasser, 1984), but Toussaint et al.'s (2001) evidence is particularly in line with our prediction that forgiveness should
become more important for health and well-being as people age.
People focus their socioemotional investments into a smaller and more
meaningful set of intimate interpersonal relationships as they age, and
the strength and stability of those relationships should become more
predictive of health and well-being in the latter years. Insofar as forgiveness helps to maintain strength and stability in those key relationships, the ability to forgive seems to become more crucial for
maintaining health and happiness into older adulthood.

More recent research by Krause and his colleagues (Krause & Ingersoll-
Dayton, 2003; Krause, 2003) corroborated this finding that forgiveness

may be particularly salubrious for elderly adults. Qualitative research by Krause and Ingersoll-Dayton found that the manner in which elderly Christian adults go about forgiving their transgressors differs: some do it automatically, some require acts of contrition, and some require admission of wrong-doing and restitution if possible. Subsequent research (Krause) using a nationwide survey showed that this distinction is important for understanding the combined roles forgiveness and religion play (at least with respect to Christianity) among the elderly. He found that: (a) forgiving others was related to enhanced psychological well-being more so than merely feeling forgiven by God; (b) forgiving others unconditionally was related to greater psychological well-being than forgiving others on the condition that they earned it through contrition; and (c) those who feel forgiven by God are less likely to expect transgressors to perform acts of contrition than those who do not feel forgiven by God. Therefore, it may be useful for people to first consider what they may do to feel forgiven by God for transgressions they may have committed, and second, to trust that engaging in such a form of catechism may, in turn, help guide others who have wronged them so that they no longer need to focus on expectations of contrition from wrongdoers. Such an approach may help elderly adults maintain strength and stability in their relationships and perhaps their psychological well-being also.

SUMMARY

The existing evidence from both cross-sectional and longitudinal studies suggests that religiousness increases as people age, and the existing cross-sectional evidence suggests that older adults are more forgiving, on average, than are younger adults. Moreover, it is clear that religiousness is encouraged by religious doctrine worldwide and seems to be more common in the lived experience of religious people. The links between age, religion, and forgiveness may be explained, at least in part, by thinking of them as responses to superordinate developmental changes in people's relational goals as they age (Carstensen, 1991, 1992, 1993, 1995; Lang & Carstensen, 1994; Van Lange et al., 1997). Forgiving becomes more important later in life because emotional gratification in relationships becomes a more important ingredient for well-being, as do close relationships with long-term friends and family.

Most of the scholarship positing links between forgiveness and health is either speculative and theoretical, or preliminary and exploratory. However, there are many reasons to believe that forgiveness is an effective means for repairing and maintaining solid, strong interpersonal relationships, and thus, that an unwillingness or inability to forgive would be a risk factor for a variety of physical, mental, and spiritual hardships. Related research from nursing and care-giving only support this notion that forgiveness becomes more beneficial later in life (Mickley, Soeken, & Blecher, 1992; Mickley, Carson, & Soeken, 1995; Mickley, Pargament, Brant, & Hipp, 1998), and exciting recent research by Toussaint and colleagues (2001) on age-related differences in the forgiveness-health relationship confirm these observations.

Nonetheless, rigorous evidence of the sort that would allow us to conclude definitively that forgiveness leads to improvements in health and well-being, or prevents declines in health and well-being, has yet to be conducted. Epidemiological research with representative samples, controlling for the many demographic, psychological, personality, social, and physical health confounds that might be responsible for the forgiveness-health relationship, has only begun (see Musick, this volume, for a report on a very good start). Moreover, investigators have only begun to conduct the laboratory-based studies that would allow for intensive observations of the biomedical pathways that could explain such associations. Clearly, research on forgiveness, health, and well-being is only beginning, and is a long way from yielding definitive conclusions.

Even more tentative are any conclusions that one might draw regarding the role of forgiveness in adjustment among older adults. In addressing this specific issue, investigators so far really have only scratched the surface. However, as theoretical and empirical work progresses, it seems not unlikely that much of this work will confirm, though perhaps also qualify, what religions have taught for millennia regarding the salutary potential of forgiveness.

AUTHOR NOTES

Preparation of this paper was supported by a grant to Michael E. McCullough from the Campaign for Forgiveness Research.

REFERENCES

Affleck, G., Tennen, H., Croog, S., & Levine, S. (1987). Causal attributions, perceived benefits and morbidity after heart attack: An 8 year study. *Journal of Consulting and Clinical Psychology, 55,* 29–35.

Allport, G. W., Gillespie, J. M., & Young, J. (1953). The religion of the postwar college student. In J. M. Seidman (Ed.), *The adolescent* (pp. 266–285). New York: Dryden.

Allport, G. W., & Ross, J. M. (1967). Personal religious orientation and prejudice. *Journal of Personality and Social Psychology, 5,* 432–443.

Al-Mabuk, R. H., Enright, R. D., & Cardis, P.A. (1995). Forgiving education with parentally deprived late adolescents. *Journal of Moral Education, 24,* 427–444.

Argue, A., Johnson, D. R., & White, L. K. (1999). Age and religiosity: Evidence from a three-wave panel analysis. *Journal for the Scientific Study of Religion, 38,* 423–435.

Aschleman, K. A. (1996). *Forgiveness as a resiliency factor in divorced or permanently separated families.* Unpublished master's thesis. Madison, WI: University of Wisconsin.

Baumeister, R., & Leary, M. (1995). The need to belong: Desire for interpersonal attachments as a fundamental human motivation. *Psychological Bulletin, 117,* 497–529.

Berry, J. W., & Worthington, E. L., Jr. (2001). Forgivingness, relationship quality, stress while imagining relationship events, and physical and mental health. *Journal of Counseling Psychology, 48,* 447–455.

Berry, J. W., Worthington, E. L., Parrott, L., & O'Connor, L. E. (2001). Dispositional forgivingness: Construct validity and development of the Transgression Narrative Test of Forgivingness (TNTF). *Personality and Social Psychology Bulletin, 27,* 1277–1290.

Bono, G. (2002). *Commonplace forgiveness among and between groups and cross-cultural perceptions of transgressors and transgressing.* Unpublished doctoral dissertation. Claremont, CA: Claremont Graduate University.

Bono, G., & Crano, W. D. (2002, August). *What kinds of apologies work, for who, and when?* Paper presented at the annual meeting of the American Psychological Society, New Orleans, LA.

Boon, S. D., & Sulsky, L. M. (1997). Attributions of blame and forgiveness in romantic relationships: A policy capturing study. *Journal of Social Behavior and Personality, 12,* 19–44.

Bradfield, M., & Aquino, K. (1999). The effects of blame attributions and offender likeableness on forgiveness and revenge in the workplace. *Journal of Management, 25,* 607–631.

Butler, R. N., Lewis, M. I., & Sunderland, T. (1998). *Aging and mental health: Positive psychosocial and biomedical approaches* (5th ed.). Needham Heights, MA: Allyn & Bacon.

Calian, C. S. (1981). Christian faith as forgiveness. *Theology, 37,* 439–443.

Carstensen, L. L. (1991). Selectivity theory: Social activity in life-span context. In K. W. Schaie (Ed.), *Annual review of gerontology and geriatrics* (pp. 195–217). New York: Springer.

Carstensen, L. L. (1992). Social and emotional patterns in adulthood: Support for socioemotional selectivity theory. *Psychology and Aging, 7,* 331–338.

Carstensen, L. L. (1993). Motivation for social contact across the life span: A theory of socioemotional selectivity. *Nebraska Symposium on Motivation, 40,* 209–254.

Carstensen, L. L. (1995). Evidence for a life-span theory of socioemotional selectivity. *Current Directions in Psychology, 4,* 151–156.

Carstensen, L. L., Isaacowitz, D. M., & Charles, S. T. (1999). Taking time seriously: A theory of socioemotional selectivity. *American Psychologist, 54,* 165–181.

Cohen, J. (1988). *Statistical power analysis for the behavioral sciences.* Hillsdale, NJ: Erlbaum.

Coyle, C. T., & Enright, R. D. (1997). Forgiveness intervention with post-abortion men. *Journal of Consulting and Clinical Psychology, 65,* 1042–1046.

Darby, B. W., & Schlenker, B. R. (1982). Children's reactions to apologies. *Journal of Personality and Social Psychology, 43,* 742–753.

Enright, R. D., & Coyle, C. (1998). Researching the process model of forgiveness within psychological interventions. In E. L. Worthington (Ed.), *Dimensions of forgiveness* (pp. 139–161). Radnor, PA: Templeton Foundation Press.

Enright, R. D., Freedman, S., & Rique, J. (1998). The psychology of interpersonal forgiveness. In R.D. Enright & J. North (Eds.), *Exploring forgiveness* (pp. 46–62), Madison, WI: University of Wisconsin Press.

Enright, R. D., Santos, M. J. D., & Al-Mabuk, R. (1989). The adolescent as forgiver. *Journal of Adolescence, 12,* 95–110.

Erikson, E. (1959). *Identity and the life cycle.* New York: International Universities Press.

Exline, J. J., & Baumeister, R. F. (2000). Expressing forgiveness and repentance: Benefits and barriers. In M. E. McCullough, K. I. Pargament, & C. E. Thoresen (Eds.), *Forgiveness: Theory, research, and practice* (pp. 133–155). New York: Guilford Press.

Exline, J., Yali, A. M., & Lobel, M. (1999). When God disappoints: Difficulty forgiving God and its role in negative emotion. *Journal of Health Psychology, 4,* 365–379.

Fincham, F. D. (2000). The kiss of the porcupines: From attributing responsibility to forgiving. *Personal Relationships, 7,* 1–23.

Finkel, E. J., Rusbult, C. E., Kumashiro, M., & Hannon, P. A. (2002). Dealing with betrayal in close relationships: Does commitment promote forgiveness? *Journal of Personality and Social Psychology, 82,* 956–974.

Freedman, S. R., & Enright, R. D. (1996). Forgiveness as an intervention with incest survivors. *Journal of Consulting and Clinical Psychology, 64,* 983–992.

Girard, M., & Mullet, E. (1997). Propensity to forgive in adolescents, young adults, older adults, and elderly people. *Journal of Adult Development, 4,* 209–220.

Gorsuch, R. L., & Hao, J. Y. (1993). Forgiveness: An exploratory factor analysis and its relationships to religious variables. *Review of Religious Research, 34,* 333–347.

Greenwald, D. F., & Harder, D. W. (1994). Sustaining fantasies and psychopathology in a normal sample. *Journal of Clinical Psychology, 50,* 707–710.

Hargrave, T. D., & Sells, J. N. (1997). The development of a forgiveness scale. *Journal of Marital and Family Therapy, 23,* 41–62.

Hathaway, S. R., & McKinley, J. C. (1946). *The Minnesota Personality Inventory* (Rev. ed.). Minneapolis: University of Minnesota Press.

Hebl, J. H., & Enright, R.D. (1993). Forgiveness as a psychotherapeutic goal with elderly females. *Psychotherapy, 30,* 658–667.

Herford, R. T. (1964). Repentance and forgiveness in the Talmud: With some reference to the teaching of the gospels. *Hibbert Journal, 40,* 55–64.

House, J. S., Landis, K. R., & Umberson, D. (1988). Social relationships and health. *Science, 241,* 540–545.

Kaplan, B. H. (1992). Social health and the forgiving heart: The type B story. *Journal of Behavioral Medicine, 15,* 3–14.

Kaplan, B. H. (1993). Two topics not covered by Aldridge: Spirituality in children and forgiveness and health. *Advances, 9,* 30–33.

Kaplan, B. H., Monroe-Blum, H., & Blazer, D. G. (1993). Religion, health, and forgiveness: Traditions and challenges. In J. S. Levin (Ed.), *Religion in aging and health* (pp. 52–77). Thousand Oaks, CA: Sage.

Kirkpatrick, L. A. (1999). Attachment and religious representations and behavior. In J. Cassidy & P. R. Shaver (Eds.), *Handbook of attachment: Theory, research, and clinical applications* (pp. 803–822). New York: Guilford.

Koenig, H. G., McCullough, M. E., & Larson, D. B. (2001). *Handbook of religion and health.* New York: Oxford Press.

Kohlberg, L. (1976). Moral stages and moralization: The cognitive-developmental approach. In T. Lickona (Ed.), *Moral development and behavior: Theory, research, and social issues* (pp. 31–53). New York: Holt.

Krause, N. (2003). Forgiveness by God, forgiveness of others, and psychological well-being in late life. *Journal for the Scientific Study of Religion, 42,* 77–93.

Krause, N., & Ingersoll-Dayton, B. (2003). Religion and the process of forgiveness in late life. *Review of Religious Research, 42,* 252–276.

Lang, F. R., & Carstensen, L. L. (1994). Close emotional regulation in adulthood and later life: A developmental view. *Annual Review of Gerontology and Geriatrics, 11,* 172–194. New York: Springer.

Levin, J. S. (1996). How religion influences morbidity and health: Reflections on natural history, salutogenesis, and host resistance. *Social Science and Medicine, 43,* 849–864.

Mauger, P. A., Perry, J. E., Freeman, T., Grove, D. C., McBride, A. G., & McKinney, K. E. (1992). The measurement of forgiveness: Preliminary research. *Journal of Psychology and Christianity, 11,* 170–180.

Mauger, P.A., Saxon, A., Hamill, C., & Pannell, M. (1996, March). *The relationship of forgiveness to interpersonal behavior.* Paper presented at the annual convention of the Southeastern Psychological Association, Norfolk, VA.

McCrae, R.R., & Costa, P. T. (1987). Validation of the five-factor model of personality across instruments and observers. *Journal of Personality and Social Psychology*, 52, 81–90.

McCraty, R., Atkinson, M., Tiller, W., Rein, G., & Watkins, A. (1995). The effects of emotion on short term power spectrum analysis on heart rate variability. *American Journal of Cardiology*, 76, 1089–1093.

McCullough, M. E. (2001). Forgiveness: Who does it and how do they do it? *Current Directions in Psychological Science*, 10, 194–197.

McCullough, M. E., Bellah, C. G., Kilpatrick, S. D., & Johnson, J. L. (2001). Vengefulness: Relationships with forgiveness, rumination, well-being, and the Big Five. *Personality and Social Psychology Bulletin*, 27, 601–610.

McCullough, M. E., Fincham, F. D., & Tsang, J. (2003). Forgiveness, forbearance, and time: The temporal unfolding of transgression-related interpersonal motivations. *Journal of Personality and Social Psychology*, 84, 540–557.

McCullough, M. E., & Hoyt, W. T. (2002). Transgression-related motivational dispositions: Personality substrates of forgiveness and their links to the big five. *Personality and Social Psychology Bulletin*, 28, 1556–1573.

McCullough, M. E., Pargament, K. I., & Thoresen, C. E. (2000). The psychology of forgiveness: History, conceptual issues, and overview. In M. E. McCullough, K. I. Pargament, & C. E. Thoresen (Eds.), *Forgiveness: Theory, research, and practice* (pp. 299–320). New York: Guilford Press.

McCullough, M. E., Rachal, K. C., Sandage, S. J., Worthington, E. L., Jr., Brown, S. W., & Hight, T. L. (1998). Interpersonal forgiving in close relationships. II: Theoretical elaboration and measurement. *Journal of Personality and Social Psychology*, 75, 1586–1603.

McCullough, M. E., & Witvliet, C. V. (2002). The psychology of forgiveness. In C. R. Snyder & S. J. Lopez (Eds.), *Handbook of positive psychology* (pp. 446–458). New York: Oxford.

McCullough, M. E., & Worthington, E. L. (1999). Religion and the forgiving personality. *Journal of Personality*, 67, 1141–1164.

McCullough, M. E., Worthington, E. L., & Rachal, K. C. (1997). Interpersonal forgiving in close relationships. *Journal of Personality and Social Psychology*, 73, 321–336.

Mickley, J. R., Carson, V., & Soeken, K. L. (1995). Religion and adult mental health: State of the science in nursing. *Issues in Mental Health Nursing*, 16, 345–360.

Mickley, J. R., Pargament, K. I., Brant, C. R., & Hipp, K. M. (1998). God and the search for meaning among hospice caregivers. *Hospice Journal*, 13, 1–17.

Mickley, J. R., Soeken, K. L., & Blecher, A. (1992). Spiritual well-being, religiousness and hope among women with breast cancer. *Journal of Nursing Scholarship*, 24, 267–272.

Miller, T. Q., Smith, T. W., Turner, C. W., Guijarro, M. L., & Hallet, A. J. (1996). A meta-analytic review of research on hostility and physical health. *Psychological Bulletin*, 119, 322–348.

Mullet, É., & Girard, M. (2000). Developmental and cognitive points of view on forgiveness. In. M. E. McCullough, K. I. Pargament, & C. E. Thoresen (Eds.), *Forgiveness: Theory, research, and practice* (pp. 111–132). New York: Guilford.

Mullet, É., Houdbine, A., Laumonier, S., & Girard, M. (1998). "Forgivingness": Factor structure in a sample of old, young, middle aged, and elderly adults. *European Psychologist, 3,* 289–297.

Nelson, M. K. (1993). *A new theory of forgiveness.* Unpublished doctoral dissertation, Purdue University, West Lafayette, IN.

Pargament, K. I., & Rye, M. S. (1998). Forgiveness as a method of religious coping. In E. L. Worthington, Jr. (Ed.), *Dimensions of forgiveness* (pp. 59–78). Philadelphia: Templeton Foundation Press.

Phillips, A. (1986). Forgiveness reconsidered. *Christian Jewish Relations, 19,* 144–156.

Poloma, M. M., & Gallup, G. H. (1991). *Varieties of prayer.* Philadelphia: Trinity Press International.

Rackley, J. V. (1993). *The relationships of marital satisfaction, forgiveness, and religiosity.* Unpublished doctoral dissertation. Blacksburg, VA: Virginia Polytechnic Institute and State University.

Rest, J. (1979). *Revised manual for the Defining Issues Test.* Unpublished manuscript, University of Minnesota, Minneapolis, MN.

Rokeach, M. (1969). The role of values in public opinion research. *Public Opinion Quarterly, 32,* 547–559.

Rokeach, M. (1973). *The nature of human values.* New York: Free Press.

Rose, A. J., & Asher, S. R. (1999). Children's goals and strategies in response to conflicts within a friendship. *Developmental Psychology, 35,* 69–79.

Rye, M. S., Pargament, K. I., Ali, M. A., Beck, G. L, Dorff, E. N., Hallisey, C., Narayanan, V., & Williams, J. G. (2000). Religious perspectives on forgiveness. In M. E. McCullough, K. I. Pargament, & C. E. Thoresen (Eds.), *Forgiveness: Theory, research, and practice* (pp. 17–40). New York: Guilford.

Schwartz, S. H., & Bilsky, W. (1995). Toward a theory of the universal content and structure of values: Extensions and cross-cultural replications. *Journal of Personality and Social Psychology, 58,* 878–891.

Shoemaker, A., & Bolt, M. (1977). The Rokeach Value Survey and perceived Christian values. *Journal of Psychology and Theology, 5,* 139–142.

Solomon, N. (1986). The forgiveness debate. *Christian Jewish Relations, 19,* 3–24.

Strasser, J. A. (1984). *The relation of general forgiveness and forgiveness type to reported health in the elderly.* Unpublished doctoral dissertation. Washington, DC: Catholic University of America.

Subkoviak, M., Enright, R. D., & Wu, C. (1992, October). *Current developments related to measuring forgiveness.* Paper presented at the Mid-Western Educational Research Association, Chicago, IL.

Subkoviak, M. J., Enright, R.D., Wu, C., Gassin, E. A., Freedman, S., Olson, L. M., & Sarinopoulos, I. (1995). Measuring interpersonal forgiveness in late adolescence and middle adulthood. *Journal of Adolescence, 18,* 641–655.

Tangney, J. P., Fee, R., Reinsmith, C., Boone, A. L., & Lee, N. (1999, August). *Assessing individual differences in the propensity to forgive.* Paper presented at the annual meeting of the American Psychological Association, Boston, MA.

Tate, E. D., & Miller, G. R. (1971). Differences in value systems of persons with varying religious orientations. *Journal for the Scientific Study of Religion, 10,* 357–365.

Taylor, R. J., & Chatters, L. M. (1989). Family, friend, and church support networks of Black Americans. In R. L. Jones (Ed.), *Black adult development and aging* (pp. 245–271). Berkeley, CA: Cobb & Henry Publishers.

Tennen, H., & Affleck, G. (1990). Blaming others for threatening events. *Psychological Bulletin, 108,* 209–232.

Thoresen, C. E., Harris, A. H. S., & Luskin, F. (2000). In M. E. McCullough, K. I. Pargament, & C. E. Thoresen (Eds.), *Forgiveness: Theory, research, and practice* (pp. 254–280). New York: Guilford Press.

Tiwari, G., Mathur, K. B., & Morbhatt, K. K. (1980). Religiosity as function of age and sex. *Asian Journal of Psychology and Education, 6,* 36–40.

Toussaint, L. L., Williams, D. R., Musick, M. A., & Everson, S. A. (2001). Forgiveness and health: Age differences in a U.S. probability sample. *Journal of Adult Development, 8,* 249–257.

Trainer, M. F. (1981). Forgiveness: Intrinsic, role-expected, expedient, in the context of divorce. Unpublished doctoral dissertation. Boston, MA: Boston University.

Tsang, J., McCullough, M., & Hoyt, W. (in press). Psychometric and rationalization accounts for the religion-forgiveness discrepancy. *Journal of Social Issues.*

Van Lange, P. A. M., Otten, W., De Bruin, E. M. N., & Joireman, J. A. (1997). Development of prosocial, individualistic, and competitive orientations: Theory and preliminary evidence. *Journal of Personality and Social Psychology, 73,* 733–746.

Weiner, B., Graham, S., Peter, O., & Zmuidinas, M. (1991). Public confession and forgiveness. *Journal of Personality, 59,* 281–312.

Williams, R., & Williams, V. (1993). *Anger kills: Seventeen strategies for controlling the hostility that can harm your health.* New York: Harper Perennial.

Witvliet, C. V., Ludwig, T., & Vander Laan, K. (2001). Granting forgiveness or harboring grudges: Implications for emotion, physiology, and health. *Psychological Science, 12,* 117–123.

Woodman, T. (1991). *The role of forgiveness in marital adjustment.* Unpublished doctoral dissertation. Pasadena, CA: Fuller Graduate School of Psychology.

Worthington, E. L., Sandage, S. J., & Berry, J. W. (2000). Group interventions to promote forgiveness: What researchers and clinicians ought to know. In M. E. McCullough, K. I. Pargament, & C. E. Thoresen (Eds.), *Forgiveness: Theory, research, and practice* (pp. 228–253). New York: Guilford Press.

Wuthnow, R. (2000). How religious groups promote forgiving: A national study. *Journal for the Scientific Study of Religion, 39,* 125–139.

Commentary

Unforgiveness, Forgiveness, Religion, and Health During Aging

Everett L. Worthington, Jr.

B ono and McCullough (this volume) defined and discussed their conception of three types of forgiveness. First, they conceptualized forgiveness as an individual's response to a transgression. They see forgiveness as a change in the forgiver's motivations (from revenge and avoidance to more benevolent motives; McCullough, Fincham, & Tsang, 2003) due to empathy (McCullough, Rachal, Sandage, Worthington, Brown, & Hight, 1998; McCullough, Worthington, & Rachal, 1997). They differentiated an unfolding of forgiveness, involving one's initial response (forbearance) versus the change in motives over time (forgiveness). Second, they discussed forgiveness as a personality disposition. Third, they viewed it as an interpersonal product of social units dependent on commitment, trust, actions of both parties, and attributions.

Their second point hypothesized that, as people age they become more religious and forgiving, and as they age, religious and forgiving people might experience fewer health risks and more positive physical health. Bono and McCullough draw on Carstensen (1991, 1992, 1993, 1995; Carstensen, Isaacowitz, & Charles, 1999) to posit that one powerful mechanism underlying the correlations between aging-religion and aging-forgiveness is socioemotional selectivity. This theory suggests that as people age, they selectively lose relationships and the remaining ones become more important. Bono and McCullough believe that the importance and salience of the relationships motivate older adults toward both religion and forgiveness. Bono and McCullough are less explicit about the *mechanisms* connecting religion and physical health and connecting forgiveness with physical health, mental health, and relationship adjustment.

In this chapter, I will address some of these mechanisms. I will agree with the social mechanisms identified by Bono and McCullough that underlie an increase in forgiveness and religion with aging. I will discuss a different (and complementary) conceptualization of forgiveness to that offered by Bono and McCullough, which will lead me to speculate on the mechanisms that connect forgiveness to physical health—especially in relation to my complementary conceptualizations of forgiveness.

AS PEOPLE AGE, WHY DO THEY BECOME MORE RELIGIOUS AND MORE FORGIVING?

Motives for Seeking Religion and Forgiveness

Sources of Meaning Become More Interpersonal.   Most elderly people have searched widely to find meaning and gratification. They may have found gratification and meaning in work, but then they retire. They may have found them in rearing a family, but children become adults and often move. Now they may not see their grandchildren very much. Or they may have suffered divorce. Basically, older adults still need love and work—hats off to Freud. For the elderly, especially the very elderly, opportunities to find meaning in work have become infrequent for most people. There is a strong movement now to do volunteer work or take new jobs after retirement. Buford (1994) calls this "the Halftime Movement."

Relationship networks do collapse, as Bono and McCullough argued. If *work* gratifications are fewer, then the person looks toward *love* for fulfillment. But the number of opportunities to receive love narrow with aging. More effort, energy, and emotional investment are poured into fewer remaining relationships as peers die, move, retire, and become less mobile. Bono and McCullough suggest that this can promote forgiveness. I would say it a bit differently, however. Socioemotional restriction (Carstensen et al., 1999) can motivate people *to reduce* unforgiveness, which might or might not involve forgiving.

As people age, increased pain, suffering, and loss force emotion-regulation strategies to change. When people are motivated to achieve fame and success in work, they will manage their emotions to make success more likely. People change the emotion-regulation strategies they employ as motivations to love increase and motivations to work decrease. As people try to cope with life's difficulties, their usual coping strategies inevitably fail. New ones are tried. Thus people widen their repertoire of coping strategies. Coping can be problem-focused or emotion-focused (Lazarus & Folkman, 1984). I hypothesize that problem-focused coping dominates the work years, and emotion-focused coping dominates the later (love) years.

Relationship of Religion and Aging

The picture I've sketched suggests this. (a) Individuals differ in the value they place on achievement and relationships. (b) Super-imposed over individual differences come pressures of aging. As people age, their world becomes relatively more dominated by a *search for meaning, a pursuit of relationship satisfaction* (i.e., love over work; partially due to socioemotional restriction, which creates a felt need), and *a drive to control negative emotion* (through an expanded emotion-focused coping orientation). Religious commitment and relationship-repair strategies are often enacted in an effort to satisfy those motives.

Religion can provide an answer to the quest for meaning. People might become more religious to have a more personal relationship with God and thus a meaningful worldview. That is, they might pursue religion due to an intrinsic motivation (Allport & Ross, 1967). People who are unable or unwilling to find their source of meaning in religion will often embrace philosophies that are sources of meaning and love. Religion can also provide an answer to the search for relationship satisfaction. People thus might become more religious to obtain more interpersonal contact within a religious community. That is an extrinsic motivation for religion (Allport & Ross, 1967). Religion, when satisfying, can provide an effective emotion-focused coping strategy. When adults find religion (or increase their religious commitment), they often discover peace, love, and fulfillment, which manage, mitigate, or overcome negative emotions.

Some meaning, relationship satisfaction, and emotional comfort can also occur in relationships. When disagreements or conflicts occur, relationship repair is strongly motivated. High negative affect can interfere with relationship repair. Emotion-focused coping is needed, and strategies developed over a lifetime might or might not be adequate. Thus, we might hypothesize that new emotion-focused coping strategies might appear in many people as they age. I hypothesize that forgiveness is one of those strategies. Bono and McCullough show that it indeed increases in prevalence as people age.

Relationship of Forgiveness and Aging

Religion Could Enhance Forgiveness. On one hand, forgiveness and religion are often related. As Rye et al. (2000) have shown, all five of the major religions value forgiveness. Some value it more than others. Marty (1998) has argued that Christianity, perhaps, values forgiveness the most. Forgiveness is the central conceptual aspect of Christianity. Ergo, many people become more forgiving because they become more religious and forgiveness is central to their faith. On the other hand, my observation—and I do not have systematic data to support this—is that very few people become more religious because they have become more forgiving.

Relational Restriction Could Cause Both Religion and Forgiveness. I believe, as Bono and McCullough suggested, that *for some people,* there is a common underlying cause—relational restriction—that can increase both religion and forgiveness as people age for people still trying to engage with the world.

Relational Restriction Could Cause Reductions in Both Religion and Forgiveness. For people who withdraw from life, relational restriction could lead to less religion (and bitterness with God) and less forgiveness (and bitterness toward those who abandoned them).

AN EMOTION-BASED VIEW OF UNFORGIVENESS AND FORGIVENESS

Transgressions and Reactions to Them

A transgression is a perceived violation either of moral boundaries or of physical or psychological boundaries. People typically react in either anger or fear. McCullough, Fincham, and Tsang (2003) argue that forbearance is suppression of initial negative motivations toward revenge or avoidance. I would add that this initial anger or fear can also be suppressed if we adopt their definition of forbearance. (I might add that forbearance could just as easily be defined as bearing the effects of the transgression over time without responding negatively. McCullough et al. focused on only one of the dictionary definitions they quoted in their article.) Nevertheless, let us say that forbearance is one response to a perceived transgression and the subsequent motivations and emotions.

A person might also respond by granting what I would call motivational-decisional forgiveness. For instance, my wife forgot to do something she had agreed to do for me, and she said, "I'm sorry. Can you forgive me?" I immediately responded, "Of course, I forgive you." She was not asking for instantaneous deep emotional change. She was asking me for an intention statement that I would not seek revenge or avoid her. I was eager to grant that. Exline and Baumeister (2000) liken that to canceling a debt. DiBlasio (1998) calls it decision-based forgiveness. I will call it *motivational-decisional forgiveness* to differentiate it from *emotional forgiveness,* which is more concerned with changing negative emotions and associated motivations over time. Motivational-decisional forgiveness can occur instantaneously because it is an intention statement of one's future motivations.

Injustice

People typically perceive hurts and offenses as unjust. Thus, an *injustice gap* is established—the magnitude of the perceived difference between one's desired outcome and the way one perceives the current status (Exline, Worthington, Hill, & McCullough, 2003; Worthington, 2000, 2001; Worthington & Wade, 1999). Thus, the perceived injustice gap changes magnitude as people experience new acts (like, for example, apologies or additional insults). People are fundamentally motivated to reduce the injustice gap. The size of the injustice gap is hypothesized to be roughly correlated with the negative emotions and motivations one feels at any given time. Importantly, as motivational-decisional forgiveness, pursuit of personal or social justice, etc., occur, they narrow the injustice gap and reduce both negative emotions and motivations).

Unforgiveness and Its Reduction

Worthington and his colleagues have written about the nature of unforgiveness and forgiveness (Worthington, 2000, 2001; Worthington, Berry, & Parrott, 2001; Worthington & Wade, 1999). *Unforgiveness* is defined as a combination of negative emotions (i.e., resentment, bitterness, hostility, hatred, anger, and fear) that arise after a transgression and motivate people to reduce the negative emotions (Worthington & Wade). Unforgiveness occurs because people perceive a transgression as a hurt or an offense (primary appraisal) and respond in anger and fear. If they cannot forbear (suppress the anger and fear) and cannot enact motivational-decisional forgiveness, then they are likely to ruminate about the event and its consequences. (Of course, there are individual differences in rumination.) Rumination is repetitive cognitive (i.e., imaginal and subvocal) activity surrounding the event. Angry rumination produces anger and often hostility and hatred. It is differentiated from anxious or depressive rumination, but transgressions might also stimulate those as well. Angry rumination might well be a mediator of unforgiveness, and might, therefore, lead to escalation of negative emotions and motivations that could result in retaliation or revenge. Rumination therefore leads further to the experience of the negative emotions that comprise unforgiveness. Note that my definition of unforgiveness includes both negative emotions and motivations to reduce them.

People reduce unforgiveness in many ways, only one of which is by forgiving (Worthington, 2001). For example, people try to reduce or avoid unforgiveness through (a) seeking justice (e.g., revenge, social or political justice, or divine justice), (b) accepting or forbearing a transgression and moving on with their life, (c) telling a different story about the event (e.g., justifying or excusing it), (d) physically avoiding the transgressor, or (e) psychologically defending against the threat of the unforgiveness through denial or projection. In fact, there are over thirty ways that reduce unforgiveness that have been identified (Worthington, 2001)—none of which involve forgiving. People might also forgive the transgression and thereby also reduce unforgiveness.

Emotional forgiveness (a term I will use for the moment to differentiate it from motivational-decisional forgiveness) is defined as the emotional juxtaposition of positive other-oriented emotions—such as empathy, sympathy, compassion, altruistic love, romantic love—against the negative emotion of unforgiveness. The positive emotions are hypothesized to neutralize the negative emotions and might, if forgiveness is complete, even fully replace the negative emotions, leaving a net positive emotional state. Thus, when people forgive, they experience (a) a reduction of unforgiving emotions, and (b) *perhaps* residual positive emotions. Note, importantly, that emotional forgiveness will lead, as I have also argued in collaborations with McCullough and others (McCullough et al., 1998; McCullough et al., 1997), to an associated reduction of negative motivations and possible increase in benevolent or conciliatory motivations.

In my conceptualization, emotional forgiveness (which for ease of discussion, I will henceforth call simply forgiveness) is seen as an emotion-regulation strategy. It can also be conceptualized as emotion-focused coping within Lazarus and Folkman's (1984) framework (see Worthington & Scherer, 2004, for a theoretical conceptualization and review).

Aging and Reduced Unforgiveness

In aging, an increased search for meaning can lead to more religious commitment, which in turn can produce forgiveness. An increased attention to fewer but more important relationships (and less attention to productivity) can lead to giving more importance to remaining relationships and more motivation to forgive if disruptions occur. An increased variety in effectiveness of emotion-focused coping strategies can lead people to try out a variety of strategies to control negative emotions—including pursuit of justice, re-storying, accepting, defending, or forgiving. Because emotion-focused coping strategies do increase over time *all of these ways are expected to increase with aging.* Thus, forgiveness is increased because it is one of many emotion-focused strategies that perhaps was not as important in some people's earlier years.

Relationship of My Theorizing to Bono and McCullough's

My conceptualization is complementary to Bono and McCullough's. Whereas they focus on motivations, I add emotions (and choose to focus on that part of the emotion-motivation connection). Whereas Bono and McCullough emphasize empathy as crucial to forgiveness, I now see it as one of five possible positive emotions that can replace unforgiveness. Whereas Bono and McCullough interpret reductions in revenge and avoidance as evidence of forgiveness, I believe that numerous strategies can reduce negative emotions and motivations to revenge and avoidance. I view the conceptualization I am presenting not as contrary to Bono and McCullough's conceptualization but as complementary to it. I think, though, that such complementarity opens additional considerations and hypotheses.

WHY DO REDUCED UNFORGIVENESS AND ENHANCED FORGIVENESS PRODUCE BETTER HEALTH?

If we accept that both religion and forgiveness produce better mental, physical, and relational health, the question still remains why? Due to limited time and space, I will focus on forgiveness and physical health.

Bono and McCullough cited Toussaint, Williams, Musick, and Everson (2001) to suggest that as people age, and especially get into the later years, those who are forgiving are relatively healthier and have fewer negative health symptoms than do those who are less forgiving as people. They mention two physiological mediating pathways—reduction in hostility and reduced sympathetic nervous system (SNS) activation. Both affect cardiovascular and immunological pathways. I will be more detailed and more speculative. Worthington and Scherer (2004) have recently thoroughly reviewed the possible physical mechanisms mediating the connection between forgiveness and health. I will summarize some of the basics here.

Indirect Mechanisms

First, both religion and forgiveness might have physical effects for some of the same reasons. Some of these involve the indirect relationships between religion and health, or forgiveness and health. For example, both religion and forgiveness contribute to larger and more supportive social networks, which provide more social and emotional support, than do non-religion and unforgiveness, respectively. Religion provides communities of people who care—often larger communities than in non-religious groups. Forgiveness contributes to reconciliation of relationships, which can make relationships more pleasant and rewarding and less likely to terminate. Second, marriage indirectly affects forgiveness. Marriage has been related to physical health (Coombs, 1991; Friedman et al., 1995). Most religions value marriage and forgiveness. Forgiving people tend to have fewer marital problems and repair problems that do exist. Third, forgiveness is related to personality traits that are related to health (Berry & Worthington, 2001). Fourth, forgiveness might be related to some relationship skills that are related to health.

Direct Effect: Psycho-neuro-immunology

People high in religion and in forgiveness have less negative, and perhaps, more positive emotions than those low in both of those. Reducing negative emotional experience affects the immune system. These effects have been summarized in several recent review papers (Kiecolt-Glaser, McGuire, Robles, & Glaser, 2002; Salovey, Rothman, Detweiler, & Steward, 2000; Sapolsky, 1994, 1999; Sternberg, 2001).

One immunological effect is in the intercellular immunological system. Negative emotions, of which unforgiveness is one, are related to and can cause dysregulation in the immune system (for a review, see Kiecolt-Glaser et al., 2002). Cytokines are protein-like materials of which there are two classes—pro- and anti-inflammatory cytokines. Pro-inflammatory cytokines involve substances like interleukin-1, interleukin-6, and tumor necrosis factor. They help fight infection and provide an early response to injury. They are secreted soon after an injury is experienced. They attract immune cells to the site of the damage and activate them. When a person is under constant stress or experiences constant infection, the intercellular immune system can be dysregulated. At the present, no researcher has investigated this with unforgiveness.

Sapolsky (1994) has reviewed the literature on the effects of stress at the neuroendocrine level. He has been most concerned about glucocorticoid production, which is one product of the hypothalamic-pituitary-adrenal axis (HPA axis). He attributes many stress-related problems to glucocorticoid production, and in particular, the production of cortisol. Berry and Worthington (2001) have shown that cortisol levels are weakly affected in unforgiving relationships, and some cortisol reactivity occurs when a person thinks about that relationship.

Salovey et al. (2000) reviewed the literature on the relationships between negative and positive emotions and physical health. They focused primarily on the relationship between negative emotions and the suppression of secretatory Immunogobulin-A (sIg-A) inhibition. Elevated levels of sIg-A affect the functioning of the immune system. This has not been investigated directly with forgiveness. Unforgiveness is a negative emotion that can be mild or strong depending on the event and other contextual variables.

Direct Effects: Cardiovascular System

Bono and McCullough have identified the reduction of hostility as being a mechanism by which forgiveness might affect physical health (see also Thoresen, Harris, & Luskin, 2000; Worthington et al., 2001). A large literature has shown that hostility is directly related to health (Smith, 1992). Hostility stretches arterial walls, creates sites for plaque deposits, and makes walls rigid over time. Attempts to date to measure cardiovascular variables have been measures of blood pressure (or the mean arterial pressure) and heart rate (Huang & Enright, 2000; Lawler, Younger, Piferi, & Jones, 2000; Witvliet, Ludwig, & Vander Laan, 2001). In the future, heart rate variability and cardiac impedance might be used to assess the degree to which unforgiveness might affect the cardiovascular system (Brosschot & Thayer, 1998; Cacioppo et al., 1998). At the present time, neither of these measures has been used to assess unforgiveness and its effects.

Direct Effects: Sympathetic Nervous System Arousal

Unforgiveness is stressful (Berry & Worthington, 2001) and thus activates the SNS. Witvliet et al. (2001) demonstrated that when people think about a person against whom they hold a grudge, or think about an unresolved hurt, they experience increased mean arterial pressure, heart rate, and skin conductance, and their facial EMGs (electromyograph; facial muscular firing) indicate the presence of negative emotions. In subsequent research, Witvliet, Ludwig, and Bauer (2002) showed that when a perpetrator commits a crime, the victim experiences similar feelings of arousal. However, if the perpetrator apologizes and offers restitution to the victim, the victim's arousal is reduced.

One might speculate that either unforgiveness effects the Vagal nerve by innervating rapid inhibition of the SNS, or unforgiveness directly effects the SNS through slower acting mechanisms such as stimulating the HPA axis, releasing glucocorticoids, or both.

Direct Effects: Central Nervous System Mechanisms

More speculatively, central nervous system processes might mediate the connection between forgiveness and physical health.

Behavioral Activation System (BAS). Gray (1982, 1984) found the BAS to be activated when an animal is aroused and motivated to engage the environment. This could occur if a person were seeking actively to reduce unforgiveness. A person who is wounded, hurt, and anxious, in contrast, would usually experience Behavioral Inhibition System (BIS) arousal. The brain structures in the BAS and BIS differ.

Prefrontal and Limbic System Activity. Researchers such as Farrow et al. (2001) have mapped areas of the brain that are stimulated when people reason about forgiveness decisions. Pietrini, Gnazzelli, Basso, Jaffe, and Grafman (2001) showed that when people become angry, they shut down rational thought. They thus lose some of the ability to control their behavior. Harmon-Jones et al. (2002) have provided EEG (electroencephalograph; neuronal brain activity) evidence that supports some of these speculations, which were determined through either functional MRIs (Farrow et al.) or PET scans (Pietrini et al.).

Structure and Function of Hypothalamus and Amygdala. Still more speculative is research showing the operation of the structures of the brain when aggression is enacted. The structures affected most are the ventral-medial hypothalamus (VMH) and portions of amygdala. The VMH affects the regulation of four basic motivations in life—eating, drinking, sexuality, and aggression. The VMH is rich in receptors for both testosterone and seratonin. One suggestion of a mechanism that might activate the inhibition of those motivations is that forgiveness might stimulate the release of seratonin in the hypothalamus. This suggests support for McCullough's theorizing about unforgiveness and forgiveness having strong motivational components.

Vagal Nerve Tonality. Vagal tonality might be another mechanism by which forgiveness and health are connected (Brosschot & Thayer, 1998). The vagus nerve is a large nerve in the parasympathetic nervous system (PSNS), which regulates the SNS by inhibiting SNS activation. Vagal tonality inhibits arousal. When a stressor is encountered, vagal tonality decreases, almost instantaneously removing SNS inhibition—releasing the "vagal brake." This allows rapid arousal (Gottman, Katz, & Hooven, 1997). Vagal tonality has been found to be related to cardiovascular disease, emotional expression, and emotion regulation (Porges, Doussard-Roosevelt, & Maiti, 1994). Forgiving people might be hypothesized to have high vagal tonality. Unforgiving people might be hypothesized to react quickly to an interpersonal threat by rapidly decreasing vagal tonality. These very speculative hypotheses have not been investigated.

CONCLUSION

In the present chapter, I have argued that Bono and McCullough identified one pathway by which religion, forgiveness, and health are related as people age. However, the picture is more complicated. Beginning with an argument about the changes that occur in aging, I stressed the emotional changes that attend relationships. Unforgiveness was conceptualized as a health-injurious emotion (with associated negative motivations). Because relationships are restricted as people age and because people widen the emotion-focused coping strategies that they have tried (though they might have settled on a few favorites), emotion-focused coping strategies in response to transgressions are important. They are important not only for aiding relationship adjustment but also because they can promote reduced health risks.

Basing my speculation on the theory that unforgiveness is an emotion (with motivational concomitants) and emotional forgiveness is one emotion-focused coping strategy, I speculated about physical mechanisms that mediate the connection between reducing unforgiveness and better physical health. I examined immunological, cardiovascular, sympathetic nervous system, and central nervous system mechanisms—some extremely speculative and others more likely to be correct. All demand future investigation in the context of reducing unforgiveness—through forgiving or otherwise.

ACKNOWLEDGMENTS

I would like gratefully to acknowledge the John Templeton Foundation, Grant # 239 and *A Campaign for Forgiveness Research,* both of which supported portions of this work.

REFERENCES

Allport, G. W., & Ross, J. M. (1967). Personal religious orientation and prejudice. *Journal of Personality and Social Psychology, 5,* 432–443.

Berry, J. W., & Worthington, E. L., Jr. (2001). Forgivingness, relationship quality, stress while imagining relationship events, and physical and mental health. *Journal of Counseling Psychology, 48,* 447–455.

Brosschot, J. F., & Thayer, J. F. (1998). Anger inhibition, cardiovascular recovery, and vagal function: A model of the link between hostility and cardiovascular disease. *Annals of Behavioral Medicine, 20,* 326–332.

Buford, R. P. (1994). *Half time: Changing your life plan from success to significance.* Grand Rapids, MI: Zondervan.

Cacioppo, J. T., Bernston, G. G., Malarkey, W. B., Kiecolt-Glaser, J. K., Sheridan, J. F., Poehlmann, K. M., Burleson, M. H., Ernst, J. M., Hawkley, L. C., & Glaser, R. (1998). Autonomic, neuroendocrine, and immune responses to psychological stress: The reactivity hypothesis. *Annals of the New York Academy of Sciences, 840,* 664–673.

Carstensen, L. L. (1991). Selectivity theory: Social activity in life-span context. In K. W. Schaie (Ed.), *Annual review of gerontology and geriatrics* (pp. 195–217). New York: Springer.

Carstensen, L. L. (1992). Social and emotional patterns in adulthood: Support for socioemotional selectivity theory. *Psychology and Aging, 7,* 331–338.

Carstensen, L. L. (1993). Motivation for social contact across the life span: A theory of socioemotional selectivity. *Nebraska Symposium on Motivation, 40,* 209–254.

Carstensen, L. L. (1995). Evidence for a life-span theory of socioemotional selectivity. *Current Directions in Psychology, 4,* 151–156.

Carstensen, L. L., Isaacowitz, D. M., & Charles, S. T. (1999). Taking time seriously: A theory of socioemotional selectivity. *American Psychologist, 54,* 165–181.

Coombs, R. H. (1991). Marital status and personal well-being: A literature review. *Family Relations, 40,* 97–102.

DiBlasio, F. A. (1998). The use of a decision-based forgiveness intervention within intergenerational family therapy. *Journal of Family Therapy, 20,* 77–94.

Exline, J. J., & Baumeister, R. F. (2000). Expressing forgiveness and repentance: Benefits and barriers. In M. E. McCullough, K. I. Pargament, & C. E. Thoresen (Eds.), *Forgiveness: Theory, research, and practice* (pp. 133–155). New York: Guilford.

Exline, J. J., Worthington, E. L., Jr., Hill, P.C., & McCullough, M. E. (2003). Forgiveness and justice: A research agenda for social psychology. *Personality and Social Psychology Review, 7,* 337–348.

Farrow, T. F. D., Zheng, Y., Wilkinson, I.D., Spence, J. F., Deakin, J. F. W., Tarrier, N., Griffiths, P. D., & Woodruff, P. W. R. (2001). Investigating the functional anatomy of empathy and forgiveness. *NeuroReport, 12,* 2433–2438.

Friedman, H. S., Tucker, J. S., Schwartz, J. E., Tomlinson-Keasey, C., Martin, L. R., Wingard, D. L., & Criqui, M. H. (1995). Psychosocial and behavioral predictors of longevity: The aging and death of the "Termites." *American Psychologist, 50,* 69–78.

Gottman, J. M., Katz, L. F., & Hooven, C. (1997). *Meta-emotion: How families communicate emotionally.* Mahwah, NJ: Lawrence Erlbaum.

Gray, J. A. (1982). *The neuropsychology of anxiety: An enquiry into the functions of the septo-hippocampus system.* New York: Oxford University Press.

Gray, J. A. (1984). Personality dimensions and emotion systems. In P. Ekman & R. J. Davidson (Eds.), *The nature of emotion: Fundamental questions* (pp. 329–331). New York: Oxford University Press.

Harmon-Jones, E., Abramson, L. Y., Sigelman, J., Bohlig, A., Hogan, M. E., & Harmon-Jones, C. (2002). Proneness to hypomania/mania symptoms or depression symptoms and asymmetrical frontal cortical responses to an anger-evoking event. *Journal of Personality and Social Psychology, 82,* 610–618.

Huang, S.-T. T., & Enright, R. D. (2000). Forgiveness and anger-related emotions in Taiwan: Implications for therapy. *Psychotherapy, 37,* 71–79.

Kiecolt-Glaser, J. K., McGuire, L., Robles, T. F., & Glaser, R. (2002). Emotions, morbidity, and morality: New perspectives from psychoneuroimmunology. *Annual Review of Psychology, 53,* 83–107.

Lawler, K. A., Younger, J., Piferi, R. A., & Jones, W. H. (2000). A physiological profile of forgiveness. *Annals of Behavioral Medicine, 22,* Symposium conducted at the meeting of the Society of Behavioral Medicine's twenty-first annual meeting, Nashville, TN.

Lazarus, R. S., & Folkman, S. (1984). *Stress, appraisal, and coping.* New York: Springer.

Marty, M. E. (1998). The ethos of Christian forgiveness. In E. L. Worthington, Jr. (Ed.), *Dimensions of forgiveness: Psychological research and theological perspectives* (pp. 9–28). Philadelphia: Templeton Foundation Press.

McCullough, M. E., Fincham, F. D., & Tsang, J. A. (2003). Forgiveness, forbearance, and time: The temporal unfolding of transgression-related motivations. *Journal of Personality and Social Psychology, 84,* 540–557.

McCullough, M. E., Rachal, K. C., Sandage, S. J., Worthington, E. L., Jr., Brown, S. W., & Hight, T. L. (1998). Interpersonal forgiving in close relationships II: Theoretical elaboration and measurement. *Journal of Personality and Social Psychology, 75,* 1586–1603.

McCullough, M. E., Worthington, E. L., Jr., & Rachal, K. C. (1997). Interpersonal forgiveness in close relationships. *Journal of Personality and Social Psychology, 75,* 321–326.

Pietrini, P., Guazzelli, M., Basso, G., Jaffe, K., Grafman, J. (2000). Neural correlates of imaginal aggressive behavior assessed by positron emission tomography in healthy subjects. *American Journal of Psychiatry, 157,* 1772–1781.

Porges, S. W., Doussard-Roosevelt, J. A., & Maiti, A. K. (1994).Vagal tone and the physiological regulation of emotion. In N. Fox (Ed.), *Emotional regulation: Behavioral and biological considerations. Monograph of the Society for Research in Child Development, 59,* 167–186.

Rye, M. S., Pargament, K. I., Ali, M. A., Beck, G. L, Dorff, E. N., Hallisey, C., Narayanan, V., & Williams, J. G. (2000). Religious perspectives on forgiveness. In M. E. McCullough, K. I. Pargament, & C. E. Thoresen (Eds.), *Forgiveness: Theory, research, and practice* (pp. 17–40). New York: Guilford.

Salovey, P., Rothman, A. J., Detweiler, J. B., & Steward, W. T. (2000). Emotional states and physical health. *American Psychologist, 55,* 110–121.

Sapolsky, R. M. (1994). *Why zebras don't get ulcers: A guide to stress, stress-related diseases, and coping.* New York: Freeman.

Sapolsky, R. M. (1999). Hormonal correlates of personality and social contexts: From non-human to human primates. In C. Panter-Brick & C. M. Worthman (Eds.), *Hormones, health, and behavior: A socio-ecological and lifespan perspective* (pp. 18–46). Cambridge, England: Cambridge University Press.

Smith, T. W. (1992). Hostility and health: Current status of a psychosomatic hypothesis. *Health Psychology, 11,* 139–150.

Sternberg, E. M. (2001). Neuroendocrine regulation of autoimmune/inflammatory disease. *Journal of Endocrinology, 169,* 429–435.

Thoresen, C. E., Harris, A. H. S., & Luskin, F. (2000). Forgiveness and health: An unanswered question. In M. E. McCullough, K. I. Pargament, & C. E. Thoresen (Eds.), *Forgiveness: Theory, research, and practice* (pp. 254–280). New York: Guilford Press.

Toussaint, L. L., Williams, D. R., Musick, M. A., & Everson, S. A. (2001). Forgiveness and health: Age differences in a U.S. probability sample. *Journal of Adult Development, 8,* 249–257.

Witvliet, C. v. O., Ludwig, T. E., & Bauer, D. J. (2002). Please forgive me: Transgressors' emotions and physiology during imagery of seeking forgiveness and victim responses. *Journal of Psychology and Christianity, 21,* 218–233.

Witvliet, C. v. O., Ludwig, T. E., & Vander Laan, K. L. (2001). Granting forgiveness or harboring grudges: Implications for emotion, physiology, and health. *Psychological Science, 121,* 117–123.

Worthington, E. L., Jr. (2000). Is there a place for forgiveness in the justice system? *Fordham Urban Law Journal, 27,* 1721–1734.

Worthington, E. L., Jr. (2001). Unforgiveness, forgiveness, and reconciliation in societies. In R. G. Helmick & R. L. Petersen (Eds.), *Forgiveness and reconciliation: Religion, public policy, and conflict transformation* (pp. 161–182). Philadelphia: Templeton Foundation Press.

Worthington, E. L., Jr., Berry, J. W., & Parrott, L., III. (2001). Unforgiveness, forgiveness, religion, and health. In T. G. Plante & A. Sherman (Eds.), *Faith and health: Psychological perspectives* (pp. 107–138). New York: Guilford.

Worthington, E. L., Jr., & Scherer, M. (2004). Forgiveness is an emotion-focused coping strategy that can reduce health risks and promote health resilience: Theory, review, and hypotheses. *Psychology and Health,* in press.

Worthington, E. L., Jr., & Wade, N. G. (1999). The social psychology of unforgiveness and forgiveness and implications for clinical practice. *Journal of Social and Clinical Psychology, 18,* 385–418.

Commentary

Multiple Forms of Forgiveness and their Relationships with Aging and Religion

Marc A. Musick

B ono and McCullough (this volume) provide an interesting look at the issue of religion and forgiveness in later life. Discussion of these issues is important because, as those authors note, increasing attention is being paid to forgiveness as a precursor of health and well-being. Their paper explores different forms of forgiveness, whether it is linked to religion and the aging process, and whether it has ties to physical and psychological well-being. All in all, Bono and McCullough provide a strong introduction to the study of forgiveness in the later part of life.

The purpose of this brief response is to discuss some of the issues raised by Bono and McCullough and to raise new issues that they did not consider in their chapter. Specifically, I will address the following items: First, I discuss several forms of forgiveness not considered by Bono and McCullough. Second, I discuss possible problems with their assertion that people become more religious and forgiving as they age. Third, using data from a national study of forgiveness, I provide insight into the two points listed above and present brief evidence linking religion to forgiveness. I conclude with some suggestions for future research in the area of forgiveness as it relates to aging, religion, and health.

VARIETIES OF FORGIVENESS

Bono and McCullough define three ways in which the term forgiveness can be used. These are forgiveness as a response, personality disposition, and as characteristics of social units. Given that the authors discussed each form in some detail, I will not do so here. It is important to note, however, that in their conceptualization, forgiveness focuses on exchanges or transactions that occur between two or more people. For example, the *response* function of forgiveness refers to how attitudes towards a transgressor change over time. As they note in their work, this form of forgiveness is explicitly inter-individual, meaning that at least two persons are involved in the forgiving process. The *personality trait* definition is clearly stated: "a traitlike tendency to forgive others across a variety of interpersonal transgressions." Again, in their conceptualization, the process of forgiveness occurs between two or more actors. The final definition, *characteristics of social units,* refers to features of social units, such as families, that resemble concepts such as "trust, intimacy, or commitment." Again, the idea behind the authors' conceptualization of forgiveness is that it is a property inherent in social relationships.

Although the authors do a good job of explaining forgiveness between individuals, they do not consider other ways in which forgiveness occurs in people's lives. Essentially, forgiveness can and does occur in at least three other major forms: forgiving oneself, feeling forgiven by God, and feeling forgiven by others.

Forgiving Oneself

People make mistakes. Indeed, the whole religious notion of sin is premised on the idea that humans are fallible and prone to making mistakes. When we make mistakes, we must make decisions about whether to forgive ourselves for those mistakes or to carry with us the burden of their consequences. It might be useful to characterize this forgiveness of oneself into different types. The first type, forgiveness for *interpersonal transgression,* is forgiving oneself for some purposeful act that, while not necessarily malicious, was a departure from normative behavior. An example of this form of self-forgiveness are spouses who commit adultery. In this instance, the act of committing adultery is a break from established customs of marriage; consequently, an act of adultery is an act undertaken with the knowledge that some custom or rule is being broken and harm can result. Once the act has been committed, there are several steps that transgressors might follow to obtain self-forgiveness. While Enright (1996) has provided a comprehensive inventory of the steps often undertaken in this process, here I briefly summarize some of the essential steps. First, offenders must recognize that some standard of conduct for a given situation has indeed been broken. Although many people break rules, self-forgiveness is not always necessary nor sought. Consequently, the second step is to recognize that some action has resulted in harm to another individual, set of individuals, a relationship, or themselves. Finally, transgressors must take the step of forgiveness, usually defined as a surrendering of the negative judgments and desire to retaliate against the transgressor (Enright & Zeil, 1989), in this case the transgressors themselves. This final step may involve contrition towards society or the aggrieved party but not necessarily so.

The second type, forgiveness for *personal mistakes,* refers to the process of forgiving oneself for lapses in judgment, opportunities taken or not taken, or decisions made that did not result in the intended consequences. Although this form of self-forgiveness is similar to the interpersonal transgression form in that it can have negative repercussions for both the individuals and others around them, it differs in intent or motivation. In the transgression instance, the individual makes a conscious decision to undertake some act that they know, from the outset, is a violation of standard conduct. The latter form, personal mistakes, results from decisions that are not violations but nevertheless result in harm. Examples of personal mistakes might include making a bad decision on the job that results in a firing or making a family decision, such as to divorce, which has long-term consequences for relationships within the family. The process of forgiveness in this type is similar to that for interpersonal transgressions. That is, first recognition of a mistaken decision is made, followed by an acknowledgment that one or more people were hurt based on the decision, then a process to forgo both self-recrimination and the desire for self-punishment is undertaken.

As stated at the outset of this section, all people make mistakes: either they violate rules or they make decisions that hurt themselves or their loved ones. Once those missteps are made, people must make decisions on whether or not to forgive themselves. In my own work I have acknowledged this important function of forgiveness. As Bono and McCullough noted in their article, my colleagues and I recently completed a study of forgiveness and health using data collected from a national survey of American adults. Data for the study were collected from 1,423 respondents via telephone interviews conducted in 1998. Our survey questions focused on forgiveness, health, religion, and other related factors. One set of questions within the survey dealt explicitly with the issue of self-forgiveness. Respondents were asked whether they agreed with the following statements: (a) I often feel that no matter what I do now I will never make up for the mistakes I have made in the past, and (b) I find it hard to forgive myself for some of the things I have done wrong.

In a recently published study (Touissant, Williams, Musick & Everson, 2001) we provide information about these questions and how they relate to health. First, we find that answers to the two questions are highly correlated ($r = .67$); that is, those who had a hard time forgiving themselves for mistakes also had a hard time forgiving themselves for things they had done wrong. Second, we find that on average respondents are more likely than not to forgive themselves, but there are a substantial number of people who have a hard time doing so. Although not reported in the paper, ancillary analyses show this pattern of results. The two-item index has a median of 4.5 on a 5-point scale, meaning that half of the respondents answered at the highest level of forgiveness for at least one question. Yet, 25% of respondents have a score of 3, indicating much lower levels of self-forgiveness for a large part of the population. Respondents are more likely to agree that it is hard to forgive themselves ($M = 3.85$) compared to making up for mistakes they had made in the past ($M = 4.08$). Further analyses also reveal that married people tend to be more self-forgiving as are people with higher levels of education. In short, based on our work it is clear that self-forgiveness varies in the population, is related to certain demographic characteristics, and is useful for predicting health outcomes.

Forgiveness by God

A large majority of adult Americans, about 95%, believe in God or some other higher power (Gallup & Lindsay, 1999). Many of those (about 86% of all adults) are affiliated with Christian religious traditions, most of which contain some notion of sin, redemption, and forgiveness (Berger, 1967). In essence, sins are affronts against God which require some form of atonement in order to reestablish a positive relationship with God (Zackrison, 1992). Atonement traditions vary, with some requiring specific acts of contrition while others require little more than a request of God that one be forgiven or an assumption that God automatically forgives all sins. Regardless of the specifics of the atonement process, at some point those who have sought forgiveness must decide whether it has been granted. There appear to be two major forms of forgiveness within this type. First, people can feel forgiven by God on an *act by act* basis; that is, they may feel forgiven by God only for certain things but not for others. This idea assumes that for every sin against God, an act of contrition or repentance is required. The second form of this type is a general orientation towards feeling forgiven by God. In other words, people may feel that, generally speaking, God forgives people for things they do wrong. As such, when an individual sins, God is ready to forgive once asked or amends are made. In the second form, forgiveness for all things is possible.

Little research has examined the issue of forgiveness by God. However, one recent study by Krause and Ellison (2003) did discuss the possible importance of this form of forgiveness. Krause and Ellison's study used data from a national sample of older adults to examine the effects of feeling forgiven by God, forgiving others, acts of contrition, and other factors on psychological well-being, including death anxiety. In measuring forgiveness by God, Krause and Ellison used an approach that taps the more specific form of forgiveness by God. That is, their measure of feeling forgiven by God asked respondents whether they agreed with the following statement, "I believe that God has forgiven me for the things I have done wrong." Interestingly, Krause and Ellison found that those who felt forgiven by God were much more likely to believe that transgressors should be unconditionally forgiven compared to those who felt that God had not forgiven them for past wrongs. This finding suggests that one's forgiveness relationship with God is associated with perceptions of forgiveness in other forms, such as forgiveness of others. It is possible that for many adults, beliefs about forgiveness by God inform or underlie all other forms of forgiveness.

Our data on forgiveness contain two questions involving forgiveness by God. Respondents were asked how much they agreed with the following items: (a) Knowing that I am forgiven for my sins gives me the strength to face my faults and be a better person; and (b) I know that God forgives me. As was the case for our measure of self-forgiveness, our two measures of feeling forgiven by God are highly correlated ($r = .64$). However, answers to these questions tend to be much more positive compared to those for the self-forgiveness items. Indeed, over half of our respondents answered in the most positive way (i.e., feeling forgiven) for both questions.

Forgiven by Others

As noted by Bono and McCullough, much of the work on forgiveness focuses on whether and how an actor forgives a transgression against the actor. In contrast, the feeling forgiven type centers on actors in terms of what steps they take to seek forgiveness from others and whether they feel forgiven for transgressions they have made. Like feeling forgiven by God, forgiveness by others can focus on single acts or sets of acts. Alternatively, it can denote a general orientation towards feeling forgiven for wrongs they've done in the past.

In contrast to forgiveness by God, it may be difficult to measure these general orientations towards feeling forgiven by others. Because many people adhere to a religious tradition in which God always forgives once asked, when actors perform the rituals needed to receive forgiveness, they can feel it been granted. In a sense, forgiveness from God can be somewhat easy to achieve once the proper steps are performed. Our data indicating universally high levels of feeling forgiven by God would support this notion. However, feeling forgiven by others is much more complicated. All of us come in contact with scores of people throughout our lives. To ask someone if they feel forgiven by all of the people against whom they have transgressed is likely an enormous undertaking. Indeed, in asking about the past, it is likely easier, and more defensible, to do so on an act by act basis.

Another approach is to ignore the actors' understanding of the feelings of those whom they have wronged and instead focus on the contrition activities or goals of the actors themselves. Enright (1996) offers a series of steps that actors might follow to complete this process. In our own work we have asked respondents how often they ask another's forgiveness when they have hurt someone, with the response categories being very often, fairly often, not too often, hardly ever, and never. For this item, we find that about 40% of respondents mention not too often or less frequently when asking for forgiveness. In short, we do find a great deal of variability among people seeking forgiveness from those whom they have wronged.

AGING, RELIGION, AND FORGIVENESS

In discussing the interplay between religion, forgiveness, and age, Bono and McCullough make several assertions that are debatable, as those authors would likely acknowledge. Although there is a logical and theoretical basis for believing each of these claims, they are not necessarily supported by the empirical data. Indeed, for some, it may be difficult to establish whether or not their assertions can be supported by the data given the nature of the question.

These assertions revolve around the idea that people become more religious and forgiving as they age. The fundamental problem with assessing these changes lies within the data. Many of the studies that attempt to examine whether attitudes, beliefs, or behavior change as people age do so with cross-sectional or limited longitudinal data. Unfortunately, research using those forms of data cannot necessarily say that any *aging* effects they observe are really due to a maturation process. Rather, they must qualify their conclusions due to the age-period-cohort (APC) problem as outlined by Glenn (1977; 1989) and others (e.g., Mason, Winsborough, Mason, & Poole, 1973; Palmore, 1978; Ryder, 1965; Schaie, 1965). In essence, the problem is that older adults who are different from younger adults on some measure could be so for one of three reasons: (a) they were like the younger adults at that age but changed as they aged, i.e., an *aging* process; (b) they are a member of a birth cohort that experienced a fundamentally different world in the earlier part of their lives and so are different due to that experience, i.e., a *cohort* effect; (c) something happened during a particular point in time that had a disproportionate effect on people living during that time or on certain people living during that time, i.e., a *period* effect. All three of these explanations are plausible—though the period effect is somewhat less so—when trying to understand age differences in some outcome. The problem is that with most survey data, especially cross-sectional data, there is no reliable statistical technique to determine which explanation is correct (Glenn, 1976). Indeed, no single explanation may be correct, as a combination of explanations might be at work.

Given the APC problem, researchers must take care when attributing age differences in some outcome to the aging process alone. Instead, researchers should make cautionary statements about interpreting age-related results based on cross-sectional data. How then do we determine whether an aging process is at work? As Glenn (1976) has argued, it may be statistically impossible to disentangle the APC problem. Yet, strides can be made through the use of prospective longitudinal data that follows multiple cohorts over long periods of time. Even then, disentangling the nature of the effect may be difficult due to sampling error and attrition (Glenn, 1977).

The APC problem is a serious one, yet as researchers continue to document age-related differences in religion and forgiveness, we can become more convinced that such changes are due to an aging process. Yet, there is an unequal amount of research on these topics, as noted below.

Aging and Religion

As Bono and McCullough observe, some work has shown age patterns in levels of religious activity. Other work using different data has revealed similar patterns. For example, using data from the *National Survey of Black Americans,* Levin and Taylor (1993) showed that older African Americans reported higher levels of religious activity than younger African Americans. Older African Americans also had higher self-ratings of religiosity and were more likely to report religion as being important when they were children. In a more recent study based on data from seven population-based surveys, Chatters, Taylor, and Lincoln (1999) found that older African Americans reported higher levels of organized and non-organized religious activity than their younger counterparts. Combined with the work cited by Bono and McCullough, this evidence suggests that the aging process might produce changes in religious activity. Yet those studies are far from conclusive given their designs.

Aging and Forgiveness

Less work has been done charting the associations between the aging process and forgiveness. Indeed, Bono and McCullough cite very few studies that have explored this relationship. Several of those cited were studies based on work by Mullet and colleagues (e.g., Girard & Mullet, 1997) and summarized in a later review chapter (Mullet & Girard, 2000). In brief, Girard and Mullet study used a small sample ($N = 236$) of adults aged 18–90 to examine age differences in forgiveness. They found, as have a few other authors, that forgiveness is increasingly likely in older cohorts. Subkoviak and colleagues (1995) revealed similar associations in a study that employed the Enright Forgiveness Inventory. However, akin to the work by Mullet and Girard, their conclusions were based on a small sample ($N = 394$), which in this case was composed of college students and their parents. As noted above, given the limited nature of these samples and the cross-sectional nature of the studies, we cannot say with any certainty that increasing forgiveness is part of the aging process. To do so, we need larger, population-based studies which contain multiple cohorts and track people over time.

Our own work has examined whether forgiveness is patterned by age (Toussaint et al., 2001). As previously noted, our work is based on a national sample of adults, an advantage over some of the work noted by Bono and McCullough. However, our work is also cross-sectional, so like the other work it is far from conclusive. In contrast to the earlier work, we examine age differences in several types of forgiveness, not just forgiveness of others. Like previous work, we find that older adults (aged 65 and older, $M = 4.22$) were more forgiving of others than middle-aged adults (aged 45–64, $M = 4.10$) and younger adults (aged 18–44,

M = 3.87). However, we did not observe the same pattern for other forms of forgiveness. For example, levels of self-forgiveness were lower among older adults (M = 3.81) than middle-aged (M = 4.00) and younger adults (M = 3.89), though these differences were not significant. In terms of feeling forgiven by God, middle-aged and older adults reported very similar levels (older: M = 4.79; middle-aged: M = 4.74) while younger adults reported significantly lower levels (M = 4.67). In terms of asking for forgiveness from others and God, no group had significantly higher levels than any other. These findings overlap with previous work in terms of forgiveness of others. However, for the other forms of forgiveness, we found no substantial evidence of an aging effect. In sum, while a theory of aging and forgiveness is appealing, the results do not yet support such an assertion. Indeed, given the only recent surge of research on these issues, it may be many years before we know for certain whether people do become more forgiving as they age.

RELIGION AND FORGIVENESS

Bono and McCullough also consider the question of whether religious people tend to be more forgiving than their non-religious counterparts. They assert that this should be true given the important role forgiveness plays in some of the world's largest religions, including Christianity. In support of this contention, the authors cite two studies based on nationally-representative samples. In the first, Poloma and Gallup (1991) sought to determine whether religious affiliation and activity was associated with higher levels of forgiveness. The authors found that more religious persons did indeed report higher levels of forgiveness. In a more recent study, Gorsuch and Hao (1993) used the same nationally-representative data and reached similar conclusions. These studies are suggestive of such a link, but more work is needed using different data and more comprehensive measurement.

Our own data on forgiveness also contain measures of religiosity that can be used to assess associations between these concepts. In Table 5.1 I present mean levels of self-forgiveness, forgiveness of others, feeling forgiven by God, and asking others for forgiveness by levels of religious service attendance. This table shows strong relationships between service attendance and three forms of forgiveness. For example, those who never attend church report a mean of 3.81 for forgiving others compared to 4.35 for those who attend more than once a week. Indeed, the pattern of mean scores shows that even among those who attend church

TABLE 5.1 Mean Levels of Forgiveness by Religious Service Attendance

	Forgiveness of self	Forgiveness of others	Forgiven by God	Asking for forgiveness
Never attend	3.84	3.81	3.87	3.49
Attend 2–3 times/month or less	3.96	3.95	4.70	3.84
Attend once/week	3.99	4.15	4.83	4.04
Attend > once/week	4.06	4.35	4.93	4.25
F value	1.01	19.62*	25.27*	13.56*

Note: All forgiveness measures range from 1–5 with higher scores reflecting more forgiveness.
*$p < .001$

at some point during the year, higher levels of attendance are associated with a greater propensity to forgive others. It is not surprising that those who attend services are more likely to feel forgiven by God. It is somewhat surprising that even among attendees, more frequent attendance leads to greater feelings of forgiveness by God. Those who attend more often also are more likely to ask for forgiveness of others when they have hurt someone. In contrast to these findings, I find no differences in respondents forgiving themselves based on service attendance. That is, levels of self-forgiveness were roughly the same across levels of attendance. All in all, our data supports the contention that religion is associated with forgiveness; however, this effect is only limited to certain forms of forgiveness and appears to exclude people forgiving themselves.

CONCLUSION

I agree with Bono and McCullough's (this volume) belief that forgiveness is an important research area, especially among older adults. Yet the field in this area still faces numerous limitations that must be overcome if our understanding of these issues is to progress. Based on a review of Bono and McCullough's work and related literature, there seem to be at least three major issues that must be addressed by the field.

First, we must pay more attention to forms of forgiveness other than those that focus on whether, how, and why actors forgive those who have hurt them. Although this form of forgiveness is important, it does not cover the myriad of ways in which people incorporate forgiveness into their lives. Other facets of forgiveness that deserve further explanation include those that I have described here: forgiveness of self, feeling forgiven by God, and feeling forgiveness by others. Yet other forms of forgiveness, such as pseudo-forgiveness (Enright & Zeil, 1989), deserve examination as well.

Second, researchers must undertake data collection efforts that improve upon earlier designs. As I have noted above, we do not yet have much research on forgiveness using data collected from community samples. Moreover, existing data from community samples are largely cross-sectional. The data used in our study of forgiveness and health are longitudinal, but because the follow-up period is only 6 months, we are very limited in our ability to chart changes in forgiveness over time. If the field does indeed want to determine whether people become more forgiving as they age, we must take steps to collect data from samples that will be re-contacted well into the future. Moreover, these data sets must collect data on multiple forms of forgiveness, not just forgiveness of others.

Finally, we must make more effort to understand the linkages between religion, forgiveness, and health. A great deal of research has begun to document the benefits of religious activity on mental and physical health (for a review see Koenig, McCullough & Larson, 2001). As noted here and in Bono and McCullough's chapter, other researchers have postulated that religion also positively influences forgiveness. If this linkage with religion does exist and is as strong as some evidence suggests, then it is possible that part of the beneficial effect of religion on health is mediated through forgiveness. As such, researchers in the area of religion and health should turn their attention towards exploring this possible mechanism.

ACKNOWLEDGMENTS

I would like to thank David R. Williams for his collaboration on the forgiveness and health study described in this chapter. I also thank the Fetzer Institute for supplying the resources needed to collect the data for the project.

REFERENCES

Berger, P. L. (1967). *The sacred canopy: Elements of a sociological theory of religion.* New York: Doubleday.

Chatters, L. M., Taylor, R. J., & Lincoln, K. D. (1999). African American religious participation: A multi-sample comparison. *Journal for the Scientific Study of Religion, 38,* 132–145.

Enright, R. D. (1996). Counseling within the forgiveness triad: On forgiving, receiving forgiveness, and self-forgiveness. *Counseling and Values, 40,* 107–126.

Enright, R. D., & Zeil, R. L. (1989). Problems encountered when we forgive one another. *Journal of Psychology and Christianity, 8,* 52–60.

Gallup, G., Jr., & Lindsay, D. M. (1999). *Surveying the religious landscape.* Harrisburg, PA: Morehouse Publishing.

Girard, M., & Mullet, E. (1997). Propensity to forgive in adolescents, young adults, older adults, and elderly people. *Journal of Adult Development, 4,* 209–220.

Glenn, N. (1976). Cohort analysts' futile quest: Statistical attempts to separate age, period and cohort effects. *American Sociological Review, 41,* 900–904.

Glenn, N. (1977). *Cohort analysis.* Newbury Park, CA: Sage Publications.

Glenn, N. (1989). A caution about mechanical solutions to the identification problem in cohort analysis: Comment on Sasaki and Suzuki. *American Journal of Sociology, 95,* 754–760.

Gorsuch, R. L. & Hao, J. Y. (1993). Forgiveness: An exploratory factor analysis and its relationships to religious variables. *Review of Religious Research, 34,* 333–347.

Koenig, H. G., McCullough, M. E., & Larson, D. B. (2001). *Handbook of religion and health.* New York: Oxford University Press.

Krause, N. & Ellison, C. G. (2003). Forgiveness by God, forgiveness of others, and psychological well-being in later life. *Journal for the Scientific Study of Religion, 32,* 77–93.

Levin, J. S., & Taylor, R. J. (1993). Gender and age differences in religiosity among Black Americans. *The Gerontologist, 33,* 16–23.

Mason, K. O., Winsborough, H. H., Mason, W. M., & Poole, W. K. (1973). Some methodological issues in cohort analysis of archival data. *American Sociological Review, 38,* 242–258.

Mullet, E., & Girard, M. (2000). Developmental and cognitive points of view on forgiveness. In M. E. McCullough, K. I. Pargament, & C. E. Thoresen (Eds.), *Forgiveness: Theory, research and practice* (pp. 111–132). New York: Guilford.

Palmore, E. (1978). When can age, period and cohort be separated? *Social Forces, 57,* 282–295.

Poloma, M. M., & Gallup, G. H., Jr. (1991). *Varieties of prayer: A survey report.* Philadelphia: Trinity Press International.

Ryder, N. B. (1965). The cohort as a concept in the study of social changes. *American Sociological Review, 30,* 843–861.

Schaie, K. W. (1965). A general model for the study of developmental problems. *Psychological Bulletin, 64,* 92–107.

Subkoviak, M. J., Enright, R. D., Wu, C., Gassin, E. A., Freedman, S., Olson, L. M., & Sarinopoulos, I. (1995). Measuring interpersonal forgiveness in late adolescence and middle adulthood. *Journal of Adolescence, 18,* 641–655.

Touissant, L. L., Williams, D. R., Musick, M. A., & Everson, S. A. (2001). Forgiveness and health: Age differences in a U.S. probability sample. *Journal of Adult Development, 8,* 249–257.

Zackrison, E. (1992). A theology of sin, grace and forgiveness. *Journal of Psychology and Christianity, 11,* 147–159.

CHAPTER 6

Race and Ethnicity in Religion and Health

Linda M. Chatters

Over the past several years, systematic programs of research have addressed questions regarding the relationship between religious involvement and health and well-being outcomes. A good deal of this work has focused on aspects of religious orientation and participation (e.g., religious beliefs, attitudes, behaviors) that may be important for physical and mental health and well-being outcomes. Additionally, special attention has been given religious institutions as locations in which distinctive types of social interactions are evident (e.g., supportive exchanges) which might have beneficial influences on health and well-being outcomes. These issues have long been a focus of work by Levin (1989, 1994a, 1994b, 1994c), Ellison (1991, 1994, 1998) and others (Idler & George, 1998), particularly in relation to the mechanisms and pathways by which religious factors impact health. Finally, research by Ellison and Levin (1998) and Krause (2002, 2003) discusses the possibility of subgroup differences in the theoretical and empirical connections between religion and health. This work provides the groundwork for a careful examination of the ways that religious involvement varies overall and, further, whether and how religion-health associations differ within and across subgroups of the population.

This chapter explores this question in relation to possible race differences in religion-health associations. The literature on race differences in religious involvement is largely concerned with group differences in rates and/or patterns of religious attitudes, belief, and behaviors. Relatively little attention focuses on the underlying basis for group differences and, further, whether they signal genuine differences in the relative significance of religion for health and well-being outcomes. However, there are compelling reasons why religion-health associations may vary across different population groups. Racial groups within the U.S. population encounter significantly different cultural, social, economic, and political circumstances and life experiences (Farley & Allen, 1989). These disparities are manifested as differences in access to resources, power, and wealth within society, as well as in relations to primary and secondary institutions. These factors constitute distinctive cultural and social-historical contexts within which various racial and ethnic groups exist.

Historically, for African Americans, religious institutions and their meaning symbols have constituted unique and distinctive social environments that have functioned as buffers and arbiters of larger societal forces. Given the noted centrality of religious institutions and high levels of commitment among Blacks, religious factors are likely important for health and related outcomes (Krause, 1992). Employing the notion of "context" (e.g., social, cultural, historical) provides a better understanding of the nature and meaning of religious involvement among African Americans and the origins of important group distinctions in religious behaviors and attitudes. In the absence of an adequate appreciation of how context shapes religious expression, comparisons across social groups are of limited value for understanding both religious involvement and the nature of religion-health associations (Chatters & Taylor, 2003).

Having said that, it is important to acknowledge that the majority of research on religion and health has been conducted in the U.S. and is almost exclusively focused on persons who belong to the Christian faith and, more specifically, identify as Protestant (Koenig, McCullough, & Larson, 2001). Although several writers examine religion and health within diverse religious groups (e.g., Buddhists, Hindus, Moslems), these treatments are often concerned with religious traditions and belief systems in relation to specific health concerns (e.g., beliefs about cancer) and identifying culturally appropriate approaches to clinical treatment (see, for example, Koenig's 1998 book and Kimble, McFadden, Ellor, & Seeber's, 1995 book on religion in aging populations).

The available research literature on religion, race, and health focuses primarily on black-white comparisons, and to a lesser extent, on studies involving Mexican Americans and Anglos (see for example, Markides, 1983; Markides & Krause, 1986; Markides, Levin, & Ray, 1987). However, the predominant focus on simple group differences in religious involvement precludes any systematic investigation of the possible meaning of those differences, whether they are consequential for health outcomes and potential differences in religion-health relationships both across (e.g., race, age, social class) and within (e.g., regional variations) defined population groups (Ellison & Levin, 1998). Analyses that focus solely on group differences ignore the possibility that social and psychological factors and processes may operate differently within specific racial and ethnic groups (Lincoln, Chatters, & Taylor, 2003) and rest on an unfounded assumption of "racial/ethnic similarity" (Hunt, 1996; Hunt, Jackson, Powell, & Steelman, 2000). Direct and systematic tests of conceptually grounded models that explore possible differential effects of religion on health (and which employ relevant controls for factors known to be associated with religion and health) are rare. Given the state of the literature, there are many unanswered questions about the connections between religion and health across religiously, racially, and ethnically diverse populations. Future examinations of religion-health connections will require investigating belief and practice as expressed within religiously and racially diverse groups within the population (Koenig et al., 2001) and systematic investigations of potential differences in the role of religion in health (Krause, 2002, 2003).

The present chapter provides a selective review of empirical research findings relating to race and ethnic differences in associations between religion and health. The chapter begins with a brief discussion of the concept of "context" and its uses in research on race differences in various social phenomena. Next, a discussion of the religious traditions and experiences of African Americans provides several examples of the concept of context as constituting distinctive personal, social, and community contexts in which to understand possible differences in religion-health connections. Following this, a review of studies addressing race, religion, and health relationships among African Americans and Mexican Americans is presented. The chapter concludes with a discussion of future research areas that are particularly promising in exploring these questions.

CONTEXTUAL PERSPECTIVES ON RELIGION AND HEALTH

Contextual perspectives have been articulated for a number of phenomena in the social, behavioral, and health sciences and across several disciplines and research fields (Anderson & McNeilly, 1991; Dilworth-Anderson & Anderson, 1994; Chatters & Taylor, 2003; Robert, 1998).

Broadly speaking, the notion of context suggests that multiple and interdependent levels of theory and analysis (i.e., social, cultural, behavioral, and biological) are important for understanding social and behavioral phenomena. A contextual perspective provides important information as to how the constructs of religion and health are defined by particular groups and how they are related to one another (Chatters & Taylor, 2003). Contextual factors are represented in the literature on religion-health associations in at least two ways which are often used interchangeably. In the first, context is taken to mean an all-inclusive and encompassing world view/ecological perspective in which aspects of personal, cultural, and social environments combine to influence broad constructs such as religion and health. This meaning of context refers to broad cultural and historical processes and events that transform fundamental definitions and understandings of religion and health and are the dynamic products of a particular set of informal groups, social institutions, and broader environmental circumstances in which individuals are embedded (Johnson et al., 1995). Accordingly, the essential meaning of a particular construct (e.g., religion, health) is informed by the influence of group-specific culture and history that characterize diverse groups and settings (Chatters & Taylor, 2003).

The second meaning of context refers to those social location factors that characterize groups and individuals (e.g., race, socioeconomic position) and that determine access to valued resources (e.g., wealth, power, prestige). The social location perspective reflects one specific approach to conceptualizing how aspects of social groups and their relative position within the social order influence individual and group status and behaviors (Chatters & Taylor, 2003) and reflects potential moderators of religion-health associations (Ellison, 1994; Ellison & Levin, 1998). Unfortunately, in common practice, the social location perspective is sometimes manifested very narrowly and defines contextual factors as ". . . a set of autonomous individual characteristics, unrelated to living and working conditions and independent of the broader political and social order" (Johnson et al., 1995, p. 602). Oftentimes, interpretation of social location differences are fairly limited in scope and only rarely involve broader notions of group history and culture. Systematic conceptual and analytic treatments of contextual perspectives in religion and health are often underdeveloped or lacking altogether and, as a result, the religious contexts of the groups under study and the complex interplay among religion, health, and other social factors are neglected (Ellison & Levin, 1998).

Notwithstanding these limitations, current conceptual and empirical research attests to the need to explore the role of group-specific culture and history (i.e., context) in understanding religion-health relationships (see for example Krause, 2002, 2003). Although ecological and social location approaches are different with respect to scope and emphasis, they bear an important relationship to one another in that contingent religion-health relationships (e.g., religion-health relationship varies dependent upon race) may indicate different meanings of religion arising from distinctive historical and cultural experiences (Ellison & Levin, 1998).

AFRICAN AMERICAN RELIGIOUS TRADITIONS

Research and writing in African American history, Black studies, religious studies, and sociology document the critical role of Black religious traditions, institutions, and affiliated organizations in African American life (see Murphy, Melton, & Ward, 1993, for a comprehensive treatment of Black religious life). Black religious traditions and institutions have been associated with the development of black communities and their internal structures and organizations (e.g., families, civic groups), as well as the well-being of individuals (see Billingsley, 1999; Frazier, 1974; Lincoln, 1974; Martin, Younge, & Smith, 2003; Nelsen & Nelsen, 1975). Historically, the mission of the African American church has been enacted within a societal and cultural environment characterized by racial oppression and discrimination. This social and cultural environment is pivotal for understanding the functions of the Black Church vis-à-vis its constituent members and communities, its institutional and programmatic responses to the larger hostile social and political environment, and the church's role in safeguarding the health and well-being of its members. Through its social and religious missions, the Black Church provided for the support and well-being of the Black community (see Lincoln & Mamiya, 1990, for a discussion of various church-based self-help and mutual help organizations). Over the past 20 years, there has been interest in Black churches as institutional settings for programmatic initiatives and community outreach in the areas of social welfare and health (Billingsley, 1999; Caldwell, Chatters, Billingsley, & Taylor, 1995; Thomas, Quinn, Billingsley, & Caldwell, 1994), the provision of social support to congregation members (particularly exchanges of support directed toward older congregation members), the use of clergy for assistance, and the personal and social factors associated with these transactions (see for example, Taylor & Chatters, 1986a, 1986b, 1988; Taylor, Chatters, & Levin, 2004).

Given the historical significance and prominence of Black religious traditions for secular efforts and concerns (e.g., the establishment of educational, social welfare, and political institutions and initiatives), religion for Black Americans was intimately connected with community and public arenas of life (Lincoln & Mamiya, 1990). Rather than being independent of secular matters, to varying degrees and among different subgroups of African Americans, religion was interdependent with the world, deeply intertwined with human affairs and was only partially differentiated from worldly concerns (Lincoln & Mamiya, 1990, p. 10). This perspective on Black religious traditions and expression suggests a radically different way of viewing the so-called "role" of religion as it is typically approached within the social, behavioral, and health sciences. Rather than seeing religion as a discrete phenomena that is reducible to specific sets of behaviors and attitudes, religion is construed as a comprehensive system of lifeways and customs that permeates daily life (Arcury, Quandt, McDonald, & Bell, 2000; McAuley, Pecchioni, & Grant, 2000).

CONTEXTUAL PERSPECTIVES ON RELIGION-HEALTH ASSOCIATIONS

As described previously, African American religious traditions embody several distinctive elements which are concerned with ameliorating adverse life circumstances and improving the social, emotional, psychological and spiritual well-being of individuals and groups (Frazier, 1974; Lincoln & Mamiya, 1990). Further, Black religious expression and narrative has historically used religious scripture and meaning to address problems of racial oppression and the economic and political disenfranchisement of Blacks in America (Lincoln & Mamiya, 1990). Historical, ethnographic, and quantitative scholarship and research on these issues suggest that various aspects of Black religious traditions are pertinent for understanding religion-health relationships. The following discussion explores four broad dimensions of Black religious expression and their relevance for religion-health associations.

Pervasiveness of Religious Content and Meaning

The nature and content of Black religious expression emphasizes the all-pervasive and encompassing nature of religious involvement, in which religious affairs are not privatized, but belong in the public domain. This is reflected in the position of religious institutions with respect to a variety of community initiatives (e.g., educational, civic, political), as well as in personal expressions of religious faith (Patillo-McCoy, 1998). Given the pervasiveness of religious content and meaning, we might anticipate that religious frameworks and coping resources would be invoked to understand and deal with a variety of problematic life situations, ranging from the relatively routine to the traumatic (Taylor, Chatters, & Levin, 2004). The ready availability and wide use of religious resources to cope with problems may have particular benefits for stress and coping processes, particularly in relation to illness.

For example, Mansfield, Mitchell, and King (2002) found that Black respondents were more likely than their White counterparts to endorse a belief in divine intervention in healing and that God acts through doctors to cure illnesses. Further, a recent study among rural elderly (McAuley et al., 2000) found that Blacks and Whites expressed different ideas concerning the centrality of religion and God in their lives and with respect to health concerns. Overall, older Blacks were more likely than older Whites to indicate that religion permeated their lives and to describe their relationships with God in personal terms. Among African American elderly, God assumed a role as comforter (ameliorates the effects of illness, makes illness easier to manage), guardian/protector (protection from illnesses), health communicator (providing health-relevant information), and miracle maker/healer/answerer of prayers (healing illness). Prayer was mentioned as the medium through which God's various roles were manifested. Similarly, Arcury et al. (2000) found that prayer was viewed as being pivotal for the maintenance of good health and in healing.

An in-depth examination of Black prayer traditions (Carter, 1976) emphasizes the varied functions of prayer for the individual as well as the group, the different purposes and orientations invoked during prayer, and the pervasiveness of prayer as a part of daily life. Further, a recent analysis of qualitative data among African Americans (Taylor, Chatters, & Levin, 2004) indicates that, among other things, prayer assumes a number of forms and functions within this group, including that of ongoing and constant communication with God (e.g., as a best friend) and in response to both everyday occurrences and major life events. These examples indicate that religious content and meaning is a pervasive feature of life for African Americans and that prayer, in addition to its use during times of duress (Poloma & Gallup, 1991), is also an ongoing and integral part of one's life (Arcury et al., 2000).

Distinctive Religious Communities

Black religious communities are distinctive social settings that are characterized by a collective orientation and communal nature. These factors give rise to interpersonal interactions that are grounded in a religious ethos emphasizing helping others and in which various forms of social support are both given and received. Further, these religious contexts support the development of close interpersonal bonds which are patterned after family relationships (i.e., church family). Such environments constitute rich sources of informal support that can be used to cope with stressful and problematic life problems and have been characterized as therapeutic communities for African Americans (Gilkes, 1980; Griffith, Young, & Smith, 1984; McRae, Carey, & Anderson-Scott, 1998). Further, similarities between participants in terms of social status factors and belief systems are thought to enhance the effectiveness of supportive exchanges (Ellison, 1994). Characterizations of aspects of congregational climate emphasize important functional elements (e.g., social support) and characteristics (e.g., sense of community, social concern, autonomy) that may be significant for psychological outcomes (Maton, 1989; Pargament, Silverman, Johnson, Echemendia, & Snyder, 1983). A focus on aspects of congregational life and the internal and external factors and processes that influence these dynamics, reflects an attempt to apply multiple levels of analysis (e.g., individual, institutional, community) to explore the role of context in associations between religion and mental health (Ellison, 1994).

Positive Core Beliefs and Values

Black religious traditions and beliefs serve to instill and reinforce positive beliefs, including a sense of hope, optimism, meaning, forgiveness, salvation, and redemption, which, in turn, may have positive influences on health outcomes (Ellison & Levin, 1998; Koenig, 1994; Krause, 2002). Within the historical context of African Americans' experiences with oppression and discrimination, the church and other faith-based institutions and settings were pivotal in sustaining the emotional, psychological, and spiritual self, as well as ensuring the physical survival of individuals and communities. These traditions of hope and other positive beliefs have become a hallmark of Black religious faith and are reflected in a variety of religious practices and orientations (Billingsley, 1999; Carter, 1976; Lincoln & Mamiya, 1990). For example, an analysis of race, religion, and psychological well-being among

Black and White college students (Blaine & Crocker, 1995) found that the salience of religious beliefs was associated with psychological well-being, but among Black students only. Further, for Blacks only, this relationship was partially mediated by attributions to God that enhance life meaning and positive social identities that were based in one's religious affiliation.

Prophetic Functions of Religion

Various aspects of Black religious traditions (i.e., the prophetic-priestly and accommodation-resistance dimensions described by Lincoln and Mamiya, 1990) embody an explicitly outward focus in relation to issues of social and economic justice (e.g., the Civil Rights Movement) and in critiquing and actively resisting dominant social, economic, and political structures and institutions. In the tradition of the Prophets of the Old Testament and in keeping with the liberating message of the Christian gospels, the Black Church and its religious traditions are called upon to critique the dominant social hierarchy that has served to oppress and discriminate against African Americans and other disadvantaged groups (Grant, 1989, 1993). Various writers on the topic of Black Theology have noted how, in the face of dehumanizing social conditions, the central tenets of Christianity have been used by African Americans to create an enduring sense of humanity, personhood, and community (Cone, 1975, 1985). These features of the Black religious tradition give rise to a diversity of cognitive and affective coping resources in the face of disadvantage and provide coherent frameworks of meaning which enhance a sense of individual and group worth and value (e.g., self-esteem, efficacy). Comparable sorts of prophetic traditions can be found in Liberation Theologies in Latin America and other Third World settings, emerging conceptualizations of Womanist Theology (Grant, 1989), and in the social and economic justice ministries evident within some liberal white denominations and congregations.

These four examples illustrate several possibilities for how cultural and historical contexts shape the nature and meaning of religious expression among African Americans in ways that are relevant to health. The next section provides a review of selected findings on religion, race, and health, including recent efforts (see for example Krause, 2002, 2003) that systematically explore race differences in religion-health connections within the context of the historical, social, and cultural experiences of African Americans.

SELECTED RESEARCH FINDINGS ON
RELIGION, RACE, AND HEALTH

The research literature on religion, race, and health (and related outcomes) is admittedly limited in its scope and variable in its quality. Further, much of this work has been conducted among samples of older persons who differ from the general population with respect to factors that are significant for these relationships (e.g., general levels of religious involvement, morbidity status, sociodemographic factors). Available studies examine general patterns of religious involvement within and across various groups (e.g., Blacks, Whites, and Mexican Americans), explore the religion-health connection within specific groups, and examine contingent (i.e., interactive) relationships involving race. Additionally, studies in the caregiver literature document the use of religious resources and coping strategies among caregivers. Finally, several recent investigations examine theoretically-derived models of religion-health associations, with a specific focus on the role of race in these relationships.

Studies Involving African Americans

A substantial body of research findings that document basic patterns of religious involvement indicate that Black Americans generally, and older Black adults in particular, are strongly invested in and committed to religious pursuits (Chatters & Taylor, 1989; Chatters, Taylor, & Lincoln, 1999; Ellison & Sherkat, 1995; Ellison & Taylor, 1996; Levin & Taylor, 1993; Levin, Taylor, & Chatters, 1994; Taylor, 1988a, 1988b; Taylor & Chatters, 1991; Taylor, Chatters, & Levin, 2004) across a variety of religious indicators, including church membership rates, public (e.g., church attendance) and private devotional practices (e.g., prayer and reading religious materials), and subjective appraisals of religiosity. Research on racial differences in religious involvement finds that African American respondents report higher levels of religious behaviors, beliefs, and attitudes than do their White counterparts (Levin, Taylor, & Chatters, 1994; Taylor, Chatters, Jayakody, & Levin, 1996) for both public and private involvement (e.g., church attendance, frequency of prayer).

With regard to religion-health associations, a small body of research among exclusively African American samples finds a beneficial effect of religious involvement on distress and depression (Brown, Ndubuisi, & Gary, 1990; Krause, 1992; Musick, Koenig, Hays, & Cohen, 1998), mortality risk (Bryant & Rakowski, 1992), and life satisfaction and other measures of psychological well-being (Ellison & Gay, 1990; Levin & Chatters, 1998; Levin, Chatters, & Taylor, 1995; Levin & Taylor, 1998), even controlling for other factors that are known to be associated with well-being. In addition, several studies (Brown & Gary, 1994; Krause, 1991; Wallace & Forman, 1998; Wallace & Williams, 1998) indicate that religious involvement among African Americans is inversely related to negative health behaviors, such as alcohol use/abuse and smoking. Both groups of studies—race differences in general levels of religious involvement and religious effects on health among African Americans—provide basic background data suggesting that religion may be differentially important for health and well-being (see Taylor, Chatters, & Levin, 2004 for a comprehensive review of studies of race differences in religious involvement and the effects of religious factors on physical and mental health among African Americans).

Finally, a group of studies directly examines the impact of race (i.e., among Black and Whites) on religion-health associations. One early investigation found that service attendance and strength of denominational affiliation were associated with higher subjective health ratings among White, but not Black respondents (Steinitz, 1980). Further, religious attendance was associated with well-being for Whites, but not Blacks. In contrast, a later study (St. George & McNamara, 1984) found that attendance was related to subjective health among Blacks, but unrelated among Whites, while strength of religious affiliation was strongly associated with health ratings and satisfaction among Black men, but only mildly related to health satisfaction among whites. Similarly, strength of religious affiliation and attendance was associated with happiness ratings for both Blacks and Whites, but effects were stronger for Black respondents. Ferraro and Koch (1994) found that an index of health was predicted by religious practice among Blacks, but not among Whites; among Blacks, however, comfort and consolation from religion were associated with poorer health status. Ellison's (1995) study of the effects of religious attendance and devotion on depressive symptoms found that religious attendance was associated with fewer depressive symptoms among Whites (they were unrelated among Blacks); lack of religious affiliation was related to more depressive symptoms among Blacks. Private devotional activities (prayer, Bible study) were related to greater depression among both groups.

Musick's (1996) study of religion and subjective health assessments found that service attendance was associated with health for both Black and White respondents. Analyses involving controls for objective health measures revealed that devotional activities were also associated with subjective health in both groups. Musick et al.'s (1998) study of the effects of religious activities (i.e., church attendance, devotional activity, religious media) on depressive symptomatology among community-dwelling elderly persons with cancer found that for Blacks, religious activity was associated with lower levels of depressive symptoms, and the effect was stronger for Blacks than Whites. These findings are in contrast to previous analyses (Idler & Kasl, 1992) in which there were no significant effects for either public or private religious factors on depressive symptoms among older Blacks and Whites. Koenig et al. (1998) found consistently lower blood pressure readings for older persons reporting frequent Bible reading and prayer; these differences were particularly notable among Black elderly. With respect to religious coping, the use of this strategy was associated with lower blood pressure readings among African Americans, but not among Whites (Steffen, Hinderliter, Blumenthal, & Sherwood, 2001).

The caregiving literature explores questions of race differences in religious involvement and the use of religious coping strategies among caregivers (Dilworth-Anderson, Williams, & Gibson, 2002). The act of caring for others and filial piety are prominent themes in many religious traditions. The giving of care to others is reinforced in Biblical texts and formalized in the norms and practices of religious institutions (i.e., caring for the sick and shut-in). Given this background, religious frameworks may be significant for the caregiving experience in several ways, including primary appraisal processes as to the stressfulness of caregiving, efforts to cope with the stresses of caregiving, and in enlisting social resources to assist in caregiving. In a major review of caregiver research Dilworth-Anderson et al. (2002), found that religious resources and coping strategies (e.g., prayer, ministerial support, help from God) were frequently identified by African American caregivers as means to cope with caregiving responsibilities. Navaie-Waliser et al.'s (2001) study of caregiving within African American, White, and Hispanic communities identified a number of similarities and differences in the caregiving experience. As compared to Whites, Black caregivers were more like to report unmet needs associated with caregiving and providing higher intensity care, but were less likely to report difficulty in providing care. Both Hispanic and Black caregivers were more likely than Whites to indicate increases in religiosity since becoming a caregiver. In a similar vein, Miltiades and Pruchno (2002) found that Black caregivers reported higher levels of religious coping which increased caregiving satisfaction, but did not reduce caregiver burden.

Despite problems in the comparability of studies (e.g., samples, instruments), a few tentative conclusions can be made regarding the differential importance of religion for coping with the caregiver experience. Overall, and similar to other reports of race differences in religious involvement, African American caregivers are more likely than whites to report that they are religious. Additionally, among African American caregivers, there is a greater tendency to identify God as a member of the informal social support system and as a primary source of social support in the caregiving role. Spiritual resources appear to be important to Black caregivers, as reflected in their reported use of prayer and religion to cope with the demands of caregiving and their reports of deriving spiritual meaning from the caregiving experience. Finally, among Black caregivers, religiosity is important in reframing the caregiving experience (i.e., threat appraisal processes) and in perceiving greater rewards in the caregiving experience. While only suggestive, these research findings indicate a number of fruitful avenues for exploring the associations among race, religion, and the caregiving experience. Additional studies are needed to verify these early findings and to determine if the use of religion in caregiving is differentially predictive of mental and physical health outcomes for caregivers of different racial groups.

Finally, a small group of recent studies focuses on the systematic evaluation of conceptual models of the relationships among race, religion, and health and is particularly useful in exploring potential group differences (including analyses of gender differences by Krause, Ellison, and Marcum, 2002) in religion-health associations. Krause (2002) explored the relationships between church-based support and health among older Black and White adults, with a specific emphasis on exploring possible mechanisms (e.g., optimism, congregational cohesiveness) for differential religious effects on health. The study findings revealed significant race differences in religious involvement (e.g., congregational cohesiveness, emotional support, spiritual support) and reported optimism. Further, the findings suggested that, among Black elderly, important social aspects of religious attendance (i.e., emotional support, spiritual support, congregational cohesiveness) were important in the overall positive association between attendance and feelings of closeness to God. In addition, church attendance was associated with greater optimism among Black elderly and a slight decline in optimism among White elderly. Notably, the specific relationships among constructs that were examined in the model were grounded in the historical and cultural experiences of African Americans, with a particular emphasis on the role of positive beliefs (i.e., optimism) that are central to Black religious traditions. Thus, in addition to providing a theoretically meaningful test of these associations, the analysis explored these relationships within the context of the social, cultural, and historical experiences of this group. Similarly, Nooney and Woodrum's (2002) findings that the protective effects of religious factors (i.e., attendance and prayer) for depression were mediated by church-based social support and religious coping, suggest that religion-health associations are complex. Although this study did not examine the model separately by race, the pattern of bivariate associations indicated that being African American was associated with greater religious involvement, suggesting that these associations may potentially vary by race.

In a further exploration of race differences in the relation between clergy interaction and feelings of self-worth, Krause (2003) found that positive interactions with clergy were significant for the self-esteem of older Blacks, but were unrelated for older Whites. Interestingly, older Whites and Blacks were no different from one another with respect to the impact of negative interactions with clergy on lowering self-esteem ratings. However, negative interactions with clergy appeared to lower self-esteem assessments of older persons who did not report using positive religious strategies in coping with problems. The conceptual model tested in this study is based on established social science theory with respect to social relationships and ties, as well as on social-historical literature on the prominent role of African American pastors for Black religious life. This study's exploration of both positive and negative social interactions with clergy, and their differential impact on a health-related outcome (i.e., self-esteem), begins to address longstanding questions about the nature and consequences of social relationships within religious settings in a much more discerning manner (see Krause, Chatters, Meltzer, & Morgan, 2000a; and Taylor, Chatter, & Levin, 2004 for discussion of church-based social interactions). Importantly, the study reflects a deep appreciation for the historical and cultural context from which African American religious expression derives.

Studies of these sorts are important because they explore religious experiences within particular racial groups and specify and test a number of functional mechanisms (e.g., coping behaviors, social support, cognitive reframing, meaning) for understanding religious effects and suggest how and why religious effects may occur differentially. Understanding religion-health association must move beyond considerations of whether religious coping strategies and resources are evident within particular groups, but must also rigorously test whether they are differentially effective with respect to pertinent health outcomes (Krause, 2002).

Studies Involving Hispanics/Latinos

Markides and associates have established a programmatic research focus on the personal and social correlates of the physical and mental health and well-being of elderly and non-elderly Mexican American and other Hispanic groups (Black & Markides, 1993, 1994). This body of work includes topics such as health status, health behaviors (e.g., smoking and alcohol use), intergenerational family relationships (Markides & Krause, 1986), and psychological well-being and distress (see for example, Chiriboga, Black, Aranda, & Markides, 2002). Several of these studies specifically examine religion and health associations (both in cross-section and longitudinal designs) within samples of older Mexican Americans (Levin & Markides, 1985, 1986; Levin, Markides, & Ray, 1996) and samples of older Mexican Americans and Anglos (Markides, 1983; Markides, Levin, & Ray, 1987). This work is based on the San Antonio longitudinal study of Mexican Americans and Anglos (Markides, 1983) and a three-generation study of Mexican Americans.

Similar to other research, a study involving data from three generations of Mexican Americans (Levin & Markides, 1985) found a link between religious factors (e.g., service attendance) and physical health (e.g., self-rated, functional health, hypertension) and psychological well-being (e.g., life satisfaction, depressive and positive affect), controlling for the effects of demographic and social factors. However, a later study (Levin & Markides, 1986) indicated that among women, the effect of religious attendance on subjective health was rendered insignificant in the presence of controls for social factors, physical capacity, and subjective religiosity. Research based on panel data from a three-generation study of Mexican Americans (Levin et al., 1996) found that the positive longitudinal effect of religious attendance on depressed affect was apparent only for the youngest generation of respondents, while life satisfaction was positively associated with attendance for the two older generations in cross-section analyses only.

Markides' (1983) analysis of religious factors and life satisfaction using longitudinal data on older Mexican Americans and Anglos found that, for both groups, subjective religiosity increased somewhat over time, while attendance and private prayer were stable over a 4-year period. Interestingly, for both groups, only church attendance was significantly associated with life satisfaction and its impact increased somewhat over time for Anglos. Finally, an 8-year longitudinal study involving a combined sample of older Mexican Americans and Anglos (Markides et al., 1987) found that religious involvement (i.e., attendance, private prayer, self-rated religiosity) remained relatively stable over time and did not increase in its ability to predict life satisfaction, despite increasing age and declines in health.

This collection of studies indicates that while the findings of a positive religion-health connection are comparable to those found in the literature, there are a number of qualifications and unanswered questions. This work indicates that among Mexican Americans, religion and health are generally positively related, but that there may be important within-group differences associated with gender and generational status. Second, overall, religious involvement remains relatively stable over time (except for, in one instance, subjective religiosity), while the relationship between religion and health remains stable. Comparative analyses revealed that Mexican Americans and Anglos are in some instances similar to one another, while in others differences emerged (i.e., increased predictive ability of church attendance for the life satisfaction of Anglos). Finally, it should be acknowledged that this is a small group of studies that requires verification in other samples of Mexican Americans.

Continuing research on the association between religion and health among Mexican Americans should focus on a variety of social and personal factors that reflect the social-historical and cultural contexts within which these relationships transpire. In addition to analyses involving basic sociodemographic characteristics (e.g., gender, social class, region of the country, urbanicity), other factors of interest should include nativity status (i.e., native born or immigrant), family generation, family structure, level of assimilation, and religious denomination (i.e., Catholic vs. Protestant). Finally, it should be acknowledged that Mexican Americans represent only one identifiable subgroup within the larger ethnic category of Hispanic/Latino. As such, there are questions about the potential significance of within-group variability in terms of racial status (e.g., Black Hispanic vs. White Hispanic) and country of origin (e.g., Puerto Rico, Cuba, Dominican Republic) for investigations of religion-health associations.

SUMMARY AND FUTURE DIRECTIONS

The noted reliance on religious worldviews and networks among African Americans, and particularly among older persons, indicates that these familiar forms of resources and ways of understanding the world are, in some respects, normative for this group (Chatters & Taylor, 1994). Religious worldviews may incorporate preferred ways of being in and understanding the world and a common language with which to comprehend and address problems of living and issues of ultimate meaning. However, it is important not to lose sight of the importance of within-group variability in the significance of religious worldviews. For particular groups of African Americans (e.g., older persons, women), religious resources and meanings may be especially important.

Current research on religion and health is slowly making progress in understanding the role of race in these relationships. Unfortunately, the vast majority of research in this area fails to fully exploit available information about the distinctive features of race and how they are associated with religion and health. A number of recent research efforts has contributed to this literature and describes the nature and functions of religion both within and between racial groups, explores these issues within the historical and current life contexts of these populations, and employs theoretically derived analytic models to examine the relationships between religion and health. In addition, recent efforts that explore the meaning of religion using qualitative information (e.g., Krause, Chatters, Meltzer, & Morgan, 2000a; Krause, Chatters, et al., 2000b; Mattis, 2002; Taylor, Chatters, & Levin, 2004), provide new insights in understanding how individuals view religion within the context of their lives. However, much work remains to be completed before a comprehensive picture of the differential impact of race on religion-health associations emerges. Central to this task is a full appreciation and utilization of a contextual perspective for understanding the nature and meaning of religion and health for diverse groups. This is particularly critical for understanding the religious experiences of groups that differ in terms of race and ethnicity (e.g., Asians, Latinos, Native Americans), social and cultural experiences (e.g., immigration processes) and religious background (e.g., non-Protestant and non-Christian). Collectively, work of this sort will enrich our understanding of religious involvement among diverse populations and its potential roles in advancing individual and group health.

REFERENCES

Anderson, N. B., & McNeilly, M. (1991). Age, gender, and ethnicity as variables in psychophysiological assessment: Sociodemographics in context. *Psychological Assessment, 3*(3), 376–384.

Arcury, T. A., Quandt, S. A., McDonald, J., & Bell, R. A. (2000). Faith and health self-management of rural older adults. *Journal of Cross-Cultural Gerontology, 15*, 55–74.

Billingsley, A. (1999). *Mighty like a river: The black church and social reform.* New York: Oxford University Press.

Black, S. A., & Markides, K. S. (1993). Acculturation and alcohol consumption in Puerto Rican, Cuban-American, and Mexican-American women in the United States. *American Journal of Public Health, 83*(6), 890–893.

Black, S. A., & Markides, K. S. (1994). Aging and generational patterns of alcohol consumption among Mexican Americans, Cuban Americans and mainland Puerto Ricans. *International Journal of Aging & Human Development, 39*(2), 97–103.

Blaine, B., & Crocker, J. (1995). Religiousness, race, and psychological well-being: Exploring social psychological mediators. *Personality and Social Psychology Bulletin, 21,* 1031–1041.

Brown, D. R., & Gary, L. E. (1994). Religious involvement and health status among African-American males. *Journal of the National Medical Association, 86,* 825–831.

Brown, D. R., Ndubuisi, S.C., & Gary, L. E. (1990). Religiosity and psychological distress among Blacks. *Journal of Religion and Health, 29,* 55–68.

Bryant, S., & Rakowski, W. (1992). Predictors of mortality among elderly African-Americans. *Research on Aging, 14,* 50–67.

Caldwell, C. H., Chatters, L. M., Billingsley, A., & Taylor, R. J. (1995). Church-based support programs for elderly black adults: Congregational and clergy characteristics. In M. A. Kimble, S. H. McFadden, J. W. Ellor, & J. J. Seeber (Eds.), *Aging, spirituality, and religion: A handbook* (pp. 306–324). Minneapolis, MN: Fortress Press.

Carter, H. A. (1976). The prayer tradition of black people. Valley Forge, PA: Judson Press.

Chatters, L. M., & Taylor, R. J. (1989). Age differences in religious participation among black adults. *Journals of Gerontology: Social Sciences, 44:* S183–S189.

Chatters, L. M., & Taylor, R. J. (1994). Religious involvement among older African Americans. In J. S. Levin (Ed.), *Religion in aging and health: Theoretical foundations and methodological frontiers* (pp. 196–230). Thousand Oaks, CA: Sage Publications.

Chatters, L. M., & Taylor, R. J. (2003). The role of social context in religion. *Journal of Religious Gerontology, 14*(2/3), 139–152.

Chatters, L. M., Taylor, R. J., & Lincoln, K. D. (1999). African American religious participation: A multi-sample comparison. *Journal for the Scientific Study of Religion, 38,* 132–145.

Chiriboga, D. A., Black, S. A., Aranda, M., & Markides, K. (2002). Stress and depressive symptoms among Mexican American elders. *Journals of Gerontology: Series B: Psychological Sciences & Social Sciences, 57B*(6), P559–P568.

Cone, J. (1975). *God of the oppressed.* New York: Seabury Press.

Cone, J. (1985). Black theology in American religion. *Journal of the American Academy of Religion, 53,* 755–771.

Dilworth-Anderson, P., & Anderson, N. B. (1994). Dementia caregiving in blacks: A contextual approach to research. In E. Light (Ed.), *Stress effects on family caregivers of Alzheimer's patients: Research and interventions* (pp. 385–409). New York: Springer Publishing.

Dilworth-Anderson, P., Williams, I. C., & Gibson, B. E. (2002). Issues of race, ethnicity, and culture in caregiving research: A 20-year review (1980–2000). *The Gerontologist, 42*(2), 237–272.

Ellison, C. G. (1991). Religious involvement and subjective well-being. *Journal of Health and Social Behavior, 32*, 80–99.

Ellison, C. G. (1994). Religion, the life-stress paradigm, and the study of depression. In J. S. Levin (Ed.), *Religion in aging and health: Theoretical foundations and methodological frontiers* (pp. 78–121). Thousand Oaks, CA: Sage Publications.

Ellison, C. G. (1995). Race, religious involvement and depressive symptomatology in a southeastern U.S. community. *Social Science and Medicine, 40*, 1561–1572.

Ellison, C. G. (1998). Religion, health and well-being among African Americans. *African American Research Perspectives, 4*, 94–103.

Ellison, C. G., & Gay, D. A. (1990). Region, religious commitment, and life satisfaction among Black Americans. *Sociological Quarterly, 31*, 123–147.

Ellison, C. G., & Levin, J. S. (1998). The religion-health connection: Evidence, theory and future directions. *Health Education and Behavior, 25*, 700–720.

Ellison, C. G., & Sherkat, D. E. (1995). The semi-involuntary institution revised: Regional variations in church participation among Black Americans. *Social Forces, 73*, 1415–1437.

Ellison, C. G., & Taylor, R. J. (1996). Turning to prayer: Religious coping among Black Americans. *Review of Religious Research, 38*, 111–131.

Farley, R., & Allen, W. R. (1989). *The color line and the quality of life in America*. New York : Oxford University Press.

Ferraro, K. F., & Koch, J. R. (1994). Religion and health among black and white adults: Examining social support and consolation. *Journal for the Scientific Study of Religion, 33*, 362–375.

Frazier, E. F. (1974). *The Negro church in America*. New York: Schocken Books.

Gilkes, C. T. (1980). The Black Church as a therapeutic community: Suggested area for research into the Black religious experience. *Journal of the Interdenominational Theological Center, 8*, 29–44.

Grant, J. (1989). *White women's Christ and Black women's Jesus: Feminist Christology and womanist response*. Atlanta, GA: Scholars Press.

Grant, J. (1993). Womanist theology: Black women's experiences as a source for doing theology. In Murphy, L. G., Melton, J. G., & Ward, G. L. *Encyclopedia of African American Religions* (pp. xlvii–lviii). New York: Garland Publishing.

Griffith, E. E. H., Young, J. L., & Smith, D. L. (1984). An analysis of the therapeutic elements in a black church service. *Hospital and Community Psychiatry, 35*, 464–469.

Hunt, M. (1996). The individual, society, or both? A comparison of Black, Latino, and White beliefs about the causes of poverty. *Social Forces, 75*(1), 293–322.

Hunt, M., Jackson, P. G., Powell, B., & Steelman, L.C. (2000). Color-blind: The treatment of race and ethnicity in social psychology. *Social Psychology Quarterly: Special Issue: The state of sociological social psychology, 63*(4), 352–364.

Idler, E. L., & George, L. M. (1998). What sociology can help us understand about religion and mental health. In H. G. Koenig (Ed.), *Handbook of religion and mental health* (pp. 51–62). San Diego: Academic Press.

Idler, E. L., & Kasl, S. V. (1992). Religion, disability, depression, and the timing of death. *American Journal of Sociology, 97*(4), 1052–1079.

Johnson, K. W., Anderson, N. B., Bastida, E., Kramer, B., Williams, D., & Wong, M. (1995). Macrosocial and environmental influences on minority health. *Special Issue: Health Psychology: Behavioral and sociocultural perspectives on ethnicity and health, 14*(7), 601–612.

Kimble, M. A., McFadden, S. H., Ellor, J. W., & Seeber, J. J. (Eds.). (1995). *Aging, spirituality, and religion: A handbook.* Minneapolis, MN: Fortress Press.

Koenig, H. G. (1994). Religion and hope for the disabled elder. In J. S. Levin (Ed.), *Religion in aging and health: Theoretical foundations and methodological frontiers* (pp. 18–51). Thousand Oaks, CA: Sage Publications.

Koenig, H. G. (Ed.) (1998). *Handbook of religion and mental health.* San Diego, CA: Academic Press.

Koenig, H. G., George, L. K., Hays, J. C., Larson, D. B., Cohen, H. J., & Blazer, D. G. (1998). The relationship between religious activities and blood pressure in older adults. *International Journal of Psychiatry in Medicine, 28*(2), 189–213.

Koenig, H. G., McCullough, M. E., & Larson, D. B. (2001). *Handbook of religion and health.* New York: Oxford University Press.

Krause, N. (1991). Stress, religiosity, and abstinence from alcohol. *Psychology and Aging, 6,* 134–144.

Krause, N. (1992). Stress, religiosity, and psychological well-being among older Blacks. *Journal of Aging & Health, 4*(3), 412–439.

Krause N. (1995). Religiosity and self-esteem among older adults. *Journal of Gerontology: Psychological Sciences, 50B,* P236–246.

Krause, N. (2002). Church-based social support and health in old age: Variations by race. *Journal of Gerontology: Social Sciences, 57B,* S332–S347.

Krause, N. (2003). Exploring race differences in the relationship between social interaction with the clergy and feelings of self-worth in late life. *Sociology of Religion, 64*(2), 183–205.

Krause, N., Chatters, L. M., Meltzer, T., & Morgan, D. (2000a). Negative interaction in the church: Insights from focus groups with older adults. *Review of Religious Research, 41,* 510–533.

Krause, N., Chatters, L. M., Meltzer, T., & Morgan, D. L. (2000b). Using focus groups to explore the nature of prayer in later life. *Journal of Aging Studies, 14*(2), 191–212.

Krause, N., Ellison, C. G., & Marcum, J. P. (2002). The effects of church-based emotional support on health: Do they vary by gender? *Sociology of Religion,* *63*(1), 21–47.

Levin, J. S. (1989). Religious factors in aging, adjustment, and health: A theoretical overview. In W. M. Clements (Ed.), *Religion, aging and health: A global perspective* (pp. 133–146). Compiled by the World Health Organization. NY: Haworth Press.

Levin, J. S. (Ed.). (1994a). *Religion in aging and health: Theoretical foundations and methodological frontiers.* Thousand Oaks, CA: Sage Publications.

Levin, J. S. (1994b). Religion and health: Is there an association, is it valid, and is it causal? *Social Science and Medicine, 38,* 1475–1482.

Levin, J. S. (1994c). Investigating the epidemiologic effects of religious experience: Findings, explanations, and barriers. In J. S. Levin (Ed.), *Religion in aging and health: Theoretical foundations and methodological frontiers* (pp. 3–17). Thousand Oaks, CA: Sage Publications.

Levin, J. S., & Chatters, L. M. (1998). Research on religion and mental health: An overview of empirical findings and theoretical issues. In H. G. Koenig (Ed.), *Handbook of religion and mental health* (pp. 33–50). San Diego, CA: Academic Press.

Levin, J. S., Chatters, L. M., & Taylor, R. J. (1995). Religious effects on health status and life satisfaction among Black Americans. *Journal of Gerontology: Social Sciences, 50B,* S154–S163.

Levin, J. S., & Markides, K. (1985). Religion and health in Mexican Americans. *Journal of Religion & Health, 24*(1), 60–69.

Levin, J. S., & Markides, K. (1986). Religious attendance and subjective health. *Journal for the Scientific Study of Religion, 25*(1), 31–40.

Levin, J. S., Markides, K., & Ray, L. A. (1996). Religious attendance and psychological well-being in Mexican Americans: A panel analysis of three-generation data. *The Gerontologist, 36*(4), 454–463.

Levin, J. S., & Taylor, R.J. (1993). Gender and age differences in religiosity among Black Americans. *The Gerontologist, 33,* 16–23.

Levin, J. S., & Taylor, R. J. (1998). Panel analysis of religious involvement and well-being in African Americans: Contemporaneous vs. longitudinal effects. *Journal for the Scientific Study of Religion, 37*(4), 695–709.

Levin, J. S., Taylor, R. J., & Chatters, L. M. (1994). Race and gender differences in religiosity among older adults: Findings from four national surveys. *Journal of Gerontology: Social Sciences, 49,* S137–S145.

Lincoln, C. E. (Ed.). (1974). *The Black experience in religion.* Garden City, NY: Anchor Press.

Lincoln, C. E., & Mamiya, L. H. (1990). *The Black Church in the African American experience.* Durham, NC: Duke University Press.

Lincoln, K. D., Chatters, L. M., & Taylor, R. J. (2003). Psychological distress among Black and White Americans: Differential effects of social support, negative interaction and personal control. *Journal of Health and Social Behavior, 44*(3), 390–407.

Mansfield, C. J., Mitchell, J., & King, D. E. (2002). The doctor as God's mechanic? Beliefs in the southeastern United States. *Social Science & Medicine, 54,* 339–409.

Markides, K. S. (1983). Aging, religiosity, and adjustment: A longitudinal analysis. *Journal of Gerontology, 38*(5), 621–625.

Markides, K. S., & Krause, N. (1986). Older Mexican Americans. *Generations, 10*(4), 31–34.

Markides, K. S., Levin, J. S., & Ray, L. A. (1987). Religion, aging and life satisfaction: An eight-year, three-wave longitudinal study. *The Gerontologist, 27*(5), 660–665.

Martin, P. P., Younge, S., & Smith, A. (2003). Searching for a Balm in Gilead: The HIV/AIDS epidemic and the African-American church. *African American Research Perspectives, 9*(1), 70–78.

Maton, K. I. (1989). Community settings as buffers of life stress? Highly supportive churches, mutual help groups, and senior centers. *American Journal of Community Psychology, 17*(2), 203–232.

Mattis, J. S. (2002). The role of religion and spirituality in the coping experience of African American women: A qualitative analysis. *Psychology of Women Quarterly, 26,* 308–320.

McAuley, W. J., Pecchioni, L., & Grant, J. A. (2000). Personal accounts of the role of God in health and illness among older rural African American and White residents. *Journal of Cross-Cultural Gerontology, 15,* 13–35.

McRae, M. B., Carey, P. M., & Anderson-Scott, R. (1998). Black churches as therapeutic systems: A group process perspective. *Health Education and Behavior, 25*(6), 778–789.

Miltiades, H. B., & Pruchno, R. (2002). The effect of religious coping on caregiving appraisals of mothers of adults with developmental disabilities. *The Gerontologist, 42*(1), 82–91.

Murphy, L. G., Melton, J. G., & Ward, G. L. (1993). *Encyclopedia of African American Religions.* New York: Garland Publishing.

Musick, M. A. (1996). Religion and subjective health among Black and White elders. *Journal of Health and Social Behavior, 37,* 221–237.

Musick, M. A., Koenig, H. G., Hays, J. C., & Cohen, H. J. (1998). Religious activity and depression among community-dwelling elderly persons with cancer: The moderating effect of race. *Journal of Gerontology: Social Sciences, 53B,* S218–S227.

Navaie-Waliser, M., Feldman, P. H., Gould, D. A., Devine, C., Kuerbis, A. N., & Donelan, K. (2001). The experiences and challenges of informal caregivers: Common themes and differences among whites, blacks and Hispanics. *The Gerontologist, 41*(6), 733–741.

Nelsen, H. M., & Nelsen, A. K. (1975). *Black church in the sixties.* Lexington, KY: University Press of Kentucky.

Nooney, J., & Woodrum, E. (2002). Religious coping and church-based social support as predictors of mental health outcomes: Testing a conceptual model. *Journal for the Scientific Study of Religion, 41,* 359–368.

Pargament, K. I., Silverman, W. H., Johnson, S., Echemendia, R., & Snyder, S. (1983). The psychosocial climate of religious congregations. *American Journal of Community Psychology, 11,* 351–381.

Patillo-McCoy, M. (1998). Church culture as a strategy of action in the Black community. *American Sociological Review, 63,* 767–784.

Poloma, M. M., & Gallup, G. (1991). *Varieties of prayer.* Philadelphia: Trinity Press International.

Robert, S. A. (1998). Community-level socioeconomic status effects on adult health. *Journal of Health & Social Behavior, 39*(1), 18–37.

St. George, A., & McNamara, P. H. (1984). Religion, race and psychological well-being. *Journal for the Scientific Study of Religion, 23,* 351–363.

Steffen, P. R., Hinderliter, A. L., Blumenthal, J. A., & Sherwood, A. (2001). Religious coping, ethnicity, and ambulatory blood pressure. *Psychosomatic Medicine: Special Issue, 63*(4), 523–530.

Steinitz, L. Y. (1980). Religiosity, well-being, and Weltanschauung among the elderly. *Journal for the Scientific Study of Religion, 19,* 60–67.

Taylor, R. J. (1988a). Correlates of religious non-involvement among Black Americans. *Review of Religious Research, 30,* 126–139.

Taylor, R. J. (1988b). Structural determinants of religious participation among Black Americans. *Review of Religious Research, 30,* 114–125.

Taylor, R. J., & Chatters, L. M. (1986a). Church-based informal support among elderly Blacks. *The Gerontologist, 26,* 637–642.

Taylor, R. J., & Chatters, L. M. (1986b). Patterns of informal support to elderly Black adults: Family, friends, and church members. *Social Work, 31,* 432–438.

Taylor, R. J., & Chatters, L. M. (1988). Church members as a source of informal social support. *Review of Religious Research, 30,* 193–203.

Taylor, R. J., & Chatters, L. M. (1991). Nonorganizational religious participation among elderly Black adults. *Journal of Gerontology: Social Sciences, 46,* S103–S111.

Taylor, R. J., Chatters, L. M., Jayakody, R., & Levin, J. S. (1996). Black and white differences in religious participation: A multi-sample comparison. *Journal for the Scientific Study of Religion, 35,* 403–410.

Taylor, R. J., Chatters, L. M., & Levin, J. S. (2004). *Religion in the lives of African Americans: Social, psychological and health perspectives.* Newbury Park, CA: Sage.

Thomas, S. B., Quinn, S. C., Billingsley, A., & Caldwell, C. H. (1994). The characteristics of northern Black churches with community health outreach programs. *American Journal of Public Health, 84,* 575–579.

Wallace, J. M., & Forman, T. A. (1998). Religion's role in promoting health and reducing risk among American youth. *Health Education and Behavior: Special issue: Public health and health education in faith communities, 25*(6), 721–741.

Wallace, J. M., Jr., & Williams, D. R. (1998). Religion and adolescent health-compromising behavior. In J. Schulenberg, J. L. Maggs, & K. Hurrelmann (Eds.), *Health risks and developmental transitions during adolescence* (pp. 444–468). Cambridge, MA: Cambridge University Press.

Commentary

Race and SES Differences in the Relationship Between Religion and Health

Keith E. Whitfield and Kimya I. Jackson

A s behavioral, medical, public health, and epidemiological researchers begin to uncover the layers of complexity around health disparities experienced by ethnic minorities, the concept of religion and spirituality has arisen as a potentially meaningful factor in understanding protective effects for ethnic minorities. The composition of the U.S. is quickly becoming more demographically diverse, particularly in the number of people of color and age (Macera, Armstead, & Anderson, 2000). The health status of the U.S. is significantly impacted by the growing number of older African Americans who disproportionately experience the burden of poor health. Fully understanding how protective factors such as religion and spirituality impact health behaviors and vary by important social factors such as socioeconomic status (SES) will be a major challenge for prevention initiatives and intervention strategies for African Americans.

This chapter responds to and expands upon Chatters' review in this volume. The goal is to contribute to the empirical concepts related to religion and spirituality she presented and to provide suggestions about alternative avenues for research in this growing field of inquiry as they relate to African Americans. Another intent of this chapter is to raise conceptual issues that may assist future research to provide explanations for how these relationships transpire differently across racial/ethnic groups. This discussion will focus on African Americans, but many of these issues are important considerations for other ethnic minorities and should be attended to in examinations of other groups.

INDIVIDUAL CHARACTERISTICS

Individual characteristics that impact the study of religion/spirituality include personality, indices of health, and individual histories that revolve around religious participation at different developmental stages. One of the most studied indices of health is physical limitations. Physical limitations significantly impact the lives of African Americans. Research suggests that African Americans are more likely to have disabilities and live with them longer (Miles & Bernard, 1992). The relationship between the pursuit of religious behavior and physical limitations may be an important direction for research. Does church attendance attenuate the impact religion has on coping or social support? Attendance may require a broad definition among African Americans, given the previously cited rates of disability among this group. Is there a difference on the impact of spirituality in those who go to church compared to those who listen to church services on the radio or watch them on TV?

Personality

One of the most popular conceptualizations of the structure of personality is the Five Factor Model (FFM) offered by Costa and McCrae (Piedmont, 1998). The FFM supposes that personality traits can be described in terms of five basic constructs or dimensions: neuroticism, extraversion, openness, conscientiousness, and agreeableness. Many propose that while personality structure is universal across cultural groups (Costa & McCrae, 1992), individual personality factors interact with other factors to differentially affect some cultural groups. For example, personality has been found to be related to physical illness (Smith & Williams, 1992) and health outcomes (e.g., Kempen, Jelick, & Ormel, 1997). Even though the structure of personality has been found to be highly similar across race, statistically significant differences in mean scores of some domains and facets exist (Heuchert, Parker, Stumpf, & Myburg, 2000). This can be explained by the Five Factor Theory (FFT) (Costa & McCrae, 1992). The FFT postulates that culture directly influences the development of characteristic adaptations, but not basic tendencies. Culture may also affect the degree to which a trait is expressed due to constraints of the context but does not instill nor eliminate traits in the individual (Jang, McRae, Angleitner, Riemann, & Livesley, 1998).

The relationship between religion and personality in late life is understudied. There are several potential reasons why understanding personality may be a key to understanding the relationship between religion/spirituality and health. The central element to variability observed in this relationship may depend on the person-religion "fit." The integration of religious messages into one's life and the utilization of support mechanisms provided by the church may depend on the fit between the deliverer (clergy) and receiver. One potential key to this relationship and fit is emotional context of the presentation of messages. Overgeneralized and exaggerated examples of personality and religious orientation include: energized and charismatic—Baptist; structured and formal—Catholic. What if there is a mismatch between an individual's personality and his religious affiliation? A mismatch in fit may mean avoiding formal religious participation or perhaps a lack of use of the support mechanisms provided by the church.

LIFE COURSE PERSPECTIVE

Cohort Issues and Regional Issues

The Civil Rights cohort is now somewhere between 55–70 years of age. Religion was woven into this movement. Given the overwhelming role of religion during this time in American history, it is not surprising to find high levels of religious participation among older African Americans. But what about the next cohort? There is a positive correlation between age and religious participation (older individuals attend more often than younger). Doing an examination of church attendance and participation over the life course seems critical to understand more about religious behavior in late life.

Raised in the Church. Most African Americans are introduced to religion during their childhood. For many, there is significant time spent by the family in the church and attending religious activities. Moral development and other dimensions of child-rearing occur from this extended contact with the church. This early indoctrination has been called being "raised in the church." This phenomenon offers an opportunity to address health disparities across the life span. Many of the health problems identified in the disparities observed among African Americans, as well as in other groups, have their origins in childhood and young adulthood. Combining spirituality with healthy-living messages and activities may be an important approach to health-disparities prevention. These messages need to be more preventative than the typical alcohol and abstinence speech. There also need to be messages that address obesity, smoking, and physical activity.

Religious activities can serve as a means for health promotion to address chronic conditions like cancer and obesity in messages in church activities. Health promotion programs have been integrated into some church activities as interventions, such as cancer reduction by infusing personalized messages about the addition of fresh fruits and vegetables, to daily meals (Demark-Wahnefried et al., 2000). Perhaps even more important are messages which provide alternatives to traditional food preparation and label reading and evaluation. There are examples where African American churches in the South have made the creation of a garden an activity to attempt to increase the amount of fresh fruits and vegetables into the diet (Demark-Wahnefried et al.). Another example includes a church-based intervention for improved nutrition and physical activity to try to reduce obesity (Resnicow et al., 2002).

DOES SPIRITUALITY REDUCE THE IMPACT OF SES ON HEALTH?

The interrelationship between religion, socioeconomic status, and health for African Americans remains unclear because previous research studies have suffered design flaws or were conceptually weak. Some of the previous research suggests that African Americans of low socioeconomic status are highly religious but there is no discussion of health outcomes for this group (Chatters, 2000). Other research studies suggest that African Americans who live in the southern region of the United States tend to have higher religious participation rates than their northern counterparts, making it difficult to determine if differences exist between the socioeconomic status groups on health outcomes (Chatters, this volume).

Chatters (this volume) states that these conceptual difficulties are based on the fundamental belief that all African Americans (no matter what their socioeconomic status) were highly religious due to being an oppressed group in the United States. Thus, African Americans' religiosity influenced to them to contribute monies to various religious institutions because they represented places of refuge and places to obtain coping skills (Chatters, this volume).

Despite the conceptual difficulties, several relationships between religious practices and positive health outcomes (apart from socioeconomic status) for African Americans have been identified. Religious practices are classified as church attendance or devotion/prayer. Regular church attendance has been linked to improved mental health (less distress and depression), and better subjective health and overall psychological well-being outcomes because individuals develop appropriate coping strategies and positive health behaviors based on their religious beliefs (Chatters, this volume). Additionally, church attendees develop social networks that lead to the experience of social support, which has been identified as an important factor for positive health outcomes. Devotion/prayer has contributed to reduced stress and lower blood pressure readings.

Future research studies need to be conducted to dissect the interrelationship between religion, socioeconomic status, and health outcomes. Chatters (this volume) suggests that culture needs to be included in this interrelationship because it is not feasible to study race without culture. Future researchers need to determine specific measures of socioeconomic status pertinent to the African American community. Moreover, they need to study different denominations that exist within the African American community and how this influences health outcomes and views of socioeconomic status.

PETITIONARY PRAYER AND HEALTH

As previously mentioned, there is a growing literature which suggests that prayer provides empowerment-coping. The focus of this research has been on petitionary prayer. The results suggest that petitionary prayer can help to cope with morbidity. This leads one to wonder, if not for spirituality, would African Americans' health be worse?

While it seems obvious to examine the protective effects that may come from prayer, there may also be outcomes that are less positive. For example, does prayer create delays in accessing health care? Delays may occur from belief in the internal strength belief provides in the short run (then one may ultimately have to go to the doctor when one's health condition is dire).

RACISM AND HEALTH

There is significant support for the notion that religious behavior provides a means for coping with stress (Chatters, 2000; Steffen, Hinderliter,

Blumenthal, & Sherwood, 2001). The relationship between religion and coping may have an interesting impact on the lives of African Americans in relation to stress. For example, directly or indirectly, does belief in God assist African Americans in coping with a racist world? Does it buffer against the daily hassles experienced by living in racist environments? These issues address more than the act of going to church or the social support from the congregation reducing stress but belief in God. However, if one doesn't acknowledge a racist world one may be putting oneself at risk. For example, African Americans may believe they are invincible when others wish them harm. As mentioned previously, they may believe health care will be good when it is not.

To provide a real-world example of the power of spirituality on health behaviors, we drew an example from some of our research conducted in Baltimore, Maryland. The following is a statement by a participant about the relationship between health, the medical field, and God.

> My health ain't the best but I keep on going, I go get my check up every year. But I can't live by the doctor, I have to live by the man up stairs. If you say you're gonna go tomorrow, I look at him (the doctor) and say **he may be good but he ain't no GOD.** I got to believe in the spirit!

One can infer from this statement that there is a strong belief in spiritual influences on health and health behaviors regardless of what one is informed by traditional medicine. This provides an example of the challenges faced in decomposing the impact of spirituality and health behaviors in health disparities research.

FUTURE DIRECTIONS

Issues of religion and health should play a significant role in the future study of SES and race among older adults. There are several interesting paths to pursue which should provide insight about the process of aging. We suggest that there are two paths which seem to involve critical issues that need to be addressed to advance this field. First, there is a need to expand the study of the relationship between religion and health by race to encompass the changing socio-demographic features of ethnic/racial aging in America (see Himes, 1992; Angel & Hogan, 1992). A review of the research on religion and race typically involves comparisons of African Americans and Caucasians and primarily one Protestant religion (Baptist). America's older adult population represents the broadest array of ethnic, racial, and cultural diversity ever witnessed in American society (Burton, Dilworth-Anderson, & Bengtson, 1992). Will the previous relationships which have been found among religion, health, coping, and other psychological assessments hold across the growing ethnic/racial groups? In addition to issues of race, what role will religious affiliation play in the link between health and religion? There may be as strong an influence on Hispanics' health related to Catholicism as on African Americans and the Baptist faith. In addition, cross-comparisons of Catholicism among Hispanics, Caucasians, and African Americans would provide interesting comparisons.

Second, the research on spirituality is in need of a greater emphasis on individual's conceptualizations of God so that the relationship between prayer and life events, health, or social relationships can be better understood. The current research implies individual relationships primarily by measuring church attendance and prayer frequency and how prayer is "applied" to life problems. What is lacking is portrayals of the belief schema that individuals have about what God's role is in their life and what He will do and won't do for them. This could be accomplished through integrating how God is conceptualized in different faiths (e.g., a vengeful God, a benevolent God, etc.). God is perhaps more difficult to operationalize than the concepts of spirituality and prayer. However, some understanding of God based on individual's conceptualizations is necessary for this field of inquiry to achieve its full potential.

CONCLUSION

The goal of this chapter was to respond to Chatters' review in this volume and to suggest some obvious opportunities to advance understanding about the relationship between religion and health as it relates to race and SES. In this chapter, we have focused more on issues related to race than to SES. Given the interrelatedness of the two, we have provided some ideas for alternative conceptualizations about the research agenda on this topic that impact both race and SES. We have also highlighted some psychological, social, and epidemiological considerations for future research. We conclude with somewhat of a challenge to researchers in this field to go beyond basic assessments and conceptualizations of spirituality and pursue older adults' perceptions of the other entity involved in the didactic relationship that is spirituality, namely, God. The perceptions about this relationship are the true foundation for how religion and health work in concert to impact individuals.

REFERENCES

Angel, J. L., & Hogan, D. P. (1992). The demography of minority aging populations. *Journal of Family History, 17*, 95–114.

Chatters, L. M. (2000). Religion and health: Public health research and practice. *Annual Review of Public Health, 21*, 335–367.

Costa, P. T., & McCrae, R. R. (1992). Four ways five factors are basic. *Personality and Individual Differences, 13*(6), 653–665.

Burton, L. M., Dilworth-Anderson, P., & Bengston, V. L. (1992). Creating new ways of thinking about diversity and aging: Theoretical challenges for the twenty-first century. *Generations, 15*(4), 67–72.

Demark-Wahnefried, W., McClelland, J. W., Jackson, B., Campbell, M. K., Cowan A., Hoben, K., & Rimer, B. K. (2000). Partnering with African American churches to achieve better health: Lessons learned during the Black Churches United for Better Health 5 a day project. *Journal of Cancer Education, 15*(3),164–167.

Heuchert, J. W. P., Parker, W. D., Stumpf, H., & Myburgh, C. P. H. (2000). The five-factor model of personality in South African college students. *American Behavioral Scientist, 44*(1), 112–125.

Himes, C. (1992). Social demography of contemporary families and aging. In L. Burton (Ed.), *Families and Aging* (pp. 23–31). New York: Baywood.

Jang, K. L., McCrae, R. R., Angleitner, A., Riemann, R., & Livesley, W. J. (1998). Heritability of facet-level traits in a cross-cultural twin sample: Support for a hierarchical model of personality. *Journal of Personality and Social Psychology, 74*(6), 1556–1565.

Kempen, G. I. J. M., Jelicic, M., & Ormel, J. (1997). Personality, chronic medical morbidity, and health-related quality of life among older persons. *Health Psychology, 16*(6), 539–546.

Macera, C. A., Armstead, C. A., & Anderson, N. B. (2000). Sociocultural influences on health. In A. Baum, T. Revenson, & J. Singer (Eds.), *Handbook of health psychology* (pp. 427–440). Mahwah, NJ: Earlbaum.

Miles, T. P., & Bernard, M. A. (1992). Health status of Black American elderly. *Journal of the American Geriatrics Society, 40*, 1047–1054.

Piedmont, R. L. (1998). *The revised NEO Personality Inventory: Clinical and research applications.* New York: Plenum Press.

Resnicow, K., Jackson, A., Braithwaite, R., DiIorio, C., Blisset, D., Rahotep, S., et al. (2002). Healthy Body/Healthy Spirit: A church-based nutrition and physical activity intervention. *Health Education Research, 17*(5), 562–573.

Smith, T. W., & Williams, P. G. (1992). Personality and health: Advantages and limitations of the five-factor model. *Journal of Personality, 60*(2), 395–423.

Steffen, P. R., Hinderliter, A. L., Blumenthal, J. A., & Sherwood, A. (2001). Religious coping, ethnicity, and ambulatory blood pressure. *Psychosomatic Medicine: Special Issue: 63*(4), 523–530.

CHAPTER 7

Religion and Health in Life Course Perspective

**Linda K. George, Judith C. Hays,
Elizabeth P. Flint, and Keith G. Meador**

R esearch on the relationships between religious participation and health grew exponentially during the past 2 decades. The result has been a deeper and richer knowledge base. We now know that specific dimensions of religious experience are typically robustly related to a variety of health outcomes. And, although longitudinal studies remain less plentiful than desired, sufficient evidence has accumulated to clarify the temporal order between religious involvement and some health outcomes. Despite these gains in knowledge, numerous issues require additional research. This paper focuses on one of those issues: the potential importance of life course patterns of religious involvement for health outcomes in late life.

BACKGROUND AND RATIONALE

There is strong and rapidly increasing evidence that religious participation is protective for health and survival. Perhaps the strongest evidence is that demonstrating that frequent attendance at religious services promotes survival—even with health and functional abilities statistically controlled (e.g., Hummer, Rogers, Nam, & Ellison, 1999; Oman & Reed, 1998; Strawbridge, Cohen, Shema, & Kaplan, 1997).

There also is considerable evidence, however, that religious involvement is prospectively associated with better physical and mental health (e.g., Koenig et al., 1997; Krause, 1998). And among persons with illness and/or disability, religious coping has been documented to increase the likelihood of survival, better illness course, and quality of life (e.g., Ai, Dunkle, Peterson, & Billings, 1998; Koenig et al., 1992; Pargament, 1997).

Religious participation is a multidimensional construct. Although consensus is lacking concerning the full range of dimensions of religious experience that are theoretically and empirically relevant to health, several dimensions have received considerable attention and varying levels of empirical evidence. *Attendance at religious services,* also referred to as public religious participation, has received the most empirical attention and has been the strongest and most consistent predictor of health outcomes. There is, of course, a potentially serious problem with selection effects when using service attendance to predict health or mortality in that illness or disability may make public religious participation difficult or impossible. However, there is now a body of research based on longitudinal research designs demonstrating that the effects of service attendance on mortality persist when health and functional status are statistically controlled (e.g., Hummer et al., 1999; Koenig et al., 1999; Oman & Reed, 1998). Longitudinal studies that examine the effects of disability onset on subsequent religious service attendance are rare, and the results are mixed. Idler and Kasl (1997) report that disability has minimal impact on frequency of attendance. In contrast, Kelley-Moore and Ferraro (2001) report that selection effects rather than social causation explain the relationships between religious participation and functional status.

Other dimensions of religious experience that have been associated with health outcomes include *private religious practices* (e.g., prayer, reading sacred texts) (e.g., Helm, Hays, Flint, Koenig, & Blazer, 2000; Koenig et al., 1999), *religious commitment* or the *perceived importance of religion to one's life* (e.g., Oxman, Freeman, & Manheimer, 1995: Wink & Dillon, 2001), and *religious coping* (Koenig et al., 1992; Pargament, 1997). The latter merits brief comment. As is more broadly true in coping research, religious coping has been examined almost exclusively among persons facing problems (i.e., one doesn't "cope" unless facing a stressor or challenge). Consequently, most studies of religious coping and health have focused on the extent to which religious coping alters the course and outcome of illness.

This raises a larger point with regard to the limitations of cross-sectional analyses of the relationships between religious participation and health. In cross-sectional studies, the health outcomes are measured in terms of prevalence. It is only with longitudinal designs that the effects of religious involvement can be separated into *preventative* and *therapeutic* effects. In studies in which religious participation is linked to the subsequent onset of illness, the potential preventative effects of religious involvement are identified. Longitudinal studies that delineate the effects of religious participation on illness course and outcome examine the therapeutic effects of religious involvement.

In addition to growing in volume, the methodological sophistication of research on religion and health has increased steadily. Recent studies routinely include multivariate analyses in which the effects of potential confounding variables and standard risk factors for morbidity and mortality are statistically controlled. And, although there are fewer longitudinal studies than is desirable, there now are at least some studies to demonstrate that religion has strong, prospective protective effects on health.

Despite substantial progress in understanding the links between religious participation and health, many issues remain unresolved. We argue that one of the most neglected issues concerns life course patterns of religious participation and their potential importance for health outcomes. In research to date, religious participation is virtually always measured in terms of *current* levels of involvement. Clearly, current religious participation tells us nothing about long-term patterns of involvement and this may be an important source of unmeasured heterogeneity. Among persons who currently attend religious services on a regular basis are those for whom this is a long-term or life-long pattern, persons who only recently established this pattern, and persons whose trajectories of religious participation exhibit substantial fluctuation over time. Similarly, among persons who now never or rarely attend religious services are those for whom this is a long-term pattern, as well as those whose participation dropped both long ago and only recently.

The rationale for studying long-term trajectories of religious involvement (or, as they will be labeled interchangeably in this chapter, religious histories) rests on at least two distinct conceptual frameworks. First, life course research has demonstrated the importance of long-term patterns of change and stability for understanding health and well-being in middle and late life. Examples of life course research examining long-term patterns of risk and/or protective factors on health outcomes include Elder and Clipp's studies of the effects of combat experience during young adulthood on health in later life (Elder & Clipp, 1988; 1989), Barrett's investigation of the effects of marital histories (rather than current marital status) on mental health outcomes (Barrett, 2000), and research by several investigators on the persisting effects of childhood traumas (e.g., physical abuse, sexual abuse, parental divorce) on the physical and mental health of adults (e.g., Kessler & Magee, 1994; Winfield, George, Swartz, & Blazer, 1990; Yama, Tovey, & Fogas, 1993). Life course perspectives also provide a powerful strategy for identifying the conditions under which early events and experiences affect subsequent health. Elder and Clipp (1988; 1989), for example, report that high levels of social support during adulthood, especially satisfying and stable marriages, substantially reduce the negative effects of combat experience on late life health.

A second rationale for investigating life course patterns of religious involvement concerns the epidemiologic concept of "length of exposure"—an issue central to epidemiologic investigation of risk factors for morbidity and mortality. The general expectation, of course, is one of dose-response: the longer and more intense the exposure to the risk factor, the stronger its effect on subsequent health. To use a stark example, epidemiologists could not have identified the health risks of smoking if they had only determined whether respondents were smoking at the time they were interviewed. It is "pack years" of smoking that has proven to be predictive of morbidity and mortality. Clearly, pack years summarizes the length and intensity of exposure to the risk factor. Currently, our knowledge of the relationships between religion and health are based on measures of religious participation that are analogous to knowing if one currently smokes cigarettes. This crude form of measurement, in terms of indexing length of exposure, has revealed robust relationships between multiple dimensions of religious participation and a variety of health outcomes. Nonetheless, examination of long-term patterns of religious involvement may provide additional, more fine-grained, knowledge about the links between religion and health.

The primary purpose of this chapter is to describe trajectories of religious involvement from childhood to old age, as retrospectively constructed by a sample of older adults, and to report initial results about the relationships between these trajectories and physical and mental health outcomes. Four dimensions of religious participation are examined: religious service attendance, time spent in private religious devotions, the importance of religion in one's life, and exposure to religious media on the television and radio. Prior to reporting our research, however, we will briefly review what is known about life course patterns of religious participation.

WHAT DO WE KNOW ABOUT LIFE COURSE PATTERNS OF RELIGIOUS PARTICIPATION?

Remarkably little is known about life course patterns of religious participation. Research to date has focused almost exclusively on attending religious services and has been based on cross-sectional studies of age differences in religious involvement. With one notable exception, the few longitudinal studies of religious participation have covered relatively short periods of time. Hypotheses about life course patterns of religious involvement have taken two primary forms. When researchers on aging first became interested in religion, they predicted that religious involvement would increase during late life as a result of declining health, loss of family and friends, and, the realization of proximity to one's own death (e.g., Becker, 1973; Berman, 1974). Scholars using developmental theories made similar predictions. Carl Jung (1964) was perhaps the first to hypothesize increased commitment to religion and spirituality during middle and late life as part of a more general reorientation toward internal concerns. Similarly, Erikson (1963) suggested that the last developmental task that individuals face is ego integrity versus despair. He suggested that issues of meaning, acceptance, and forgiveness of self and others were important components of the journey toward integrity and that religious principles are frequently used as a framework for that journey (Erikson & Erikson, 1997). More recently, in a book based on Erikson's notes and private papers, Hoare (2002) documents the pivotal roles that Erikson attributed to religion, morals, and ethics in adult development. Erikson defined morals as the conventional guidelines transmitted to societal members and ethics as the guiding principles that individuals develop via personal experience and contemplation. In his view, the mature adult has moved beyond conventional morals to a richer and more complex set of ethical principles. Hoare claims that Erikson viewed organized religion as the bastion of conventional morality rather than promoting complex ethical reasoning. Recall, however, that Erikson's two major psycho-biographies are of religious leaders: Luther (Erikson, 1958) and Gandhi (Erickson, 1969). These religious leaders are viewed by Erikson as having transformed religious dogma by means of mature ethical reasoning, backed by behavioral commitment to that reasoning. Wright (1982) presents another view of Erikson's work that aligns it more closely with the development of organized religion.

A variant of the developmental perspective suggests that life crises play a special role in triggering concerns about religious and spiritual issues—ultimately generating growth from adversity. Scholars who subscribe to this tenet suggest that crises and challenges, ranging from the death of loved ones to personal health problems to confronting age discrimination, often play a pivotal role in focusing one's attention on larger issues of meaning (e.g., Atchley, 1997; Idler, 1995). Recently, several investigators have turned their attention to the benefits that adverse experiences can have for growth (e.g., Affleck & Tennen, 1996; McMillen, Smith, & Fisher, 1997). Although the research base remains small, there is convincing empirical evidence that large proportions of individuals who experience severe traumas report benefits (as well as problems) resulting from their experience (e.g., Lehman et al., 1993; McMillen, Zuravin, & Rideout, 1995). Evidence concerning the mental health benefits of perceived benefits is mixed, however (McMillen & Cook, 2003; McMillen et al., 1997).

A potentially important contribution of the life crisis hypothesis is its potential for explaining individual differences in patterns of religious experience. Both the occurrence and the timing of increased commitment to religious experience may be, in part, a function of exposure to stressors. For example, McMillen and Cook (2003) report that increased spirituality is a common outcome of severe psychological trauma. On the other hand, life crises can trigger an accompanying crisis of faith, leading some individuals to turn away from religious commitment and involvement. Indeed, 70 years ago, in a now-classic study, Vetter and Green (1932–1933) demonstrated that more than half of the members of the American Association for the Advancement of Atheism had turned away from religion and the notion of God after experiencing major life crises, typically the death of a close family member. Thus, the life crisis hypothesis may help explain both dramatic increases and decreases in religious involvement over the life course. Health and well-being also may depend, in part, on the individual's ability to grow from the experience of adversity rather than succumbing to it.

Family researchers developed a different hypothesis, based on their theoretical template of the family life cycle. These investigators suggest that the major activities of adulthood are defined by family roles and that there is substantial uniformity in responses to those roles. With regard to religious involvement, family life cycle theory suggests that individuals typically decrease involvement in religious organizations during adolescence and early adulthood, followed by an increase in religious participation after children are born, and that religious involvement will remain quite stable until very late in life when health problems interfere with public religious participation (Duvall & Miller, 1985).

The developmental hypothesis has been conceptually applied to multiple dimensions of religious involvement (e.g., public and private participation, the importance of religion in one's life). Nonetheless, empirical tests of this hypothesis have focused almost exclusively on public religious participation. The family life course hypothesis has focused specifically on attending religious services because of the assumption that the increase in participation after the birth of children reflects parents' desires to provide religious socialization experiences to their offspring. Empirical tests of both hypotheses are relatively rare.

Before turning to available empirical evidence concerning life course patterns of religious participation, a brief note about "faith development" is merited. Fowler (1981) developed and tested a model of faith development. Like Kohlberg and Piaget, Fowler posits a stage theory of faith development, with successively higher stages representing more complex views of morality, ethics, and meaning. Although Fowler labels his theory as developmental, his stages of faith are only loosely linked to age. To date, this theory has been tested only cross-sectionally with mixed results. Because Fowler's theory focuses on patterns of cognition rather than the more behavioral indicators of religious experience considered here, his work will not be examined further.

The Developmental Hypothesis: Empirical Evidence

Early cross-sectional studies of religious participation focused on age differences in rates of religious service attendance. The hypothesis that service attendance would be higher among older than younger adults received considerable support (e.g., Alston & McIntosh, 1974; Moberg, 1965). What could not be determined, of course, was whether these differences were a function of age changes, cohort differences, or both. In the mid-1970s, Blazer and Palmore (1976) examined patterns of service attendance over time among middle-aged and older adults, although the period of observation was relatively short (i.e., 8 years). The results suggested relatively stable patterns of attendance over time. Because the study observed individuals who were middle-aged and older at baseline and the follow-up interval was relatively short, the question of whether religious involvement increases after young adulthood could not be answered.

Investigators using developmental theories of religious involvement also have been hampered by the lack of long-term longitudinal data, relying on cross-sectional and retrospective data. Moreover, because the emphasis in these studies tends to be on linking religious experience to psychological issues such as self-acceptance and concerns about younger generations, the boundaries of "religious experience" tend to be vague—indeed, there is seldom an effort to define religious experience. Nonetheless, several investigators claim to have identified a shift toward religious or spiritual issues during middle or late life. For example, using in-depth retrospective interviews with a small sample, Bianchi (1987) reported a midlife transformation in which religious beliefs become less moralistic and rigid. Using a somewhat larger sample, Tornstam (1999) found evidence of a shift toward transcendence in later life, arguing that this represents a distinct developmental shift. It is unclear, however, whether and how this transcendence is linked to religion (although respondents often used religious concepts and metaphors to describe transcendence).

One recent study, however, appears to have broken new ground with regard to life course patterns of religiousness and spirituality. Using data from the Berkeley Growth Studies, with observations spanning more than 40 years, Wink and Dillon (2002) examined patterns of religious and spiritual involvement from early adulthood through old age (late 60s–mid-70s). These authors defined spirituality in terms of two criteria: (a) spiritual quest—i.e., explicit concern about spiritual issues such as purpose and meaning in life and (b) commitment to spiritual practices such as prayer, meditation, or reading spiritual literature. Religious participation was measured as involvement in organized religion. Clearly, these definitions of the boundaries between religion and spirituality are open to dispute. In particular, as defined in this study, "spiritual practices" are similar to the concept of "private religious practices" frequently studied as a dimension of religious involvement.

Wink and Dillon (2002) report several findings relevant to the developmental perspective. First, patterns of religious participation tended to be established in early adulthood and remain quite stable thereafter. Second, there was a clear ascendance of spirituality in middle age that continued into later life. This modal pattern or "trajectory" is based on group means. There was undoubtedly substantial individual variation that is not captured by the modal pattern. Third, the two cohorts in the Berkeley Growth Studies differed somewhat in life course patterns of spirituality. By midlife the cohorts looked much the same, but during young adulthood there was substantial evidence of spirituality in the younger, but not the older cohort. The authors attribute this cohort difference to the increase in public attention to spirituality as distinct from religion that emerged after World War II and affected the younger cohort earlier in the life course. For our purposes, it is important to note that religious participation was a strong predictor of spirituality both concurrently and prospectively.

One can argue with the methods of measurement in the Wink and Dillon (2002) study. Specific questions about spirituality were not asked at any of the interviews and even religious participation was not assessed at each interview. The authors coded religion and spirituality by extracting segments from the interviews in which participants spontaneously mentioned issues relevant to religion and/or spirituality. Despite these potential measurement problems, this study merits attention as the first to trace long-term patterns of religious and spiritual involvement across the adult life course.

The tenet that stressors are associated with higher levels of religious and/or spiritual involvement receives some support in previous research. Several cross-sectional studies report higher rates of religious/spiritual involvement among persons who have experienced serious personal or interpersonal crises (Atchley, 1997; Idler, 1995). The problem with these studies, of course, is that temporal order cannot be established. In their longitudinal study, however, Wink and Dillon (2002) found stressful life events and other adversities to prospectively predict increases in spirituality. The effects of stressors were additive with general age changes—that is, increased spirituality from midlife on was typical and the experience of stressors augmented this general pattern.

The Family Life Cycle Hypothesis

The family life cycle hypothesis has received less empirical attention than the developmental hypothesis. Virtually all empirical tests of the family life cycle hypothesis have relied on cross-sectional data. Recall that the major feature of this hypothesis is that the birth of children ignites increased religious participation as indexed by attending religious services and other activities sponsored by religious organizations. In addition, those increased levels of participation are expected to continue into middle and old age.

The life cycle hypothesis has received limited support in the two major tests to date (Firebaugh & Harley, 1991; Stolzenberg, Blair-Loy, & Waite, 1995). Although young adults with children are significantly more likely to attend religious services than young adults who are not married or those who are married and childless, the pattern is not strong—certainly not sufficiently strong to merit the label of a predictable life course pattern. The pattern also is complex, depending in part on factors including gender, age of the parents, and age of the children (Stolzenberg et al., 1995). Patterns of divorce, cohabitation, and remarriage also complicate the picture. As examples, divorced women are substantially more likely to attend religious services than divorced men and cohabiting couples are less likely to attend services regardless of the presence of minor children.

A somewhat different question has emerged from research on the life cycle hypothesis of religious participation. Because this hypothesis rests on the assumption that families with young children increase participation in organized religion in order to provide religious socialization to the children, some investigators have studied religious socialization itself. The key question in this research is whether socialization "works"—i.e., the extent to which religious socialization elicits long-term patterns of religious participation after childhood. Results from studies of this form of "religious inheritance" show strong and consistent results: the stronger the religious socialization, the more likely that adults will reproduce their parents' patterns of religious participation (e.g., Myers, 1996; Wilson & Sherkat, 1994). Indeed, religious socialization is a stronger predictor of religious participation than family life cycle status, although the latter also is significant. In addition, religious socialization is partially mediated by parents' marital happiness (Myers) and continued close ties to family of origin (Wilson & Sherkat).

For our purposes, research on the life cycle hypothesis and religious socialization suggests two patterns that might be expected in individuals' religious histories. First, although the pattern is less consistent than expected, religious participation may increase during child-rearing. Second, strong religious socialization during childhood may set the stage for lifelong commitment to religious involvement.

Life Course Patterns of Religious Participation and Health

To date, possible links between life course patterns of religious participation and health have received little attention. Again, the work of Wink and Dillon (2001) is an exception to the general pattern. These authors examined the relationships between religious participation and multiple measures of health and well-being. They did not, however, investigate trajectories of religious participation. Rather they first examined concurrent relationships between religious involvement and health in late life. Subsequently, they determined whether religiousness/spirituality earlier in the life course also predicted health and well-being in late life.

Physical health was rated by coders who had access to both interviews with participants and their answers to questions about self-rated health, perceived energy, and physical complaints. There was no significant relationship between religious participation in late life and the physical health ratings; the same pattern emerged when religious involvement at earlier ages was examined. There also was no main effect of concurrent religious participation on life satisfaction during late life.

A significant interaction was observed, however: religious participation buffered the effects of physical health problems on life satisfaction. This same interactive effect was observed when religious participation was measured 30 years earlier than life satisfaction during old age. Mental health was measured using multiple scales that assessed both inner-directed (e.g., personal growth, self-acceptance) and outer-directed (e.g., generativity, positive relations with others) concerns. Both concurrently and prospectively, religious participation predicted other-focused, but not inner-focused, dimensions of mental health.

Although the topic of the relationships between long-term patterns of religious participation and health outcomes is similar in Wink and Dillon's (2001) study and that reported here, the strategies used are very different. Wink and Dillon included prospective predictions of these relationships with long intervals between measurement of the independent and dependent variables. But they did not examine long-term patterns of religious involvement. In contrast, our goal was to link life-long trajectories of religious participation to health outcomes in late life. We turn to our study now.

THE DUKE RELIGIOUS/SPIRITUAL HISTORY STUDY

Study Design and Methods

The data reported here are from a study designed to develop measures of religious history. As described below, a "life calendar" approach was used to assess multiple dimensions of religious involvement across the life course. Thus, this study is based on retrospective reports of religious participation. In addition, because the focus of the larger study was instrument development, both qualitative and quantitative methods were used to measure religious participation.

Developing a Measure of Religious History

When we began our study, there were no standardized instruments for measuring religious history. In a conference paper, Benson (1991) presented a 100-item survey of religious biography. In terms of content, the survey emphasized public religious participation and private religious practices. A major component of the survey was religious participation during childhood. In addition, Benson asked respondents about dramatic increases and decreases in religious faith. The conference paper provided no information about the psychometric properties of the survey or relationships between religious history and health. Beyond

Benson's work, we identified a few studies that included measures of both current religious participation and familial practices during childhood (e.g., Chatters, Levin, & Taylor, 1992; Levin, Chatters, & Taylor, 1995). None of these previous efforts provided an efficient, comprehensive method of measuring religious history. Benson's survey is very rich, but it is (a) too long for inclusion in most research projects and (b) lacks psychometric analysis. Measures of childhood religious involvement are incomplete.

Because of the lack of extant measures, we launched a two-phase project to develop methods for assessing religious history. The first phase consisted of in-depth open-ended interviews with a small number of respondents. The second phase involved structured interviews with a larger number of older adults whom we had studied for a decade and about whom we had extensive health information.

All study participants, in both phases of the project, were age 65 and older. Restriction of the age range of participants reflects both practical and scientific issues. In terms of practicality, one of the goals of this project was to examine the relationships between religious history and health. By focusing the religious history project on older adults, we were able to link it to our ongoing study of a representative sample of community-dwelling older adults from whom we have detailed health information for 10 years, as well as to reports of religious participation over the same decade. Scientifically, if the measures of religious history generated by the project are intended to cover all of adulthood, it makes sense to focus on older adults, who have the longest religious histories.

Phase I. The purpose of Phase I was to obtain information from older adults about their religious histories. Because we wanted to hear how respondents described their life course patterns of religious involvement in their own words, semi-structured, open-ended interviews were conducted with 30 persons age 65 and older from the Duke University Aging Center Subject Registry. This registry includes more than 1,900 community-dwelling adults in the Durham/Chapel Hill/Raleigh area who are willing to participate in research. Although intense efforts are made to insure heterogeneity in the Subject Registry, it is ultimately a pool of research volunteers. The 30 subjects who participated in Phase I had the following characteristics: 60% were women; one-third were African American and two-thirds were white; the age range was 65 to 88 years; and with regard to religious affiliation, 13% were Jewish, 10% were Roman Catholic, and 77% were Protestant. This distribution of religious affiliation is characteristic of the geographic area.

The interviews were open-ended, but the interviewers obtained information about seven topics: demographic characteristics; religious affiliation across the life course; earliest religious memory; periods of particular religious significance (including "turning points"); patterns of public religious participation, private religious practices, and the importance of religion across the life course; primary positive and negative influences on religiousness across the life course; and current beliefs about selected theological issues (e.g., belief in an afterlife, original sin).

The 30 interviews ranged in length from 1.5 to 3 hours. All the interviews were transcribed and the constant comparative method (e.g. Patton, 1990) was used to extract themes and common issues. Identification of the themes and efforts to translate them into closed-ended interview questions for Phase II were performed by three of the authors of this paper. The interviews proved to be a successful strategy for eliciting a life course view of religiousness in multiple dimensions, identifying both dramatic turning points and long-term patterns of religious experience.

Phase II. During Phase II, items derived from the open-ended interviews were administered to 157 respondents participating in the Duke University Established Populations for Epidemiologic Studies of the Elderly (Duke EPESE). The Duke EPESE began with a multistage, stratified sample of older adults living in five North Carolina counties. The first in-person interview was administered in 1986 to 1,462 persons age 65 and older. In 1996, the fourth in-person interview was administered to survivors of the EPESE cohort. Two other in-person interviews were administered to EPESE participants between the first and fourth interviews. Approximately 2,000 respondents participated in all four in-person interviews. More than 85% of the attrition between the first and last interviews was the result of respondent death.

The sampling frame for Phase II consisted of Duke EPESE respondents who (a) had participated in all four in-person interviews and (b) were cognitively intact and capable of being interviewed in the 1996 survey—i.e., who scored no more than one error on the Short Portable Mental Status Questionnaire (Pfeiffer, 1975). This pool of EPESE respondents was then stratified by religious affiliation as reported in the baseline interview. In order to ensure diversity of religious affiliation, we attempted to interview a randomly selected one of every seven Fundamentalist and Pietistic Protestants, one of every two Mainline Protestants, and all affiliated and non-affiliated others (i.e., Roman Catholics, Jews, Mormons, Unitarian Universalists, Jehovah's Witnesses, agnostics, and atheists). Of the 228 respondents selected for Phase II,

15 had died and 6 had moved from the tracking area since 1996. Of the remainder, 76% (N = 157) consented to in-person interviews in their homes by a trained interviewer. A subgroup of 20 of these respondents agreed to participate in a test-retest reliability study, in which the interview was repeated approximately 2 weeks later.

The Phase II interview consisted of 108 questions that were developed on the basis of themes that emerged during analysis of the Phase I qualitative data. We subsequently performed psychometric analyses to reduce the number of items in the scale (Hays, Meador, Branch, & George, 2001). One major component of the interview, of special relevance to this paper, was the retrospective measures of religious service attendance, private religious practices, the perceived importance of religion in the respondents' lives, and use of religious media (television and radio). A "life history calendar" strategy (Freedman, Thornton, Camburn, Alwin, & Young-DeMarco, 1988) was used in which respondents reported levels of these religious dimensions on a decade-by-decade basis, from early childhood to the present. Information about dramatic religious events and or "turning points" was also obtained.

Developing Life Course Trajectories of Religious Experience. Life history data collected in Phase II permitted the construction of retrospective life course trajectories for four dimensions of religious experience: public participation (i.e., service attendance), private religious practices, exposure to religious programs on television and radio, and the perceived importance of religion in respondents' lives. Respondents reported their levels of involvement on each of these dimensions during childhood and for every decade of their adult lives. Response categories for all four dimensions ranged from 1–6 (i.e., from never to once a week or more for service attendance and use of religious media, from never to once a day or more for private religious practices, and from unimportant to utmost importance for religious commitment).

The trajectories were then sorted, on the basis of visual inspection, into the number of discrete patterns observed for a given dimension of religious experience. Once the visually-generated trajectories were identified, they were scrutinized so that the "decision rules" underlying the set of trajectories could be extracted (e.g., consistent moderate religious importance = a score of 3 or 4 on religious importance for at least 5 decades, with no deviations above 5 or below 2). These decision rules insured that the final trajectories were reliably constructed.

These procedures generated nine distinct trajectories of service attendance, private religious practices, and religious importance; six trajectories of religious media use were identified. Because of the small sample sizes for several trajectories in each domain, consolidation of trajectories was required prior to data analysis. After consolidation, there are six trajectories for service attendance, five trajectories for private religious practices, and four trajectories each for importance of religion and use of religious media.

Other Measures Used in Analysis

A major purpose of this paper is to examine the relationships between trajectories of religious participation and health outcomes. We also examined the relationships between life course patterns of religious involvement and both demographic characteristics and social support in late life. We view these variables as encompassing broader indicators of well-being than traditional health outcomes. Three categories of variables other than religious history were used in the analysis: demographic variables and social support were taken from the fourth in-person EPESE interview; health and well-being measures were obtained during the religious history interviews.

Demographic Variables. Several demographic variables are known risk or protective factors for health outcomes in late life and are related to one or more dimensions of religious participation. The demographic variables examined are age (measured in years), race (African American vs. White), gender, marital status (a simple dichotomy of married versus unmarried), and education (measured in years).

Social Support. The Duke Social Support Index (DSSI) elicits information about four dimensions of social support (see Landerman, George, Campbell, & Blazer, 1986, for details about the scale and its psychometric properties). *Social Network Size* is the most objective structural component of social support measured. It tallies the number of close friends and family upon whom the respondent can depend during times of need or crisis. Household members are not counted in the tally. *Social Interaction* measures the amount of time that respondents spend talking to and being with members of their support networks. *Instrumental Support* measures the types of tangible and intangible assistance that respondents receive from members of their social support networks. *Perceived Support* measures the extent to which respondents feel cared for and can depend on network members.

Health and Well-Being. Four health measures are examined in this paper. *Self-Rated Health* is assessed using the standard single-item measure.

Because so few respondents reported poor health, we aggregated fair and poor health, resulting in three responses: poor/fair, good, and excellent. *Instrumental Activities of Daily Living (IADL)* (George & Fillenbaum, 1985) measure functional status. *Depressive Symptoms* are measured with a modified version of the Center for Epidemiologic Depression Scale (CES-D) (Radloff, 1977). (See Blazer, Burchett, Service, & George, 1991 for details of this version of the CES-D.) *Life Satisfaction* is examined as an indicator of overall well-being and was measured using the Life Satisfaction Index originally developed by Neugarten and colleagues (Neugarten, Havighurst, & Tobin, 1961).

RESULTS

Trajectories of Religious Participation

Table 7.1 provides descriptions and sample sizes for the consolidated trajectories for the four dimensions of religious involvement. North Carolina is in the Bible Belt and the distributions of respondents across trajectories clearly emphasize that point. Slightly more than a third of the respondents reported lifelong high levels of attending religious services and engaging in private religious practices. Nearly half of the respondents reported either high lifelong use of religious media or steadily increasing use across time. And more than half (53%) of the respondents indicated that religion had been consistently of utmost importance throughout their lives.

Despite these very high rates of lifelong religious involvement, other patterns were reported by reasonable, albeit smaller numbers of EPESE participants. Increases in religious involvement were more common for all four dimensions than were decreases or lifelong patterns of low involvement. The trajectories for service attendance were most distinctive. About 15% of the sample exhibited a substantial decline in attendance in early adulthood, followed by a rebound prior to middle age—a pattern that may reflect the presence of minor children, as predicted in family life course theory.

We were surprised that nearly one-third of the respondents reported a precipitous decline in service attendance around the age of 50, with two-thirds of these individuals reporting a later rebound to high levels of attendance and one-third remaining at low levels of attendance after age 50. When respondents reported precipitous "turning points" on any of the religious variables, they were asked the reason for or circumstances surrounding the dramatic change. With regard to the precipitous decline in service attendance at approximately age 50, a

TABLE 7.1   Trajectory Types and Distributions

Trajectory Type	Code	n	%
Religious Service Attendance			
1. Lifelong high	Lifehigh	57	36.3
2. Gradual unidirectional change	Chng1way	15	9.6
3. Early decline with rebound, multiple fluctuations	Other	24	15.3
4. Precipitous decline after 50, rebound	50+downup	17	10.8
5. Precipitous decline after 50, no rebound	50+down	34	21.7
6. Lifelong low	Lifelow	10	6.4
Private Religious Practices			
1. Lifelong high	Lifehigh	55	35.0
2. Increase over life	Increase	13	6.3
3. Precipitous decline, rebound	Downup	41	26.1
4. Decrease over life	Decrease	39	24.8
5. Lifelong low	Lifelow	9	5.7
Religious Media Use			
1. Lifelong high	Lifehigh	74	47.1
2. Fluctuations across life course	Fluctuate	19	12.1
3. Increase, then precipitous decline	Updown	35	22.3
4. Lifelong low or no use	Lifelow	29	18.5
Religious Importance			
1. Lifelong very important	Lifehigh	84	53.5
2. Gradual increase over life course	Gradinc	22	14.0
3. Dramatic increase, sustained	Biginc	26	16.6
4. Decrease and lifelong low	Dec/low	25	15.9

variety of reasons were reported. Among those who experienced a precipitous decline and then a rebound, illness was the most common attribution for the decline, with recovery or improvement in health accounting for the subsequent rebound. Among those who did not rebound, the most common reason given for decreasing or stopping service attendance was interpersonal differences with the clergy, lay church leaders, and/or congregational peers.

Correlates of Trajectories of Religious Involvement

Analyses were performed to examine the relationships between religious history trajectories and the three categories of other variables: demographic characteristics, dimensions of social support, and the indicators of health and well-being. Unfortunately, because of the small sample size, analysis is restricted to bivariate relationships. Religious history trajectories are, of course, categorical variables. When the correlate also was categorical, chi-square tests were used; for continuous variables, analysis of variance was used to generate means for the religious trajectories and determine whether the differences observed were statistically significant.

In the following sections, the correlates of religious trajectories for each of the four domains of religious involvement are described. Given 4 religious domains, 4–6 trajectories per domain, and 12 correlates per trajectory, the results are extremely detailed and complex. Table 7.2 presents a summary of the significant (and, in the case of gender, nearly significant) correlates identified. This table may help to summarize the details presented in Tables 7.3 to 7.6.

Correlates of Religious Service Attendance

Table 7.3 presents the relationships between the trajectories of religious service attendance and demographic, social support, and health and well-being measures. (Means and percentages for the total sample are reported in parentheses beside the variable names.) Many of the 12 possible correlates examined differed across the trajectories of service attendance.

Demographic Variables. Two demographic variables were significantly associated with the trajectories of religious service attendance. Blacks were significantly more likely than whites to report lifelong high levels of attending religious services; alternatively, they were far less likely than whites to report either a precipitous decline in attendance after age 50 or a lifelong pattern of infrequent attendance. Marital status also was significantly related to trajectories of service attendance (not tabled). The unmarried were more likely to report lifelong high levels of attendance; conversely, the married were more likely to report both fluctuating patterns of attendance (trajectories 2 and 3) and lifelong patterns of infrequent attendance. Two notes about the unmarried respondents in this sample are merited. First, because this is a sample of older adults, the unmarried participants were overwhelmingly widowed. Second, keep in mind that we are looking at marital status at age 70 and older; current marital statuses reflect a variety of marital *histories*. The important point is that for many respondents, current marital status was measured at a time that is temporally far removed from at least the early decades of the religious history.

TABLE 7.2   Summary of Correlates of Religious History Trajectories in Four Domains

	Religious History Domain			
	Service Attendance	Private Religious Practices	Religious Media Use	Religious Importance
Trajectory Type				
Lifelong High	Unmarried** Women	Women	Women	Women**
Fluctuating Pattern	Married** Men			
Precipitous Decline After 50	Whites** Women Low Self-Rated Health** High IADL Impairment** High Depression** Low Life Satisfaction**			

Religious History Domain

	Service Attendance	Private Religious Practices	Religious Media Use	Religious Importance
Precipitous Decline After 50, Then Rebound	Women Low Self-Rated Health** High Depression**			
Lifelong Low	Whites** Married** High Education** Low Social Interaction** High Self-Rated Health**	Whites** High Education**	Whites** High Education** Low Social Interaction** Young-Old** Low Instrumental Support** High Life Satisfaction**	Whites** High Education** Low Social Interaction** Low Social Network** Low Perceived Support** High Self-Rated Health**

** $p < .01$

TABLE 7.3　Correlates of Religious Service Trajectories

						Trajectory Type						
	1 Lifehigh		2 Chng1way		3 Other		4 50+downup		5 50+down		6 Lifelow	
Variable	%	M	%	M	%	M	%	M	%	M	%	M
Demographic Variables												
Age (79.9)		79.6		79.7		79.9		81.4		80.4		78.0
Male (33.8%)	29.8		60.0		45.8		17.7		29.4		30.0	
Female (66.2%)	70.2		40.0		54.2		82.4		70.5		70.0	
Black (31.2%)	47.4		33.3		25.0		23.5		17.7		10.0*	
White (68.8%)	52.6		66.7		75.0		76.5		82.4		90.0	
Education in years (12.1)		12.4		10.3		12.6		11.9		11.7		13.2
Social Support												
Social Network Size (11.5)		12.3		12.5		11.3		11.1		11.4		7.6
Social Interaction (14.0)		15.6		14.7		12.9		13.2		13.5		9.8*
Instrumental Support (8.7)		8.6		9.0		9.5		8.1		8.8		7.1
Perceived Support (5.6)		5.7		5.7		5.7		5.5		5.4		5.2
Health and Well-Being												
Self-Rated Health												
Excellent (23.6%)	24.6		13.1		20.8		17.7		17.7		70.0*	
Good (43.3%)	45.6		53.3		50.0		29.4		41.2		30.0	
Fair/Poor (33.1%)	29.8		33.3		29.2		52.9		41.2		00.0	
IADL (0.5)	0.2		0.1		0.3		0.4		1.5		0.8*	
Katz ADL (0.2)	0.1		0.1		0.2		0.4		0.5		0.1	
Depressive Symptoms (2.2)	1.7		2.3		1.5		2.2		3.8		1.2*	
Life Satisfaction (19.1)	19.9		18.3		20.1		18.2		16.9		21.5*	

* $p < .01$

Although they did not achieve statistical significance, visual inspection reveals fairly dramatic differences across trajectories by both gender and education. Men were substantially less likely than women to report lifelong patterns of frequent religious attendance and more likely to report fluctuating patterns or lifelong levels of infrequent attendance. In addition, the declines in attendance after age 50, whether or not they were followed by a rebound in public religious participation, were overwhelmingly reported by women. With regard to education, respondents with more than a high school education were dramatically over-represented among respondents reporting lifelong patterns of infrequent attendance. In a larger sample, these differences would undoubtedly be statistically significant.

Social Support. One of the four dimensions of social support was significantly related to the trajectories of religious service attendance. Respondents who reported lifelong infrequent service attendance reported significantly lower levels of social interaction than other respondents, especially those with lifelong patterns of frequent attendance. Indeed, this pattern was observed for all the social support measures, although it was statistically significant only for social interaction.

Health and Well-Being. All four indicators of health and well-being were significantly associated with the religious service trajectories. The relationships between the religious service trajectories and self-rated health were surprising in light of previous research. Persons who reported excellent health also were significantly more likely to report lifelong patterns of low religious attendance. At the opposite end of the health spectrum, none of the respondents who reported their health to be fair or poor reported lifelong infrequent attendance. Persons reporting fair or poor health were disproportionately represented in the two trajectories characterized by a precipitous decline in attendance after age 50 (trajectories 4 and 5). We believe that this pattern, in large part, reflects the high levels of education among those who report stable patterns of infrequent attendance. Unfortunately, sample size does not permit us to test this hypothesis.

For IADL impairments, the significant contrast is between (a) persons who reported a dramatic decline in attendance after age 50 and whose attendance did not subsequently rebound and (b) all other trajectories. It is possible that this trajectory reflects the consequences of disability for service attendance, but we cannot test this hypothesis because we do not know the age at onset of functional impairment. (Also, as noted previously, most respondents who reported this trajectory attributed their precipitous and long-term decreases in attendance to conflicts with church members and/or clergy). The same pattern is observed for depressive symptoms and life satisfaction. That is, depressive symptoms are significantly higher, and levels of life satisfaction significantly lower, among persons who reported precipitous declines in service attendance after age 50 with no subsequent increase in attendance.

Correlates of Private Religious Practices

As shown in Table 7.4, there are fewer statistically significant differences across trajectories of private religious participation than for religious service attendance.

Demographic Variables. Among the demographic variables, race was significantly related to life-course patterns of private religious practices. African Americans were significantly more likely to report lifelong high levels of private religious practices than whites. In contrast, whites were disproportionately represented in all the other trajectories. Education was also significantly associated with patterns of private religious practices, although the relationship is complex. The major contrast is between respondents with more than a high school education and their less-educated peers. Participants with more than a high school education were disproportionately represented in two trajectories: a pattern of increase across adulthood followed by a decline (trajectory 4) and lifelong low levels of private religious practices (trajectory 5).

Although not statistically significant, rather dramatic gender differences were observed in life course patterns of private religious practices. Women were substantially more likely than men to report lifelong high involvement in private religious practices (trajectory 1) and increasing involvement in private religious practices across adulthood (trajectory 2). In contrast, men were more likely to report fluctuating and lifelong low levels of involvement in private religious practices (trajectories 3–5).

Social Support. None of the measures of social support were significantly related to the trajectories of private religious practices. For three of the measures—social network size, social interaction, and instrumental support—substantially lower levels of support were reported by persons with lifelong low levels of private religious practices. But these differences did not achieve statistical significance.

TABLE 7.4   Correlates of Private Religious Practices Trajectories

	1 Lifehigh		2 Increase		3 Downup		4 Decrease		5 Lifelow	
Variable	%	M	%	M	%	M	%	M	%	M
Demographic Variables										
Age (79.9)		80.8		77.8		79.9		79.5		79.9
Male (33.8%)	21.8		23.1		41.5		41.0		55.6	
Female (66.2%)	70.2		40.0		54.2		82.4		70.5	
Black (31.2%)	43.6		7.7		39.0		18.0		11.1*	
White (68.8%)	56.4		92.3		61.0		82.1		88.9	
Education in years (12.1)		11.6		9.8		11.9		13.1		14.9*
Social Support										
Social Network Size (11.5)		11.7		12.9		12.1		10.8		9.4
Social Interaction (14.0)		15.0		15.8		14.0		13.3		9.4
Instrumental Support (8.7)		9.1		9.4		8.8		8.2		6.8
Perceived Support (5.6)		5.6		5.8		5.6		5.5		5.6
Health and Well-Being										
Self-Rated Health										
Excellent (23.6%)	21.8		15.4		24.4		20.5		55.6	
Good (43.3%)	47.3		53.9		39.0		43.6		22.2	
Fair/Poor (33.1%)	30.9		30.8		36.6		35.9		22.2	
IADL (0.5)		0.5		0.2		0.7		0.6		0.6
Katz ADL (0.2)		0.2		0.0		0.3		0.2		0.7
Depressive Symptoms (2.2)		2.1		2.2		2.4		2.3		1.9
Life Satisfaction (19.1)		19.3		17.7		19.5		18.8		18.0

Trajectory Type

* $p < .01$

Health and Well-Being. There were also no significant associations between life course patterns of private religious involvement and the indicators of health and well-being. A strong pattern is observed among persons who report lifelong low levels of involvement in private religious practices, indicating that self-perceived excellent health is more prevalent for that trajectory than for others. Despite this dramatic difference, however, the overall association between trajectories of private religious involvement and self-rated health is not significant.

Correlates of Religious Media Use

Analyses of the correlates of the religious media use trajectories are presented in Table 7.5. Again, the number of significant correlates is small.

Demographic Variables. Three demographic variables were significantly related to patterns of religious media use. Religious media use is the only dimension of religious participation significantly related to age. Among this old-old sample, the youngest members were significantly more likely to report lifelong patterns of low or no use than their older peers. Compared to whites, African-American respondents were significantly more likely to report lifelong or increasing media use (trajectory 1). Conversely, white respondents were much more likely to report lifelong patterns of low or no use of religious media. Education was also significantly associated with trajectories of religious media use. Respondents with more than a high school education were significantly more likely to report lifelong low or no use of religious media than their less-educated peers.

Social Support. Two dimensions of social support were significantly related to life course patterns of religious media use. Respondents reporting lifelong low or no religious media use reported significantly lower levels of social interaction and instrumental assistance than respondents reporting other life course patterns.

Health and Well-Being. Among the indicators of health and well-being, only life satisfaction was significantly related to the trajectories of religious media use. Respondents who reported a life course pattern of low or no religious media use reported higher life satisfaction than those reporting other patterns. Overall, there is little evidence that trajectories of religious media use are related to health and well-being.

TABLE 7.5 Correlates of Religious Media Use Trajectories

| | Trajectory Type | | | | | | | |
| | 1 Lifehigh | | 2 Fluctuate | | 3 Updown | | 4 Lifelow | |
Variable	%	M	%	M	%	M	%	M
Demographic Variables								
Age (79.9)		80.5		80.8		79.7		78.2*
Male (33.8%)	32.4		42.1		28.6		37.9	
Female (66.2%)	67.6		57.9		71.4		62.1	
Black (31.2%)	47.3		10.5		28.6		6.9*	
White (68.8%)	52.7		89.5		71.4		93.1	
Education in years (12.1)		11.1		11.3		12.5		14.7*
Social Support								
Social Network Size (11.5)		12.9		12.3		9.8		9.5
Social Interaction (14.0)		15.6		13.8		13.1		11.3*
Instrumental Support (8.7)		9.1		8.3		9.0		7.5*
Perceived Support (5.6)		5.6		5.7		5.8		5.3
Health and Well-Being								
Self-Rated Health								
Excellent (23.6%)	16.2		26.3		25.7		37.9	
Good (43.3%)	44.6		36.8		42.9		44.8	
Fair/Poor (33.1%)	39.2		36.8		31.4		17.2	
IADL (0.5)		0.6		0.5		0.3		0.8
Katz ADL (0.2)		0.3		0.1		0.2		0.3
Depressive Symptoms (2.2)		1.9		2.8		2.8		1.8
Life Satisfaction (19.1)		19.2		19.5		17.1		20.7*

* $p < .01$

Correlates of Religious Importance

The final set of religious trajectories describes life course patterns of the perceived importance of religion (see Table 7.6).

Demographic Variables. Three demographic characteristics were significantly associated with trajectories of perceived religious importance. Women were significantly more likely than men to report lifelong patterns of highly valuing religion; men, in contrast, were much more likely to report lifelong patterns of low religious importance. The significant association between race and trajectories of religious importance is driven by the dramatic difference for lifelong patterns of low religious importance. Whites are disproportionately likely to report this life course pattern; African Americans are highly unlikely to report this pattern. Education is also significantly related to trajectories of religious importance, with the highly educated most likely to report that religion has not been important to them throughout their lives. This finding parallels education differences observed for the other dimensions of religious participation.

Social Support. There is a general pattern regarding trajectories of religious importance and social support: participants who report lifelong low levels of religious importance generally report the lowest levels of social support. This pattern achieves statistical significance for three dimensions of social support: social network size, social interaction, and perceived support.

Health and Well-Being. Trajectories of religious importance are significantly related to only one indicator of health. Persons reporting lifelong low religious importance are disproportionately likely to describe their health as excellent; those who report a pattern of increasing, then declining religious importance (trajectory 3) are over-represented among those who describe their health as fair/poor.

DISCUSSION AND IMPLICATIONS

The study reported in this paper makes two contributions to our understanding of life course patterns of religious involvement and their potential implications for explicating the links between religion and health. First, we demonstrated that the life history calendar can be used to obtain retrospective information about long-term patterns of religious

TABLE 7.6   Correlates of Religious Importance Trajectories

Variable	1 Lifehigh %	1 Lifehigh M	2 Gradinc %	2 Gradinc M	3 Biginc %	3 Biginc M	4 Lifelow %	4 Lifelow M
Demographic Variables								
Age (79.9)		80.2		80.2		79.1		79.6
Male (33.8%)	26.2		31.8		34.6		60.0**	
Female (66.2%)	73.8		68.2		65.4		40.0	
Black (31.2%)	36.9		40.9		26.9		8.0**	
White (68.8%)	63.1		59.1		73.1		92.0	
Education in years (12.1)		12.3		10.5		11.5		13.3**
Social Support								
Social Network Size (11.5)		11.1		15.5		11.9		9.1*
Social Interaction (14.0)		13.8		17.4		15.2		10.5**
Instrumental Support (8.7)		8.7		8.7		8.8		8.5
Perceived Support (5.6)		5.6		5.9		5.7		5.2*
Health and Well-Being								
Self-Rated Health								
Excellent (23.6%)	20.2		22.7		15.4		44.0**	
Good (43.3%)	52.4		31.8		34.6		32.0	
Fair/Poor (33.1%)	27.4		45.5		50.0		24.0	
IADL (0.5)		0.4		0.5		0.3		1.1
Katz ADL (0.2)		0.2		0.3		0.2		0.3
Depressive Symptoms (2.2)		2.0		2.1		2.2		2.9
Life Satisfaction (19.1)		19.0		18.8		18.9		19.6

* *p* < .05
** *p* < .01

participation. This information also informs the two hypotheses about religious participation across the life course: the developmental hypothesis and the family life cycle hypothesis. Second, we took a first and admittedly limited look at the relationships between trajectories of religious participation and health and well-being in late life.

Life Course Patterns of Religious Participation

The life history calendar technique proved valuable in obtaining respondents' retrospective reports of religious participation in four dimensions across the life course. Even in this small sample, diverse trajectories were observed. Indeed, after substantial consolidation, 4–6 distinct trajectories were needed to capture the basic categories of religious histories. And this diversity existed despite a sample that resides in the midst of the Bible Belt. It is not surprising that lifelong patterns of high religious involvement were the modal religious trajectories in this sample. More surprising was the diversity of patterns reported by participants. Religious histories in samples located where religion is a less pervasive social institution would undoubtedly reveal even greater diversity.

Two conceptual frameworks provide hypotheses about life course patterns of religious involvement: the developmental perspective and family life cycle theory. Neither perspective garnered substantial support in this study. With regard to the family life cycle hypothesis, for which religious service attendance is the most relevant dimension of religious participation, only about 7% of the sample (half of the trajectory in which this pattern is embedded) reported declines in service attendance in early adulthood followed by increases during the child-rearing years.

There is also, at best, modest support for the developmental hypothesis. There was no evidence that private religious practices increased from midlife through old age. Religious media use did not support this hypothesis either, although it is not clear that developmental theorists would expect it to do so. For service attendance, only 10% of the sample reported a significant increase in public religious participation after age 50—and this was invariably after a precipitous decline. The importance of religion to one's life is arguably the dimension of religious experience most relevant to developmental issues. It is also the dimension that provides the strongest support for the developmental hypothesis. Approximately 30% of the sample report increases in religious importance across the adult life course.

It is not clear what "drives" life course patterns of religious participation. But the processes that do so are apparently too complex to be adequately represented by developmental or family life cycle perspectives.

Correlates of Religious Histories

We examined three categories of potential correlates of religious histories: demographic characteristics, social support, and health/well-being. Among the most consistent patterns observed were those between demographic variables and trajectories of religious involvement. Race (African Americans and Whites in this sample) was the most consistent correlate of life course patterns of religious participation. For all four dimensions of religious involvement, African Americans were significantly more likely than Whites to report lifelong high levels of participation. Conversely, lifelong patterns of low religious involvement were reported almost exclusively by Whites. Education was significantly related to religious history in three dimensions (all but service attendance) and the differences were dramatic. Persons reporting lifelong patterns of low religious involvement had the highest levels of educational attainment in the sample. There was a statistically significant gender difference for only one of the dimensions of religious experience (religious importance), but substantial gender differences were observed across all four dimensions. Women were consistently concentrated in trajectories representing high levels of religious involvement; conversely, men were disproportionately represented in trajectories representing low lifelong involvement and declining involvement over time.

Indicators of social support were significantly related to religious history for three of the four dimensions of religious participation. In line with previous research, persons who reported lifelong patterns of low religious participation reported lower levels of social support than respondents reporting other life course patterns. Although not all tests of the relationships between religious history and social support were significant, the overall pattern of findings is consistent.

Given the large and growing body of research on religious participation and health, we were especially interested in the relationships between trajectories of religious participation and health/well-being—even though only bivariate relationships could be examined because of small sample size. Overall, significant relationships between religious trajectories and health/well-being in late life were small in number and surprising in direction.

All of the significant relationships between life course patterns of religious involvement and health or well-being indicated that persons reporting lifelong patterns of low religious participation were the healthiest and happiest. As previous literature suggests, the most important dimension of religious participation was service attendance—four of the six significant relationships between religious history and health/well-being were observed for trajectories of service attendance. But all six significant relationships were opposite in direction to what that same research base reports. These unanticipated findings are especially ironic in light of the fact that research that my colleagues and I performed, based on the Duke EPESE data, has consistently demonstrated that religious participation prospectively predicts better health and longer survival (e.g., Koenig et al., 1998; Koenig et al., 1999).

One obvious possibility is that the bivariate relationships examined in this study are affected by the failure to incorporate important control variables, especially race and education. The well-known inequalities in health between Blacks and Whites may swamp the health benefits of religious participation, although at the advanced ages of study participants, the Black-White mortality cross-over may have diminished health inequalities observed at earlier ages. Similarly, education is known to be a strong and consistent predictor of better health and longer survival and its effects may override any risk resulting from lack of religious involvement.

Another possibility for the unexpected findings concerning religious history and health/well-being may be the sampling scheme used in this study. Recall that we sampled small proportions of Protestants, especially members of Fundamentalist and Evangelical denominations, and selected all agnostics and atheists. The distribution of religious affiliation/non-affiliation is much different than that in the EPESE sample as a whole and may have had strong effects on the results observed in this small sample.

From a conceptual perspective, it is tempting to view these findings in terms of the "comfort hypothesis" (Glock, Ringer, & Babbie, 1967). This hypothesis suggests religious participation is especially important to persons who are socially disadvantaged and/or marginal to society—that deprivations and injustices in the secular world are compensated for by participation in religious organizations that focus on the non-secular. These authors used the comfort hypothesis to explain gender, race, age, and SES differences in frequency of attending religious services. It is possible that a compensation process is part of the effects of religious participation on health as well—i.e., that religion is especially important to the health and well-being of persons who lack other health-protecting resources.

If the findings reported here were replicated using data from a larger sample, the comfort hypothesis would merit consideration. As it is, however, we believe that methodological issues are the more likely explanations for the patterns observed.

Limitations of the Study

The major limitations of this study have been previously noted. To briefly reiterate, the most serious limitation of this study is the small sample size, which precludes multivariate analysis. The sampling strategy, which resulted in distributions of religious affiliation/non-affiliation that are much different from those representative of the geographic area, also may have strongly affected the results. These are major threats to the internal validity of the study.

Use of retrospective data is always a concern and is heir to a variety of problems (e.g., Scott & Alwin, 1998). Although we are well aware of the problems with retrospective data, we also would argue that, for many topics, we can either use retrospective data or not study them at all. Religious history seems to be such a topic. We believe that it is better to study religious histories retrospectively than not to study them at all, but we are well aware that prospective data covering birth to late life would undoubtedly have generated somewhat different patterns.

External validity is a concern as well. Study participants reside in the Bible Belt and distributions of religious participation are known to vary substantially by geographic region. In addition, participants are members of the oldest-old. This not only means that generalization to other age groups is not possible, but also that this is a sample of survivors who represent, in terms of health and longevity, the elite of their cohorts.

Future Prospects

Despite its limitations, we hope that this paper will stimulate future research on the links between life course patterns of religious participation and health during middle and later life. As previously noted, it is interesting that both the developmental and family life cycle hypotheses received little support, based on the retrospective religious histories reported in this sample of older adults. Less obvious is the fact that two variants of these hypotheses garner substantial indirect support from the results reported here.

First, the life crisis hypothesis received substantial support, although it was tested only indirectly. Significant minorities of our respondents reported precipitous declines, increases, or more complex fluctuations in religious involvement over the life course. This is especially the case for service attendance. We asked respondents to explain dramatic "turning points" in their religious histories. Overall, those attributions focused on life crises. One of the major crises reported was dramatic decreases and increases in health. Using a typical life events checklist, dramatic decreases in health would be identified, but dramatic upswings in health or functioning would not. Interaction problems with clergy or congregational peers were also frequently endorsed as the cause of sharp declines in service attendance. This type of crisis would not be captured in traditional measures of acute stressors. Thus, one profitable area for future research on religious histories would be to systematically explore the perceived reasons for dramatic declines and increases in religious involvement. Investigators answering this challenge should be careful, however, not to fall into the trap of relying solely on pre-existing measures of life events or crises. Moreover, some of the factors that motivate increased religious participation will be positive rather than negative experiences (e.g., recovery/improvement in a chronic illness) and should not be ignored despite the fact that positive experiences are rarely included in studies of life crises.

Second, substantial previous research has demonstrated the importance of early religious socialization for adult religious participation. Those studies have overwhelmingly focused on whether religious participation as a child predicts religious participation as a relatively young adult. For all four domains of religious involvement, the modal category was "lifelong high" involvement (range of 35.0%–53.5% across the four domains). Although much smaller percentages, a minority of respondents reported "lifelong low" involvement (5.7%–15.9% across domains). These are strong patterns of life course stability. It is certainly plausible that these patterns of stability are due to the persisting effects of childhood religious socialization. Although these patterns are compatible with a socialization explanation, convincing evidence of this will require careful measurement of varying levels of childhood religious socialization that are systematically used to predict subsequent religious involvement during adulthood. If socialization explains the large proportions of life course stability, this will constitute compelling testimony to the power of early life socialization.

There are many debates raging about the implications of research demonstrating that religious participation promotes health and longevity—especially about the extent, if any, that individuals can and should turn to religion to protect their health and whether religious interventions should be offered to persons seeking to protect or improve their health. The hypothesis that one can promote health in any immediate or dramatic way by simply turning to religion seems untenable to us. It is much more likely that long-term (not necessarily lifelong, but long-term) religious participation has indirect effects on health via a variety of mechanisms. Much larger and more detailed studies of religious histories are one potentially valuable strategy for beginning to understand these dynamics.

REFERENCES

Affleck, G., & Tennen, H. (1996). Construing benefits from adversity: Adaptational significance and dispositional underpinnings. *Journal of Personality, 64,* 899–922.

Ai, A. L., Dunkle, R. E., Peterson, C., & Billings, S. F. (1998). The role of private prayer in psychological recovery among midlife and aged patients following cardiac surgery. *Gerontologist, 38,* 591–601.

Alston, J. P., & McIntosh, W. A. (1974). An assessment of the determinants of religious participation. *Sociological Quarterly, 20,* 49–62.

Atchley, R. C. (1997). Everyday mysticism: Spiritual development in later adulthood. *Journal of Adult Development, 4,* 123–134.

Barrett, A. E. (2000). Marital trajectories and mental health. *Journal of Health and Social Behavior, 41,* 451–464.

Becker, E. (1973). *The denial of death.* New York: Free Press.

Benson, P. L. (1991, August). *Patterns of religious development in adolescence and adulthood.* Invited address at the annual meeting of the American Psychological Association, San Francisco, CA.

Berman, A. L. (1974). Belief in afterlife, religion, religiosity, and life-threatening experiences. *Omega, 5,* 127–135.

Bianchi, E. (1987). *Aging as a spiritual journey.* New York: Crossroad.

Blazer, D. G., Burchett, B. M., Service, C., & George, L. K. (1991). The association of age and depression among the elderly: An epidemiologic exploration. *Journal of Gerontology: Medical Sciences, 46,* M210–M215.

Blazer, D. G., & Palmore, E. B. (1976). Religion and aging in a longitudinal panel. *The Gerontologist, 16,* 82–85.

Chatters, L. M., Levin, J. S., & Taylor, R. J. (1992). Antecedents and dimensions of religious involvement among older Black Americans. *Journal of Gerontology: Social Sciences, 47,* S269–S278.

Duvall, E. M., & Miller, B. C. (1985). *Marriage and family development* (6th ed.). New York: Harper & Row.

Elder, G. H., Jr., & Clipp, E. C. (1988). Wartime losses and social bonding: Influences across 40 years in men's lives. *Psychiatry, 51,* 177–198.

Elder, G. H., Jr., & Clipp, E. C. (1989). Combat experience and emotional health: Impairment and resilience in later life. *Journal of Personality, 57,* 311–341.

Erikson, E. (1958). *Young man Luther.* New York: Norton.

Erikson, E. (1963). *Childhood and society.* New York: Norton.

Erikson, E. (1969). *Gandhi's truth.* New York: Norton.

Erikson, E. H., & Erikson, J. (1997) *The Life cycle completed.* New York: Norton.

Firebaugh, G., & Harley, B. (1991). Trends in U.S. church attendance: Secularization and revival, or merely lifecycle effects. *Journal for the Scientific Study of Religion, 30,* 487–500.

Fowler, J. W. (1981). *Stages of faith: The psychology of human development and the quest for meaning.* New York: Harper & Row.

Freedman, D., Thornton, A., Camburn, D., Alwin, D. F., & Young-DeMarco, L. (1988). The life history calendar: A technique for collecting retrospective data. *Sociological Methodology, 18,* 37–68.

George, L. K., & Fillenbaum, G. G. (1985). The OARS Methodology: A decade of experience in geriatric assessment. *Journal of the American Geriatrics Society, 33,* 607–615.

Glock, C. Y, Ringer, B. B., & Babbie, E. R. (1967). *To comfort and to challenge.* Berkeley: University of California Press.

Hays, J. C., Meador, K. G., Branch, P. S., & George, L. K. (2001). The History of Religion and Spirituality Scale in Four Dimensions (HRSS-4): Validity and reliability. *Gerontologist, 41,* 239–249.

Helm, H. M., Hays, J. C., Flint, E. P., Koenig, H. G., & Blazer, D. G. (2000). Does private religious activity prolong survival? A six-year follow-up study of 3,851 older adults. *Journal of Gerontology: Medical Sciences, 55A,* M400–M415.

Hoare, C. H. (2002). *Erikson on development in adulthood.* New York: Oxford University Press.

Hummer, R. A., Rogers, R. O., Nam, C. B., & Ellison, C. G. (1999). Religious involvement and U.S. adult mortality. *Demography, 36,* 273–285.

Idler, E. L. (1995). Religion, health, and nonphysical senses of self. *Social Forces, 74,* 683–704.

Idler, E. L., & Kasl, S. V. (1997). Religion among disabled and nondisabled persons II: Attendance at religious services as a predictor of the course of disability. *Journal of Gerontology: Social Sciences, 52B,* S306–S316.

Jung, C. G. (1964). *Man and his symbols.* New York: Laurel.

Kelley-Moore, J. A., & Ferraro, K. F. (2001). Functional limitations and religious service attendance in later life: Barrier and/or benefit mechanism? *Journal of Gerontology: Social Sciences, 56B,* S365–S373.

Kessler, R. C., & Magee, W. J. (1994). Childhood family violence and adult recurrent depression. *Journal of Health and Social Behavior, 35,* 13–27.

Koenig, H. G., Cohen, H. J., Blazer, D. G., Pieper, C., Meador, K. G., Shelp, F., Goli, V., & DiPasquale, B. (1992). Religious coping and depression among elderly, hospitalized medically ill men. *American Journal of Psychiatry, 149,* 1693–1700.

Koenig, H. G., George, L. K., Cohen, J. C., Hays, J. C., Blazer, D. G., & Larson, D. B. (1998). The relationship between religious activities and blood pressure in older adults. *International Journal of Psychiatry in Medicine, 28,* 189–213.

Koenig, H. G., Hays, J. C., George, L. K., Blazer, D. G., Larson, D. B., & Landerman, L. R. (1997). Modeling the cross-sectional relationships between religion, physical health, social support, and depressive symptoms. *American Journal of Geriatric Psychiatry, 5,* 131–144.

Koenig, H. G., Hays, J. C., Larson, D. B., George, L. K., Cohen, J. C., McCullough, M. E., Meador, K. G., & Blazer D. G. (1999). Does religious attendance prolong survival? A six-year follow-up study of 3,968 older adults. *Journal of Gerontology: Medical Sciences, 54A,* M370–M376.

Krause, N. (1998). Neighborhood deterioration, religious coping, and changes in health during late life. *The Gerontologist, 38,* 653–664.

Landerman, R., George, L. K., Campbell, R. T., & Blazer, D. G. (1989). Alternative models of the stress buffering hypothesis. *American Journal of Community psychology, 17,* 625–642.

Lehman, D., Davis, C., DeLongis, A. Wortman, C. Bluck, S., Mandel, D., et al. (1993). Positive and negative life changes following bereavement and their relations to adjustment. *Journal of Social and Clinical Psychology, 12,* 90–112.

Levin, J. S., Chatters, L. M., & Taylor, R. J. (1995). Religious effects on health status and life satisfaction among Black Americans. *Journal of Gerontology: Social Sciences, 50B,* S154–S163.

McMillen, J. C., & Cook, C. L. (2003). The positive by-products of spinal cord injury and their correlates. *Rehabilitation Psychology, 48,* 77–85.

McMillen, J. C., Smith, E. M., & Fisher, R. H. (1997). Perceived benefit and mental health after three types of disaster. *Journal of Consulting and Clinical Psychology, 65,* 733–739.

McMillen, J. C., Zuravin, S., & Rideout, G. B. (1995). Perceived benefit from child sexual abuse. *Journal of Consulting and Clinical Psychology, 63,* 1037–1043.

Moberg, D. O. (1965). Religion in old age. *Geriatrics, 1,* 977–982.

Myers, S. (1996). An interactive model of religious inheritance: The importance of family context. *American Sociological Review, 61,* 858-866.

Neugarten, B. L., Havighurst, R. J., & Tobin, S. (1961). The measurement of life satisfaction. *Journal of Gerontology, 16,* 134–143.

Oman, D., & Reed, D. (1998). Religion and mortality among the community-dwelling elderly. *American Journal of Public Health, 88,* 1469–1475.

Oxman, T. E., Freeman, D. H., & Manheimer, E. D. (1995). Lack of social participation or religious strength and comfort as risk factors for death after cardiac surgery in the elderly. *Psychosomatic Medicine, 57,* 5–15.

Pargament, K. I. (1997). *The psychology of religion and coping.* New York: Guilford Press.

Patton, M. Q. (1990). *Qualitative evaluation and research methods* (2nd ed.). Beverly Hills, CA: Sage.

Pfeiffer, E. (1975). A short portable mental status questionnaire for the assessment of organic brain deficit in elderly patients. *Journal of the American Geriatrics Society, 23,* 433–441.

Radloff, L. (1977). The CES-D Scale: A self-report depression scale for research in the general population. *Applied Psychological Measurement, 1,* 385–401.

Scott, J., & Alwin, D. F. (1998). Retrospective vs. prospective measurement of life histories in longitudinal research. In J. Z. Giele & G. H. Elder (Eds.), *Crafting life studies: Intersection of social and personal history* (pp. 98–127). Newbury Park, CA: Sage Publications.

Stolzenberg, R., Blair-Loy, M., & Waite, L. (1995). Age and family life cycle effects on church membership. *American Sociological Review, 60,* 84–103.

Strawbridge, W. J., Cohen, R. D., Shema, S. J., & Kaplan, G. A. (1997). Frequent attendance at religious services and mortality over 28 years. *American Journal of Public Health, 87,* 957–961.

Tornstam, L. (1999). Late-life transcendence: A new developmental perspective on aging. In L. E. Thomas & E. Eisenhandler (Eds.), *Religion, belief, and spirituality in late life* (pp. 178–202). New York: Springer.

Vetter, G. B., & Green, M. (1932–1933). Personality and group factors in the making of atheists. *Journal of Abnormal and Social Psychology, 27,* 179–194.

Wilson, J., & Sherkat, D. (1994). Returning to the fold. *Journal for the Scientific Study of Religion, 33,* 148–161.

Winfield, I., George, L. K., Swartz, M. S., & Blazer, D. G. (1990). Sexual assault and psychiatric disorders among women in a community population. *American Journal of Psychiatry, 147,* 335–341.

Wink, P., & Dillon, M. (2001). Religious involvement and health outcomes in late adulthood: Findings from a longitudinal study of women and men. In T. G. Plante & A. C. Sherman (Eds.), *Faith and health: Psychological perspectives* (pp. 75–106). New York: Guilford.

Wink, P., & Dillon, M. (2002). Spiritual development across the life course: Findings from a longitudinal study. *Journal of Adult Development, 9,* 79–84.

Wright, J. E., Jr. (1982). *Erikson: Identity and religion.* New York: Seabury Press.

Yama, M. F., Tovey, S. L., & Fogas, B. S. (1993). Childhood family environment and sexual abuse as predictors of anxiety and depression in adult women. *American Journal of Orthopsychiatry, 63,* 136–141.

Author Index

Subject Index

Springer Publishing Company

Keeping the Faith in Late Life

Susan A. Eisenhandler, PhD

"Eisenhandler's well-grounded report of 'bedrock socialization' and the folkways of faith provides a long-needed counterbalance for our understanding of American elders. This book belongs on its own shelf—even better, it belongs in the hands of all who have ever wondered about the fate of faith in later life."

–Robert J. Kastenbaum, PhD
Professor Emeritus of Gerontology and Communication
Arizona State University, Tempe, AZ

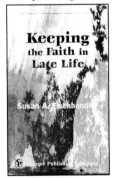

"Intelligently argued and compellingly written, this book is a welcome addition to a gerontological literature that now increasingly considers the place of spirituality in older people's everyday lives...Powerful and grounded in the ordinary, the book provides marvelous insights into the nexus of religious sensibility and the practice of daily living."

–Jaber F. Gubrium, PhD, Professor and Chair
University of Missouri

Contents:

- Introduction: Faith as a Feature of Identity and of Late Life: The Theoretical and Methodological Context of the Study
- The Bedrock of Faith and Religion—Socialization
- The Folkways of Prayer in Late Life
- Other Folkways of Faith in Late Life
- A Grown-Up Faith with Musings, Doubts, and Questions
- Folkways of Faith in Long Term Care Settings: Self, Soul, and Space
- Conclusion: Beyond A Reflexive Faith
- References • Appendix A: A Closer Look at Several Steps in the Research Process
- Appendix B: Some Social Characteristics of the Sample

2003   208pp   0-8261-1775-9   hardcover

536 Broadway, New York, NY 10012
Order Toll-Free: 877-687-7476 • Order On-line: www.springerpub.com

Springer Publishing Company

Religion, Belief, and Spirituality in Late Life

L. Eugene Thomas, PhD, and
Susan A. Eisenhandler, PhD, Editors

This volume examines the importance of beliefs within psychologically-relevant issues from self-identity to recovery from grief. The editors provide a broad framework for viewing religion in the lives of the elderly by drawing on insights derived from the humanities, and those mined from qualitative social science research, as well as from empirical and quantitative research.

Contents:

I. Creating and Understanding the Text of Late Life Spirituality
- A Handful of Quietness: Measuring the Meaning of Our Years, *S. Bertman*
- Joan and Erik Erikson/Sarah and Abraham: Parallel Awakenings in the Long Shadow of Wisdom and Faith, *A. Achenbaum* and *S. Modell*

II. Spirituality Writ Large and Small in Late Life
- Spiritual and Ethical Striving in Late Life: Three Paths to Integrity, *M. Miller*
- Aspects of Transcendence in Everyday Worlds: Reading and Spirituality in Late Life, *S. Eisenhandler*

III. The Nature of Beliefs: Cross-Cultural Perspectives
- Quarreling with God: Belief and Disbelief Among Elderly Jewish Immigrants from the Former USSR, *E. Thomas*
- Some Correlates of Religiosity Among Turkish Adults and Elderly, *O. Imamoglu*

IV. Glimpses of Gendered Spirituality
- Spirituality: A Continually Evolving Component in Women's Identity Development, *P. Burke*
- Surprised by Joy and Burdened with Age: The Letters of John Casteel, *S. McFadden*
- Quest Religiosity and the Search for Meaning in Later Life, *A. Futterman*
- Late Life Transcendence: A New Development Perspective on Aging, *L. Tornstam*
- Afterword by *Robert Kastenbaum*

1998   248pp   0-8261-1235-8   hardcover

536 Broadway, New York, NY 10012
Order Toll-Free: 877-687-7476 • Order On-line: www.springerpub.com